Spiritual Needs and Pastoral Services
Readings in Research

Larry VandeCreek

(Editor)

Research in Pastoral Care and Counseling:
Quantitative and Qualitative Approaches

ISBN   0-929670-12-4

Cover design
by
Darwin Melnyk
Cathedral Graphics
23250 NE Bald Peak Road
Hillsboro, OR 97123

Contents

Preface

Larry VandeCreek

Pastoral caregivers are increasing their interest in and attention to quantitative research. My goal in editing this book is to nurture that interest and attention. Hopefully this is accomplished by placing between these covers 23 previously published but widely scattered research reports which can inform the work of general hospital chaplains and parish pastors.

Many chaplains and pastors assume that few, if any, research results exist that can enlighten their pastoral practice. In truth, the literature contains many such studies; so many, in fact, that I set strident standards for inclusion in this volume. Without these guidelines, decisions concerning individual research reports would have been impossible.

What were the inclusion/exclusion criteria? I considered only published quantitative research reports concerning pastoral care carried out within a general hospital, outpatient setting, or a congregation. What does this exclude? It excludes qualitative as well as theory building articles; McSherry's contribution included here is the least empirical but it merits inclusion because it is a ringing challenge to chaplains to be more quantitative in their work. It excludes new materials; all reports in this book are previously published. It excludes material about pastoral care in settings such as psychiatric hospitals and prisons. It excludes research concerning training for pastoral care as found in clinical pastoral education as well as studies that focus on the personal or educational factors that influence ministry. Finally, it excludes studies in which the only respondents were college students or community persons, except as they are part of a religious congregation.

Some materials which qualify according to the above standards are excluded for other reasons. Using an additional, more subjective standard, I determined whether a report contained a sufficiently strong sample size, research design and analysis to generate confidence in the results. Further, each study needed to show promise of being instructive to pastoral caregivers. Interested readers will find many of the materials excluded here annotated in the bibliography (Matthews, Larson, & Barry, 1993) listed below.

These materials examine many areas, including a description of spirituality among hospital patients and parish members. Some studies describe the benefits of spirituality in the process of recovery, the role of prayer, and the evaluation of pastoral care. Authors include chaplains, nurses, physicians, persons in public health, and psychologists of religion.

Readers of this volume who provide pastoral care face several difficult tasks. The difficulties arise from the lack of exposure to and training in scientific methodology among pastors and chaplains. This, in turn, is fed by a lack of motivation to view pastoral care scientifically. Most pastors and chaplains have few compelling reasons to let research results influence their work. It will not likely lead to either professional or financial gain. And historically, many reasons exist to stay away from science and from research. After all, the great gulf which separates science and religion was, in part, created because of scientific methodology and the value placed on research. Historically, the sciences separated from religion on this very point.

This leads to the first challenge–learning how to read these reports. Frequently I hear chaplains complain that research articles are dull and boring. Much depends on expectations. The reports are intended to communicate information and, in this instance, quantitative information. In the background of each report are the references, which can often be as valuable as the results themselves, and assumptions that the reader is somewhat knowledgeable about selected principles of science. Understanding the Methodology section requires some knowledge concerning issues related to sample selection and size, the use of a comparison group as well as the choice of data collection instruments. An understanding of the Results section requires knowledge concerning the nature of the data and what statistical tests are appropriate. And the reader's critical analysis of how the author handled these issues is necessary to evaluate the outcome of the research. Without this critical and curious attitude, the reader does, indeed, become bored. Equipping the reader for this task is beyond the scope of this volume, but I have provided "Editor's Comments" at the end of some reports to facilitate an understanding of the process and the results. Many of these comments are critical, citing limitations of the design and results. These comments are made in the spirit of scientific critique; they also interrupt the tendency of non-scientific readers to over-interpret the results.

The second task grows out of the first. Upon finishing a specific report (or the entire book), the challenge is how to incorporate these research results into the day-to-day provision of pastoral care. The pastoral care community has not done well in the past with this crucial task. Rather than shaping their own practice of pastoral care on the basis of research, chaplains and pastors usually want others, such as administrators, to read reports such as these so that they once and for all appreciate and support this ministry. It is worth noting that this requires "them" to change rather than ourselves. The truth is, that while chaplains and parish pastors carry out their hospital ministry in highly scientific settings where research results constantly mold medical and nursing practices, their own work is largely shaped by tradition and a reliance on trained intuition. The practice of pastoral care will benefit by attention to research results which further inform intuition. Chaplains can then tailor their work accordingly, all the while acknowledging that the practice of pastoral care can never be as thoroughly driven by research results as is medicine and nursing.

I hope the reader faces these challenges at every juncture, asking, "What are the implications for my practice?" For example, Pargament (1990) reports that persons who use their religious faith to cope with "negative life events" report better outcomes. Our challenge, then, is how to respond to that finding. It is not sufficient to say, "Well, I already knew that!" Previously it may have been a "clinical impression"; now it is known in quite a different way because a detailed research design carried out with scientific controls verified the impression. This requires response, but what response? Does such a result mean that chaplains must make deliberate efforts to help patients mobilize their faith because this will contribute to a better recovery? If that is true, then is a passive "ministry of presence" or a pleasant, supportive pastoral visit enough? Such challenges can be found throughout these materials.

These two challenges facing the readers who are chaplains are further complicated by the continuing expectation, indeed, the demand among some, that pastoral research prove that chaplains are essential to hospitals. Usually it also incorporates the expectation that hospital-funded chaplains must be proven to be so valuable that job security is guaranteed. Those who search for such assurances from pastoral research will be disappointed. Pastoral research will never achieve job security for chaplains. It can–and does within this volume, generate results which strongly suggest that hospital patients possess spiritual needs, that religious faith, ritual, and practice are helpful to patients, that the mobilization of such spiritual resources produce better outcomes among populations which have been studied, and that patients and families strongly endorse the work of chaplains, reporting it to be helpful to them. Consequently, administrators may decide for these and other reasons to employ chaplains. But that will always be an administrative decision. Demonstrating patient and family needs as well as the benefits of spirituality, even by scientific means, does not in itself compel administrators to employ chaplains. While these reports may encourage hospital administrators to support chaplains, hopefully they will also encourage chaplains to determine more carefully how they can be of help to patients and families. A skeptical chaplain once told me that pastoral research was useless because it did not affect practice. He went on to imply that, in addition to producing relevant research results, it was also my duty to see to it that such an impact on practice took place. That I cannot do. It is the challenge faced by each reader who provides clinical care. It is altogether possible that many will yawn and continue as they are.

These reports do not imply that all the answers are in hand; our present knowledge possesses many limitations. Some readers may extol these articles as a rich treasure of results from decades of devotion to pastoral research. It is not so. The reports are, for the most part, isolated studies from here and there with limited replication of results. A number of my own publications are included in this volume, but they too are opportunistic in nature, relying on the availability of medical students to gather data. The basic fact, therefore, with which the field of pastoral care must contend is that it does not possess a bank of quantitative research which informs its work nor research programs which produce them. These studies, therefore, cannot be called "a literature"; they represent only scattered reports largely unrelated to each other although each contains results which can inform the pastoral practice of chaplains and pastors.

I have organized the reports in chronological order, beginning with three from the decades of the 1960's and the 1970's. These solid studies possess historical interest among chaplains but have not been widely available. Reports from the decades of 1980's and 1990's describe increasingly complex and more powerful research designs. A larger number of reports are also available from these decades, reflecting an increased interest in the role of religion and spirituality. I have broken with the chronological order only once by placing four articles at the end of the volume concerning the evaluation of hospital pastoral care. These can best be understood if read together.

Finally, some readers of this volume, such as graduate students, may be searching for examples of the quantitative research process and how to report results. The authors represented here demonstrate how to manage, analyze, and report large amounts of data, although with varying amounts of skill. That, in itself, can be helpful.

I wish to acknowledge the support of two persons. Orlo Strunk, Jr., editor of the Journal of Pastoral Care Publications, Inc., suggested the volume and has graciously supported my efforts. Marjorie Lyon, the secretary of the Pastoral Care Department, has conscientiously helped prepare the materials.

There is much work to do. Hopefully, this book will stimulate both our interest and our production.

REFERENCE

Matthews, D., Larson, D., Barry, C. (1993). *The Faith Factor: An Annotated Bibliography Of Clinical Research On Spiritual Subjects.* Washington D.C.: National Institute of Healthcare Research.

1

Acceptance and Healing

Randall C. Mason, Jr.
Graham Clark
Robert B. Reeves, Jr.
S. Bruce Wagner

The speed of healing following retinal detachment surgery is a critical factor in determining whether or not the patient will recover his vision. This investigation grew out of a concern for those who healed so slowly that their chances of recovering vision were minimal and out of a general interest in the sources of variability in the speed of wound healing. Prior clinical observation by Clark had indicated the possible relevance of psychological factors to the speed of healing. The task of this investigation was to isolate and describe these factors.

Before focusing on psychological differences, we attempted to locate non-psychological determinants. An examination of the records for 116 retinal detachment patients previously treated by Clark, however, revealed no significant relationships between the speed of healing and such factors as the extent of surgery, type of surgery, type of detachment, the presence or absence of other diseases, sex, and socioeconomic status. The one significant relationship between age and the speed of healing was minimal and in a direction opposite to that expected, with the older patients healing more quickly than the younger. (Age range between 40 and 80.) These results permitted the investigation to be focused more precisely on psychological sources of variability.

Various attempts were made to utilize current theories and concepts in psychosomatic medicine. While these theories provided many promising leads,

Reproduced with permission of the Plenum Publishing Company from the *Journal of Religion and Health*, (1969), 8, 123-142.

their pursuit led only to negative results. Despite such results, we still felt that psychological differences between the rapid and the slow healers were present and that the problem was either with the means of testing the theories or with the theories themselves. One suggestion was that the theories were based for the most part on studies of diseases of spontaneous origin, while this investigation was concerned with the response to surgical insult. Furthermore, the theories had not been subjected to adequate testing, so that they were the products more of speculation than of adequately designed research.

At this stage in the investigation, Reeves (1960) reported on his use of the concept of acceptance in a study of terminal cancer patients. He used acceptance as a descriptive concept to characterize their behavioral and attitudinal responses to their actuation, and related variability in acceptance to other phenomena he had observed while ministering to these patients as a hospital chaplain. The acceptance concept appeared to have the potential for capturing observed behavioral and attitudinal differences between rapid and slow healers; its potential was further suggested by the work of Wright (1960), who independently had used acceptance to describe psychological responses to disability. She distinguished between those whose acceptance of their disability enabled them to achieve an adequate level of functioning and those whose lack of acceptance created psychological complications that prevented adequate functioning. Both the problem of response to disability and the concept of acceptance seemed pertinent to the retinal detachment patient. Retinal detachment creates a temporary and potentially permanent disability, and the concept of acceptance appeared relevant to the question of variability in speed of healing.

A review of the psychological and healing patterns of those patients seen in the preliminary studies made the usefulness of the concept increasingly apparent and also led to a better understanding of the meaning of acceptance. A high degree of acceptance is shown when the patient, so to speak, is able to take in stride the shock of having a retinal detachment and having to undergo surgery. He sees his eye problem as an unfortunate but surmountable one that will not interfere with the ongoingness of his life. He may, indeed, experience some fear about possible pain and be disgruntled by the inconvenience of hospitalization, but he does not lose sight of the temporary quality of his experience. He usually has a high degree of confidence that the surgery will be successful, and that he soon will be able to resume his usual life pattern. Even when he has been told that the success of the surgery is in his particular case unlikely, the threat of blindness does not impair his confidence in a meaningful continuation of his life.

By contrast, the patient with low acceptance gives evidence of having lost perspective; his concern about the possible results of surgery is central and pervasive. The way he expresses this concern is dependent on his personality, but there is no question about the overwhelming quality of his concern.

STUDY I

The hypothesis of this study was that the speed of healing is positively related to the degree of acceptance. To test this hypothesis, five persons on the retinal detachment staff rated each patient on the degree of acceptance; the surgeon also rated the speed of healing for each patient. The results were obtained by a correlational analysis of the relationship of the ratings of speed of healing to those of acceptance.

Subjects

The subjects were 52 persons suffering from retinal detachment who were admitted to the Ophthalmological Institute of Columbia-Presbyterian Medical Center as patients of Dr. Graham Clark. All persons seeking treatment were accepted as patients unless there was a medical reason precluding the possibility of successful surgery. All but two patients were accepted as subjects. One had a language difficulty and the other was treated with a procedure that prevented observation of the speed of healing.

Hollingshead's (1957) Index of Socioeconomic Status based on occupation and education was used to determine socioeconomic status. The distribution of the sample was fairly normal, so that, going from the highest to the lowest status level, there were 6, 11, 19, 10, and 6 persons respectively. The sample contained 31 males and 21 females ranging in age from 37 to 77, with a mean of 58.9 years. While the distributions of the sample according to age and sex differ from the general population, they do represent the retinal detachment population.

Raters

The five raters included a surgeon, an office secretary, two nurses, and a clergyman. The surgeon was an ophthalmologist specializing in retinal detachment surgery. The nurses were not members of the regular nursing staff of the hospital. One nurse assisted the surgeon by carrying out routine medical duties. The other served as a research assistant administering a questionnaire and carrying out physiological tests. The clergyman was a clinically-trained chaplain, and at the time of the study was doing graduate work in clinical psychology.

Method

Each rater rated each patient on a 7-point scale with a 1 indicating the highest degree of acceptance and a 7 the lowest. The surgeon and nursing assistant made their ratings after their first contacts with the patient and prior to the surgery to prevent their observations during surgery from unconsciously influencing their ratings. The ratings of the secretary were based on telephone conversations with the patient prior to his admission to the hospital and personal contacts during his hospitalization. Both the research assistant and the chaplain made their ratings toward the end of the patient's stay in the hospital. The research assistant's ratings were based on her contacts with each patient during the administration of the questionnaire and the physiological tests. The chaplain's ratings were based on one to four visits with each patient, with the majority of patients being seen 4 times.

The surgeon made two additional ratings. At the same time that he made his rating of acceptance, he used a 5-point scale to indicate the seriousness and complexity of the detachment and the condition of the eye tissues—factors that might be related to the speed of healing independently of the degree of acceptance. Just prior to the patient's discharge from the hospital, the surgeon, using a 5-point scale, rated the speed of healing with a 1 indicating the fastest and a 5 the slowest healers.

In the early stages of the study, a conference was held following the discharge of each patient from the hospital to discuss the success of each rater in predicting the speed of healing by his rating of acceptance. The conferences were not held, however, until all ratings had been completed. They were helpful in reaching a better understanding of the practical and theoretical meaning of acceptance.

Results

The first step in the analysis of the results was to determine the relation of speed of healing to age, sex, socioeconomic status, and the seriousness of the detachment. Pearson Product-Moment Correlation coefficients were computed between the ratings of speed of healing and these variables. The correlation coefficients obtained were small and insignificant. Pearson Product-Moment Correlation coefficients were then computed between the rating of the speed of healing and the ratings of acceptance. For various reasons, the raters were not always able to see all of the patients. The number of patients seen by each rater together with the obtained matrix of correlations and intercorrelations are presented in Table 1. The correlations between the major variables of acceptance and healing were all significant, with two being significant at the .001 level, one at the .01 level, and two at the 0.5 level. The level of agreement between the raters was high, with all of the intercorrelations being significant at the .001 level except for two significant at the .01 level.

As noted above, ratings of speed of healing were not significantly related to the seriousness of the detachment, socioeconomic status, sex, or age of the patient. There were, however, some correlation coefficients significant at the .05 level between such variables and ratings of acceptance. There was a tendency among some of the raters to find a higher degree of acceptance in females, in older persons, and in those with a less serious detachment.

TABLE 1

Correlation Coefficients* Between Ratings of Acceptance and Speed of Healing

	N	1	2	3	4	5	6
1. Secretary	41	—	.61c	.53c	.48b	.54c	.51c
2. Nursing Assistant	52			.58c	.51c	.52c	.31a
3. Research Assistant	51				.68c	.54c	.33b
4. Chaplain	43					.48b	.27a
5. Surgeon	51						.56c
6. Speed of Healing							—

[a]significant at the .05 level
[b]significant at the .01 level
[c]significant at the .001 level

*For those untrained in statistics the numbers in the tables and the concept of significance may be confusing. Correlational coefficients range from -1.00 to +1.00. If acceptance ratings perfectly and positively corresponded to speed of healing ratings (5,5; 4,4; etc.), the obtained correlation coefficient would be +1.00, whereas if the ratings corresponded perfectly but inversely (5,1;4,2; etc), the obtained correlation coefficient would be -1.00. The departure of a correlation coefficient from either +1 or -1 toward 0 indicates a less than perfect relationship, and correlation coefficients close to 0 indicate the absence of a demonstrated relationship between two variables. A correlation coefficient is lowered when the hypothesized relationship is minimal or when the methods of measuring the variables are inadequate.

If ratings on the variables of acceptance and healing were simply assigned to each patient randomly by picking numbers from a hat, the obtained correlational coefficient would usually be low; but infrequently a high correlation coefficient will occur. The concept of significance levels is a way of determining, based on probability theory, how often a correlation coefficient of a given size occurs by chance alone. When the chances of obtaining a correlation coefficient of a given size by chance alone is equal to or less than 5%, 1%, or .1%, this is indicated by stating that the level of significance of that correlation coefficient is either .05, .01, or .001 respectively. When the probability of a correlation coefficient of a given size occurring by change is greater than 5%, it is interpreted as having occurred by change, but when less than 5%, a genuine relationship between the two variables is assumed operative (Du Bois, 1965).

COMMENT

The results obtained clearly demonstrate the validity and the relevance of acceptance to the problem of the speed of healing. Indeed, the correlations obtained were higher than had been anticipated in this initial study. The ratings were less accurate in the early stages of the study. Even though there had been extended discussions among the raters prior to the study about the meaning of acceptance, much remained to be learned. As the study progressed, the meaning of acceptance became clearer and the ratings more accurate.

A more detailed analysis of the results suggests that two factors reduced the accuracy of the ratings throughout the study. One factor is related to the fact that age, sex, and the seriousness of the detachment correlated significantly with the degree of acceptance, but not with speed of healing. A possible explanation is that there is an aspect of acceptance unrelated to speed of healing. Why, however, would this particular dimension of acceptance correlate positively with the seriousness of the detachment? A greater possibility is that the raters assumed that such variables were related to the speed of healing, and these assumptions both influenced and decreased their accuracy in rating acceptance. Even though the staff was unaware of the surgeon's ratings of the seriousness of the detachment, they tended to make such judgments based on information received from the patients.

Another factor is that some raters paid too much attention to psychological phenomena other than acceptance. The lowest correlation coefficients between acceptance and healing were based on ratings obtained from those persons with the most recent training and experience in making psychological diagnostic judgments. By contrast, the second highest correlation coefficient was based on the ratings of the office secretary, who had no prior psychological training. While there are other possible explanations for the differences in the correlation coefficients, this explanation is consistent with other observations and indicates that in future studies naive observers may make the best raters of acceptance.

As a final step in analyzing the data, scatter diagrams were prepared showing the relation between each rater's ratings of acceptance and the ratings for speed of healing. An inspection of these diagrams suggests that the correlation coefficients would have been higher if only three categories for speed of healing and degree of acceptance had been used. Raters were more successful in predicting by their ratings of acceptance whether a patient was a very quick, a very slow, or a moderate healer than in distinguishing differences within the moderate group. This analysis suggests that the acceptance variable is relevant to the broader differences in speed of healing, but not to the finer differences in the moderate group. There are some personality variables potentially relevant to these differences, but they have not as yet been adequately studied.

STUDY II

This study was, with one important exception, a replication of Study 1. Upon completion of the previous study, the staff developed a set of ten scales for measuring acceptance. They did this in order to achieve greater precision in the measurement of acceptance and to make the meaning and measurement of acceptance clearer to others who might desire to do research in this area. These ten scales were used in this study for measuring acceptance rather than having the raters make an over-all rating of acceptance.

Subjects

The subjects were 46 persons suffering from retinal detachment. There were no significant differences in the distributions by age, sex, and socioeconomic status between this group of subjects and the group used in Study 1. The one difference is that, although both groups were treated by the same surgeon, this group was treated at St. Luke's Hospital in New York rather than at Columbia-Presbyterian Medical Center.

Raters

The speed of healing was rated by the same surgeon who rated speed of healing in the previous study. Only one person was used to rate acceptance: a clergyman who, at the beginning of this study, had had no prior experience in this area. Prior to his participation in the project, he had served for several years in the parish. During the time of the study he was also doing advanced training in pastoral counseling.

Method

Upon completion of Study 1, the raters were asked to indicate why they rated each patient as they did. Their answers, together with further staff discussions, led to the formation of ten 5-point acceptance scales. These scales, together with a brief verbal description of the five points on each scale, are presented in Table 2. To help those who may wish to use these scales, a manual is being prepared to indicate more precisely the rationale for giving specific ratings on each scale.

The chaplain rated each patient on these scales on the basis of his pastoral visits. Rather than trying to rate each patient on all 10 scales, however, he made ratings only on those scales for which he had definite information. The surgeon, as in Study 1, used a 5-point scale to rate the speed of healing. The surgeon and the chaplain avoided talking to each other about patients so as not to influence each other's ratings.

Results

Upon completion of the study, a single score for degree of acceptance was obtained by taking the mean of the scores on those scales on which the chaplain made ratings and multiplying by 10. With 10 scales and 5 points on each scale, potential scores ranged between 10 and 50. Since an analysis of the previous study had suggested that the variable of acceptance was relevant to only three levels of healing speed, the obtained scores for degree of acceptance and speed of healing were grouped so that there were three levels for each variable and the distribution of scores on both variables were as nearly similar as possible. The correlation coefficient obtained between speed of healing and degree of acceptance was .61 significant at beyond the .001 level.

COMMENT

The results of this study clearly support the finding of the previous study that the degree of acceptance is related to the speed of healing. Furthermore, it has validated as a group the 10 scales used in this study, thereby giving greater clarity to the meaning of acceptance and increased specificity in its measurement. This replication has further merit in that it was carried out at a different hospital and that the chaplain rating acceptance had not participated in the previous study. While it would have been desirable to use a different surgeon in this study, it was simply not possible.

DISCUSSION

There are no implications of causality associated with the concept of acceptance. The correlational method of analysis does not permit causal interpretations. Furthermore, such an interpretation obscures the theoretical function of acceptance as a descriptive and intermediary concept. The usefulness of acceptance as a descriptive concept is illustrated by the scales developed for use in the second study: measuring the state of the patient without implying within that description either the underlying causes or results of that state.

As an intermediary concept, it serves as a bridge between the sources and correlates of acceptance. Since results of the preliminary studies suggested that variability in speed of healing could not be attributed to any single factor or set of factors, a concept was needed that permitted measurement of the sum effect of all relevant factors. The speed of healing should be more highly related to the sum effect of all relevant factors than to any factor taken singly. Such an intermediary or bridge concept also permits the research to be divided into two areas: the relation of acceptance to hypothesized correlates, such as speed of healing, and the identification and description of the sources or components of acceptance.

The studies reported here are the first (in the) area relating acceptance to healing. Since the results support the existence of this relationship, further investigations in this area are indicated. First these studies should be replicated in another hospital with different personnel conducting the research. If independently obtained data supported the findings reported here, the way would be prepared for examining the relation of acceptance to problems of wound healing other than retinal detachment, and then to other kinds of psychosomatic problems.

Consideration of the sources of acceptance constitutes a quite distinct area of investigation. While the research reported here does not bear directly on this question, there are some theoretical and clinical observations relevant to understanding and to developing a theory about the sources of acceptance as a basis for future research.

The most common-sense explanation views low acceptance as a function of reality factors in the life situation. While the occurrence of a retinal detachment would be upsetting to anyone, there are additional factors making a retinal detachment more intolerable to some patients than to others; e.g., the printer dependent on his eyesight for earning his livelihood as compared with the independently wealthy man.

The sociologists add sophistication to common sense by noting that the impact of reality factors is always modified by the person's cultural framework. Thus, the independently wealthy man, if deeply imbued with the spirit of Weber's Protestant Ethic, may be more distressed by his inability to work than the printer who does not view his own value as determined by the ability to produce. Thus one must understand both the reality factors in the life situation and the patient's interpretation of their meaning. Our own observations suggest that the common-sense approach and the modifications of the sociologists are valuable but insufficient. Complete dependence on such explanations usually results from the research error of being primarily concerned with patients with low acceptance and of finding post-facto explanations. Upon finding that a patient with low acceptance happens to be a printer, there is a natural tendency to assume an understanding of his state. Studying each patient systematically quickly reveals patients with similar backgrounds and reality factors in their life situation but showing high acceptance. While systematic study does not permit the significance of reality and cultural factors to be ruled out, it does necessitate a reformulation of the problem: under what conditions do reality and cultural factors become operative in producing low acceptance?

Seeking an answer to this question by focusing on the psychodynamics of patients with low acceptance revealed the presence, either singly or in combination, of three psychological processes. For some the presence of a retinal detachment together with the institutional procedures of the hospital activates regressive dependency wishes to be relieved of responsibility and to be completely cared for by others. Some can accept such wishes with comfort and enjoy the opportunity to regress. More commonly, however, patients find such wishes unacceptable, and their activation is accompanied by guilt and anxiety.

A related yet different regressive process concerns the problem of power, the Freudian concept of castration anxiety, and the symbolic meaning of blindness as castration. Here the regression is a retreat from the use of power or competitiveness rather than a wish to be cared for by others. One man, though recovering his vision, utilized his retinal detachment as an opportunity for a sharp and permanent regressive change in style of life. Explaining that he needed to protect his eyes, he sold his share in the family business and retreated to his home, venturing forth only to do the family marketing. Patients for whom the use of power is the source of primary conflict are often distinguished either by their troubled passivity or their fluttering helplessness.

Patients suffering from either regressive process are also likely to experience guilt and anxiety. While the guilty will seek desperately in the past for an explanation of their present predicament, and the anxious will ruminate about the possibility of blindness, both the guilt and anxiety appear primarily related to the unconscious and unacceptable regressive wishes. In the unconscious where the wish is equivalent to the deed, the guilty patient perceives his wishes as causing his detachment (the punishment) and fears further that his wishes may create permanent blindness. These tendencies are enhanced by a lack of definitive understanding of the causes of retinal detachment.

The third and less frequent process was that in which the meaning of the retinal detachment was influenced by pre-existing guilt related to broken human relationships and unresolved grief reactions. For example, a recently bereaved woman expressed the feeling that she ought to have done more for her husband while he was alive. She went on to indicate that although she knew intellectually that God did not punish people by giving them a retinal detachment, she sometimes wondered, especially when feeling depressed, whether her detachment might not be the result of her failure to give sufficient care to her husband.

These psychological processes, however, even when combined with significant reality and cultural factors, do not explain the differences in acceptance. Attributing these differences to such psychological processes results from the same research error noted above with respect to reality and cultural factors; that is, giving post-facto explanations for distress in patients with low acceptance. Examination of all patients indicates that many have the psychological potential for the processes described above to occur, but they do not. Furthermore, psychological make-up does not account for shifts in levels of acceptance. Sometimes the shifts occur within a single hospitalization, but they are more marked and obvious when a second hospitalization is necessary. While there are no differences in level of acceptance for most patients between the first and second, for some there is a shift to a lower level, and somewhat surprisingly, for some there is a shift to a higher level. The increased stress of a second hospitalization could account for a decrease, but not for an increase.

Though we acknowledge the importance of the three psychological processes described above, they appear either to be associated with or activated by, rather than causing, low acceptance. Thus, the problem of understanding the sources of acceptance must again be reformulated; when do reality and cultural factors become operative in producing low acceptance and the above-described psychological processes occur?

Even before the concept of acceptance had been introduced into this research, Clark had noted that the slow-healing patients reminded him more of soldiers suffering from war neurosis than of any other psychological condition. As the study of acceptance progressed, two similarities became strikingly obvious. While both the detachment patient and the soldier in combat live with the threat of danger, the reality factors are not in either case sufficient by themselves to create a breakdown (war neurosis or low acceptance). Thus Kardiner (1959), in his discussion of the war neuroses, raises a similar question to the one raised above with respect to reality and cultural factors: when does an objective threat become a traumatic event? The intensity of the threat is not an adequate answer, as exemplified by the calmness of the Japanese pilots during the Second World War while preparing for suicidal missions, and more recently, the peacefulness of the Buddhists preparing for self-immolation in protest against the Vietnamese war.

A second similarity exists at the psychological and behavioral levels. It appears (in contrast to other neuroses) that the behavioral manifestations of the war neuroses cannot be grouped into a single syndrome and that the symptoms vary according to the pre-trauma psychological make-up of the patient. Likewise (as was noted above in describing patients with low acceptance) while the concern about possible blindness is central and pervasive, the method of expressing that concern (the symptoms) varies. Presumably, as is true in the case of patients with low acceptance, there are a variety of psychological processes activated with the onset of the war neuroses. This variety in psychological processes and behavioral manifestations may explain in part why the personality trait and emotional specificity theories current in psychosomatic medicine were not helpful in the study of variations in healing patterns of retinal detachment patients. The question remaining with respect both to the low-acceptance patient and to the victim of war neuroses is: how do the associated psychological processes and behavioral manifestations become activated?

The investigations of Frank (1961) are pertinent to the issue of physical healing: the question of when reality, cultural, and psychological factors become significant, and the understanding of acceptance and slow healing. His work focuses on similarities with respect to the healing process in modern methods of psychotherapy, the placebo effect in medicine, brain-washing, and religious forms of healing in both primitive and modern societies. He finds that a prerequisite for all forms of healing is a conceptual framework or world view that offers the patient a "... rationale, however absurd, for making sense of his illness and the treatment procedure, and places the healer in the position of transmitter or controller of impressive healing forces" (p. 60). This conceptual scheme provides the believer an explanation of why he became ill and what he must do to be well–a function historically fulfilled by the varied religious stories of man's fall from the state of bliss ("illness") and the way to salvation (healing), and now for many, by the scientific ideologies underlying modern methods of psychotherapy and medicine. The ideology must successfully legitimatize the healer and the methods or rituals he uses, as well as make relevant the means of healing to the believer's understanding of why he became ill. The apparent success of varied ideologies and healing methods suggests that the validity of the ideology is irrelevant; the important issue is the power of the ideology to evoke expectant faith — a state of mind closely related to high acceptance. The state of expectant faith is further supported by the acceptance of the ideology within the believer's community and by the personal magnetism or charisma of the healer (perhaps related to the healer's belief in the ideology and his personal power to heal).

These comments on the healing process are both illustrated by, and in turn clarify, some familiar phenomena. First, with respect to the healer, one often hears patients in the hospital or former patients devote a great deal of their conversation to the personal qualities and skills of their physician, often going to great lengths to explain the way they secured his particular services. Often the patient's preoccupation with this issue is passed off as "small talk," but in light of Frank's comments on the significance of the healer, it is likely that the patient is dealing with what is for him a central and significant issue. Secondly, with respect to methods of treatment, those familiar with the hospital must be aware that many hospital procedures and treatment methods have a sacred quality in that they are accepted without question and are ritualistic in that they continue to be practiced even when shown unnecessary. Many stress-producing procedures for the treatment of retinal detachment are still widely used, even though shown ineffective ten to fifteen years ago. Thirdly, retinal detachment patients are quite preoccupied with the issue of causality to the point that each one has one or more theories to advance as to why he became ill–explanations ranging anywhere from a bump on the head to having committed the unpardonable sin. Certainly the patient is in part concerned with the issue of causality so that he may avoid future mishaps, but also because he wishes to be assured that the methods of treatment are relevant. All of modern treatment methods may prove ineffective for the primitive tribal man convinced that he is ill because of a curse.

Kardiner (1959) finds similar factors significant for the soldier in battle:
... the soldier is protected by his teammates, by his trust in effective leadership, and by the effectiveness of his weapons. In addition, he is

protected by the idea of invulnerability. The latter lasts only as long as no one in his team is injured or killed. This breaks it up. (p.248)

What happens when the faith is lost or the idea of invulnerability broken, when the ideology is powerless to evoke expectant trust, or when the charismatic leader and/or his methods become suspect? For the retinal detachment patient these appear to be the factors responsible for the move from high to low acceptance, to the reality of the patient's situation becoming an overwhelming threat, to the onset of regressive psychological processes, and to despair and poor healing.

How is the faith lost? Sometimes it is insufficiently aroused. A woman of Christian Science faith failed to heal despite the relative simplicity of the surgical procedure. Afterwards, she indicated to the surgeon that having surgery was in conflict with Christian Science beliefs. Before operating, the surgeon made clear to her that he was only doing a mechanical task akin to realigning a broken bone, and that her faith was the major factor in the actual healing. His statements helped her reconcile her Christian Science beliefs with the necessity of surgery, and she healed quickly after the second operation. Similar problems were encountered with a Roman Catholic priest concerned about entering a Protestant hospital and a married man involved in a sexual affair who felt that blindness was to be his punishment. As strange as it may seem to the scientifically sophisticated, even well-educated people, on an emotional level, still believe that blindness may result from sin. The speed of healing for the latter man changed sharply when he decided to end his infidelity. Other patients are well known to practicing psychotherapists, who describe their initial relationships to healers by the term "negative transference." For example, an experimental psychology student entering therapy spent his first hour informing the therapist that he had little hope of any help from him because of the conflicting research on the value of psychotherapy. While negative transference is often a prelude to intensely positive transference, both the psychotherapist and the surgeon are well advised to give attention to resolving it prior to employing their healing procedures, or else the patient's prophesies of the healer's inability to heal may well be self-fulfilling.

Other patients may begin with an expectant faith, but lose their faith. Some patients who whole-heartedly trust and praise both the surgeon and God may shift rapidly from high to low acceptance if the first operation is unsuccessful. While most will accept the surgeon's explanations of why the second operation should be successful even though the first was not, some will reject the explanations and doubt either the healer and his methods or their own worthiness for being healed. Once such doubts appear, low acceptance ensues and the patient's doubts are actualized. To put the matter in rather cavalier fashion, the surgeon needs a good public relations department for both himself and his methods. On the practical level this discussion does not imply that nurses and chaplains should either suppress or ignore doubts the patient may have. Such methods will only increase the patient's doubts. Rather, the nurse or chaplain should help the patient express and work through his doubts, which he may be able to do if the nurse and chaplain do not become anxious themselves.

The thrust of this whole discussion suggests that high acceptance and rapid healing occur, despite the psychological make-up of the person or the intensity of the threat, when the patient has faith in the healer, his method of healing, and feels that these methods are relevant to the cause of his illness. Low acceptance and poor healing occur when such beliefs are undermined. Furthermore, this discussion suggests that the person seeking to help the slow healer should not be concerned with either the intrapsychic make-up of the patient (which may take years to change) or with environmental factors. Rather, he should focus primarily on what variables enhance or destroy the patient's attitude of expectant faith.

While the validity of ideology may be irrelevant as long as it has the power to produce expectant faith, future research should isolate variables relevant to the power of the ideology (Frank, 1961, p. 60). Preliminary observations point to at least three variables: comprehensiveness, transcendence, and specificity. Comprehensiveness refers to the ability of the ideology to comprehend or handle reality factors. For example, the ideology of the woman of Christian Science faith did not comprehend the necessity of surgery and that of the provincial Roman Catholic priest was not able to handle the problem of going to a Protestant hospital.

A second variable is the transcendence of the ideology. A very common statement made by patients is: "I have faith in God–faith that God will give me back my sight." To such persons blindness is such a terrible tragedy that they feel life would not be worth living if they were to become permanently blind. The issue of blindness becomes a practical equivalent to the issue of survival. This type of faith is usually quite brittle, easily destroyed or challenged by adverse circumstances. Any negative word about the surgeon, his methods, or the outcome of the surgery becomes an immediate source of concern. From a normative point of view, this kind of faith is distortion of the nature of faith certainly in the Christian tradition and probably within most religious traditions. Nevertheless, most patients appear to have been taught that faith is believing intensely that you will receive what you wish, and that if you believe and pray sufficiently, reality can be changed.

By contrast, the ideology of some patients is sufficiently transcendent to make the issue of blindness relatively irrelevant, and thus to some degree the qualities of the healer and his methods. These are people whose world view is such that they are sincerely convinced that life will continue to be meaningful whether they see again or not. The faith aroused by their ideology permits them to be relatively unconcerned about the exigencies of their situation. This is the transcendent faith displayed by St. Paul in his affirmation: "Whether I live or die, I am the Lord's!" These patients affirm in either secular or religious language: "Whether I see or go blind, life will continue to be meaningful and rich."

Lest these comments be interpreted as a polemic for the Christian faith, let it be quickly stated that this type of transcendent faith was found only in one or two per cent of the retinal detachment population, and even more rarely among the self-consciously religious. Indeed, problems occurred so often among the latter group that a third variable is suggested: the specificity or applicability of the ideology. The self-consciously religious most often exhibited a split ideology: they were enough influenced by the scientific culture to acknowledge the necessity of the scientific medical procedures, but also felt that to regain their vision they needed to trust God in a way that did not include the surgeon and his methods. An idealogy with low specificity is one in which the ideology is not applicable to what is happening to the patient in the hospital, and is not sufficiently specific to the situation to enhance the role of the healer and his methods. Indeed, the personal qualities and skills of the surgeon may be irrelevant compared to the question of whether the patient is believing "hard enough." By its very nature, an ideology with low specificity may elicit a compelled faith, but have great difficulty evoking an expectant trusting faith.

REFERENCES

Du Bois, P. (1965). *An Introduction to Psychological Statistics.* New York, Harper & Row.

Frank, J. (1961). *Persuasion and Healing.* Baltimore: The Johns Hopkins Press.

Hollingshead, A. (1957). *A Two-Factor Index of Social Position.* 1965 Yale Station, New Haven, CT.

Kardiner A. (1959). Traumatic neuroses of war. In S. Arieti (Ed.), *American Handbook of Psychiatry*, Vol. 1. New York: Basic Books, Inc., Publishers.

Reeves, R. (1960). Study of terminal cancer patients. *Journal of Pastoral Care, 14,* 218-223.

Wright, B. (1960). *Physical Disability—a Psychological Approach.* New York: Harper.

TABLE 2
Acceptance Scale
Scale Points

Scales	Accepts Totally	Accepts Cautiously	Accepts with Reservations	Accepts with Resignation	Rejects
1. Reaction to Detachment	Confronts directly	Shaken but goes on	Advances fearfully	Bogged Down	Trapped- Back-to-wall
2. Reaction to Surgeon	Trusts	Praises hopefully	Seeks reassurance	Submits	Suspects
3. Reaction to Surgery	Optimistic about results	Hopefully certain of success	Vacillates in expectation	Unwilling to hope	Pessimistic
4. Reaction to Chaplain	Seeks companionship in interpreting life	Seeks agreement for positive philosophy	Seeks consolation and avoids discussion of inner conflict	Seeks respect for virtue and wisdom of compliance	Perceives as alien force or expects him to mourn
5. Reaction to Others	Meets on equal terms	Acts as host	Is not sure how to react	Expects sympathy and concern	Gives sense that no response to him is adequate
6. Coping Ability	Confident he can cope	Hopeful he can cope	Ambivalent about coping ability	Doubtful he can cope	Convinced he cannot cope
7. Self-care Ability	Able to do things for self and be helpful	Tries to do things for self and cooperate	Torn between desire to do and inability to do	Helpless and makes obvious display of it	Acts as if entitled to services
8. Self-Image	Accepts self and situation (without special concern)	Displays positive image (embarrassed by dependence)	Keeps things in check (ambivalent about dependence)	Self-pitying (recognizes dependence with pity)	Sulking or detached (angry over dependence)
9. Conversational Style	Willing to converse in depth	Pursues pleasant conversation	Caught between response and preoccupation	Talks mostly about affliction of self	Avoids open contacts with others
10. Philosophy of Evil	Accepts bad with good	Wonders how the bad fits	Seeks assurance this is not all bad	"What can you do?" (It's God's will.)	"It's a dirty trick."

Editor's Comments

Reading research requires critical analysis. This includes the reader's careful attention to whether the authors have accurately interpreted existing work they cite in their literature review and whether, later in the article, they discuss their results in realistic terms. Most of the scrutiny, however, is devoted to the methods and results sections because what the authors find is strongly influenced by the methods they use.

From the Methods section, the reader should be able to identify the variables which the author studied. A "variable" is anything that varies, what changes and which likely has the capacity to influence the outcome of what is being studied. It is crucial that such influences be identified and managed during the project.

Two kinds of variables exist. Independent variables presumably have the capacity to be active or influential agents in what is being studied. One purpose of the research is to determine if these independent variables are, in fact, significant contributors. Dependent (or response) variables are the ones that are affected. They are often the test scores, outcomes, or other measures which demonstrate that a difference was identified.

The reader should be able to plot the design of the project on an X-Y axis, listing the independent variables in a column (Y axis) and the dependent (or response) variables horizontally in a row across the top of the page. Drawn in this fashion, the reader can develop a clear image of the authors' intentions.

What does the design of Study 1 look like? The independent variables of the 52 subjects such as age and sex are described first, after noting how subjects were selected. Occupational status and education were measured by the Hollingshead scoring system. The authors then go on to describe how additional independent variables were created. Concerning the acceptance rating, they describe the profession of the raters and their patient contact. They note that the surgeon made ratings concerning seriousness and complexity of the detachment as well as the condition of the eye tissue. The design is completed by noting that before discharge, the surgeon made a ranking which described the speed of healing. This is the response (or dependent) variable, the one they are seeking to explain and it is placed on the horizontal axis. The total design is displayed in Figure 1. The "X"s designate the intersection of the independent and response variables and the results section should contain data for each "X". The research question is, "Where will significant correlations be found?" and the hypothesis is that it exists at the intersection of "acceptance" and the "speed of healing."

FIGURE 1	
Methods	
Subjects	Speed of Healing
Age	X
Sex	X
Occupational status and education	X
Measurements	
Seriousness of detachment	X
Condition of the tissue	X
"Acceptance" rating	X

So what did they find? Now we enter the results section. They immediately report the no significant relationship was found between the speed of healing and age, sex, occupational/education level, or the seriousness of detachment. The next paragraph describes the relationship between acceptance ratings and the speed of healing, resulting in Table 1 in their report.

In the next paragraph, the authors go on to note an item of considerable interest. They report that the acceptance ratings, the data that most clearly correlated with the mysterious variations in healing speed, may have been influenced by undesirable factors because "there was a tendency among some of the raters to find a higher degree of acceptance in females, in older persons, and in those with less serious detachments." It seems clear that the authors interpret this to mean that some bias may have existed in the raters. This finding cast some doubt on the results and is the motivation for the second study.

Understanding each research report will be enhanced if readers plot the design on such an X-Y axis at least in their minds. This effort helps understand the logic of the authors and to track the results.

One additional comment is necessary. As the authors themselves note in the discussion section, this is correlational research and the results can never be interpreted in a cause-effect manner. The results suggest only that the speed of healing and a higher "acceptance" rating rise and fall together. The cause for a more rapid healing remains unknown. A different research design is required to study cause-effect relationships.   The concept of "acceptance" has not been given an adequate conceptual context in this or subsequent work. This is a severe limitation because the concept itself would be more easily understood if placed in a wider cognitive context. I suggest that further exploration of this matter needs to give attention to Lazarus' (1984) model of coping with stress. Their work is referenced by a number of authors represented in this book. Patients who possessed a high degree of acceptance seemed to make a "primary appraisal" (Lazarus' description) that their surgery would be "stressful" (as opposed to "irrelevant" or "benign") and that this stress was a "challenge," as compared to one involving "harm-loss" or a "threat" (again, Lazarus' terms). These patients also seemed to evaluate their internal strength to be sufficient to meet this challenge, a process Lazarus called "secondary appraisal."

In the meantime, the authors' advice is still sound: the pastor/chaplain "should focus primarily on what variables enhance or destroy the patient's attitude of expectant faith."

REFERENCES

Lazarus, R., & Folkman, S. (1984). *Stress, appraisal and coping*. New York: Springer.

2

Crisis Intervention in Orthopedic Surgery— Empirical Evidence of the Effectiveness of a Chaplain Working with Surgery Patients

John L. Florell

In the past 10 to 20 years there has been considerable growth in the establishment of departments of pastoral care, social work, psychiatry and broader nursing services that have augmented the traditional medical procedures with spiritual and emotional support within the hospital setting.

Spokesmen for these helping professions say that they take some of the patient load off already over-taxed physicians and nurses. They claim they are accessible and place few demands on the patients. The problem has been that little of an empirical nature has been done to evaluate the impact of these professions on the hospitalized patient.

For over 20 years studies have been reported that seemed to confirm that emotional preparation can aid healing. In the early 1950's pediatric patients

Reproduced with permission of John L. Florell from the *Bulletin of the American Protestant Hospital Association,* (1973), pp. 29-36.

were prepared for hospitalization and surgery by visits to the hospital, rehearsing surgery and allowing the family to be close throughout the hospitalization (Jackson, *et.al.*, 1953). Janis' (1958) research indicated psychological preparation could lower postoperative anxieties in patients. In the early 1960's Egbert *et.al.* (1964) showed preparation also seemed to have a positive effect on the healing process of adults. Mason *et.al.* (1969) found in certain types of surgery the speed of healing was dependent on the patient's faith in the healer, his method and the feeling that the method was relevant to the cause of the illness. Andrew (1970) even found that tape recorded preparation could be helpful to the healing process with certain types of patients.

In relation to the hospitalized patient, chaplains have long practiced a supportive stance that seems consistent with the findings of the research cited above. The primary aim of the chaplain is to show the patient he is cared for and that any feelings the patient has are acceptable to deal with.

Crisis intervention theory, which refers to treating people around one of the crucial points in their lives, advocates an intense relation between the person in crisis and a professional who can help the person deal with his problem. The basic presupposition of crisis intervention work is that people are more open to help when they are under intense stress. Actual intervention seems to help because another person, who is more stable, is participating in the crisis with the person who is under stress assuring him that his feelings and reactions are acceptable and that the crisis can be resolved in certain ways.

DEVELOPMENT OF TREATMENTS

To find how the basic techniques of chaplain's support and crisis intervention could be applied to the hospitalized patient, 44 orthopedic patients were interviewed, before any research was done, to find what patients felt helped or hindered their recovery. Generally, these patients seemed to lack elemental information about the way that the hospital was operated and they wondered whether their feelings about their operation were normal. Those patients who had a positive attitude about their operation emphasized their relationship with the staff or their physician. Thirty-six out of 44 felt that there had been an attempt by a member of the staff to deal with their feelings about surgery.

Two treatments were devised on the crisis intervention model to help patients deal with surgery. The first treatment, called support, was based on the primary stance of the chaplain. In the treatment the treater showed his concern for the patient through regular visits where the patient's feelings and anxieties were talked about. The patient was assured his feelings were acceptable and that the counselor would be with him if needed.

A second treatment, called support-information, was devised to augment the basic supportive treatment with information that would help explain the hospital rhythm, role expectancies that hospital personnel had for patients, and practical knowledge of how to gain relief from pain, who to ask about recovery procedures, ordering food, etc. It was felt that this information would help prepare patients emotionally for surgery through anticipation and reinforce the patient's confidence in the counselor and the entire hospital staff.

METHOD

Several different measures were used to evaluate the impact these treatments had on the healing process. These included identifying material such as age and sex; surgical-medical history, such as the number of previous hospitalizations, length of stay in the hospital and the type of surgery being performed; basic psychological make-up, such as the Spielberger (1969) transitory anxiety scores and treatment ratings; and physiological and nonreactive measures from medical records and calls for service, such as pulse and respiration rates, amount of pain medication used, lines of nursing notes written and calls for the bedpan, medication and other services.

Orthopedic surgery patients were studied before, during and after hospitalization in the following areas: Length of stay in the hospital, use of pain medication, state anxiety, physiological measures, comparison of physician and patients' ratings of the patients' pain, stress and satisfaction, the patients' rating of their treatment, and the amount written about each patient in nursing notes.

Patients were divided by three different phases in the study. In all there were three groups: The control group (N=50), a support group (N=30), and a support-information group (N=70). In the first phase group number one, called the control group received normal hospital care. During the second phase two groups were formed using random number selection. Group two, called support (N=30) received the support treatment and group three, called support-information (N=30) received the support-information treatment. During the final phase group three with N=40 was continued from the second phase and received support-information treatment.

Groups were compared on the variables listed above, using a one-way analyses of variance. Patients were measured on certain variables before and after surgery and with the type of data gathered on these variables, sign tests were constructed and chi square scores were calculated to compare the impact of the treatments on the healing process.

RESULTS

All groups were found to be relatively equivalent presurgically on all the following variables: age, sex, number of previous hospitalizations, type of surgery, manifest anxiety, pulse, respiration, temperature, amount of pain medication, lines of nursing notes written and calls for bedpan, medication and service. Therefore, it was postulated that any differences among the three groups post-surgically on these variables would be a function of the treatments given to them.

Both the support and support-information groups were found to have significant impact on healing when compared with the control group. Though less dramatic, the support-information group seemed to have a greater impact than the support treatment alone. All results reported were significant at the .05 level of significance using ANOVA.

FIGURE 1
Days Stay in the Hospital from the Day of surgery

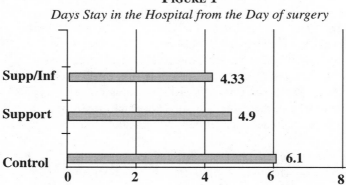

As shown in Figure 1, the control group stayed in the hospital after their operation almost a day longer than the support group and two days longer than the support-information group. Figure 2 shows that treatments given before surgery raised the transitory anxiety of both treatment groups almost four points higher than the control group. However, Figure 3 demonstrates that the transitory scores of the control group increased almost five points after surgery, while the support group decreased 1.8 points and the support-information group 3.3 points. Thus the control group had transitory anxiety scores over two points higher than the support group and four points higher than the support-information group. Figure 4 indicates that the control group made many more calls for service than either treatment groups, and that the support group made more calls than the support-information group. The control group patients were more incongruent in their assessment of the pain and stress they endure during surgery with their surgeon's assessment than either treatment group as shown in Figure 5.

FIGURE 2

Transitory Anxiety Scores After Treatment and Before Surgery

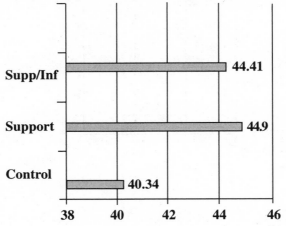

FIGURE 3

Transitory Anxiety Scores the Second Day After Surgery

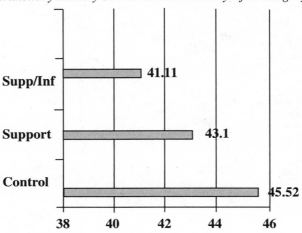

FIGURE 4

Comparison of Monitored Calls by Group Using Standardized Scores

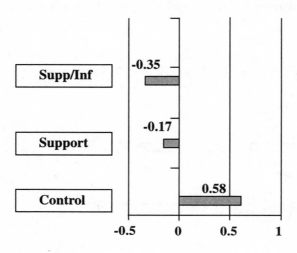

FIGURE 5

*Standardized Congruency Scores Comparing Physician and Patient
Ratings of Pain and Stress*

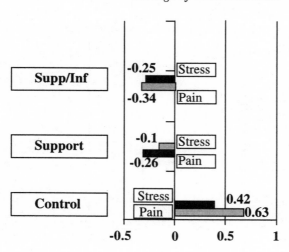

Table 1 provides additional evidence of the affect that the crisis intervention treatments had on the surgery patient. Treatment groups used less pain medication, had lower physiological responses, and had less written about them in nursing notes than did the control group.

TABLE 1
Measure Taken the First and Second Days after surgery
and
the Third Day after Surgery Till Release

A. THE QUANTITY OF PAIN MEDICATION USED BY GROUP

	1st and 2nd Day	3rd day till Release
Support-Information	3.76	1.76
Support	4.47	2.60
Control	5.16	3.30

B. RESPIRATION RATE BY GROUP

Support-Information	17.84	17.83
Support	17.93	17.78
Control	19.18	18.42

C. PULSE RATE BY GROUP

Support-Information	81.36	76.87
Support	80.47	75.69
Control	86.42	80.02

D. LINES OF NURSING NOTES WRITTEN FOR EACH GROUP

Support-Information	9.26	4.60
Support	9.93	5.17
Control	13.30	7.50

DISCUSSION

The most pragmatically significant result of this study appears to be that patients were able to leave the hospital from one to two days sooner in the groups that received crisis intervention treatment. The implication of this for hospital administration is obvious in terms of bed availability, physician time, cost and patient satisfaction.

Another significant finding could be seen in the change of transitory anxiety scores from after treatment and before surgery to after surgery scores. These scores indicated that treatments raised patients' anxiety in anticipation of their surgery. Control patients, though their anxiety scores raised before surgery, were far below the treatment groups raises. It seems helping patients face their fears of surgery raised their anxiety initially, but helped them adapt to recovery and lower their anxiety post-surgically. Patients who received support and information were significantly less anxious than the support group (Figures 2 and 3). The present study indicates that the anxiety of the treatment groups presurgically was helpful in that it was directly related to the realistic threat of surgery.

Recent research conducted by Spiegel has show that the level of a patient's anxiety can influence his perception of pain. The correlation of the use of pain medication and the transitory anxiety of patients seem to support this thesis. In addition, it indicates intervention treatment can affect the use of pain killing drugs.

The calls each patient made to the nursing station were noted on a prepared check list. The control group made many more requests for service from the staff than either of the treatment groups. It appears that the treatment team which consisted of chaplains, social workers and nursing staff was able to lower the demands patients made on the regular staff and their physicians. Use of auxiliary personnel already present in many hospitals may make a significant impact on patient healing, especially if such personnel can give information that will help orient the patient to his treatment and to the operations of the hospital.

Both the support and the support-information groups appeared to affect the physiological responses of the patients. These responses were seen in the lower respiration and pulse rates (Table 1), indicating less anxiety and physical tension. Thus, it appears the treatments used aided the patients' physical recovery.

Patients in the support and support-information groups were more realistic in their attitudes about their operations than were the control group patients.

Figure 4 shows their rating of pain, stress and satisfaction were closer to the more objective ratings of their physicians.

These same patients were also more satisfied with their treatment than were the control group patients. An important part of the attitude treatment patients had was related to their feeling less pain, recovering more quickly and being released ahead of the control group. The positive attitude these patients had holds important potential for the hospital. It is good for the hospital image in the community, and it could be of benefit if the patient needs hospitalization in the future.

SUMMARY

In conclusion, it appears that the crisis intervention technique used in this study had a significant impact on the healing process. Evidence seems to show chaplains were effective in using these techniques.

This study indicates that giving the patients a reference point, helping them focus on the experience of surgery, aiding them in making sense out of the whole experience of surgery and recovery through information and letting the patients know they were cared for has a significant impact on the healing process.

REFERENCES

Andrew, J. (1970). Recovery from surgery, with and without preparatory instruction, for three coping styles. *Journal of Personality and Social Psychology, 15*, 223-226.

Egbert, L., *et.al.* (1964). Reduction of postoperative pain by encouragement and instruction of patients. *New England Journal of Medicine, 270*, 825-827.

Jackson, K., *et.al..* (1953). Behavior Changes Indicating Emotional Trauma in Tonsillectomy Children. *Pediatrics, 12*, 23-28.

Janis, Irving. (1958). *Psychological Stress*, New York: John Wiley and Sons.

Mason, R., Clark, G., Reeves, R., Wagner, S. (1969). Acceptance and healing. *Journal of Religion and Health, 8*, 123-142.

Spielberger, C. *et.al.* (1969). *The S.T.A.I. Manual*, Tallahassee, Fla: Mimeograph copy.

EDITOR'S COMMENTS

This is a solid study which should continue to be of interest to hospital chaplains. It is an "intervention study" in which one variable was manipulated: the kind of attention received from the chaplain. The author, therefore, can argue that the data of the response variables among the three groups demonstrate the effects of that attention.

The author's statement of the problem at the date of publication (1973) continues to be true today:

Spokesmen for these helping professions (previously described as "departments of pastoral care, social work,.....") ...claim they are accessible and place few demands on the patient. The problem has been that little of an empirical nature has been done to evaluate the impact of these professions on the hospitalized patient.

So, what did the author find? He reports a shorten length of stay in the hospital when patients receive emotional/spiritual support and information about the hospital process. At least some chaplains today would argue that the author's work was not explicitly spiritual in character and thus the results can not be interpreted as demonstrating the unique benefits of hospital chaplains. The fact that it was carried out by a chaplain, however, does suggest that they can successfully provide this service which is humane and at least implicitly spiritual. Readers who wish further discussion of this project should consult the author's chapter in *At the Point of Need: Living Human Experience* (1988). This chapter further describes the context within which the research took place and alludes to a subsequent project "conducted in six Midwestern hospitals" (p.265) although no published report of this work seems to exist.

The chief finding in this project is very relevant today. Hospital administrators are increasingly interested in shortening the length of stay and these results suggest that the support and information given by this chaplain accomplished that in a substantial manner.

REFERENCES

Florell, J. (1988). Effective pastoral care in the hospital. In J. Ashbrook & J. Hinkle Jr. (Eds.), *At the point of human need* (pp.263-269). New York: University Press of America.

Prediction of Results in Open Heart Surgery

Mitchell Mills
Donald Mimbs
Edward E. Jayne
Robert B. Reeves, Jr.

S urgeons know that there are certain depressed, pessimistic patients who have an unusually high operative risk. Recognition of such patients takes experience and demands that considerable time be spent getting to know the person. Even then, the evaluation is subjective and difficult to communicate to others.

Hospital chaplains have shown an increasing willingness to serve as consultants on the patient-care team. Their depth of knowledge concerning man's interpersonal relationships and their religious concern for the wholeness of sick patients combine to generate data that physicians can use in planning their patients' care.

Data that are most useful to physicians are quantitative and amenable to statistical analysis. The chaplains at the National Naval Medical Center suggested that the Acceptance Scale developed by Mason, Clark, Reeves, and Wagner (1969) might provide such data preoperatively in a variety of surgical illnesses other than retinal detachment. It was decided to test this hypothesis for open heart surgery.

Reproduced with permission of the Plenum Publishing Company, from the *Journal of Religion and Health*, (1975), 14(3), 159-164.

METHODS

One hundred adult patients scheduled for open heart surgery between March 21, 1972, and January 17, 1974, were interviewed preoperatively by a chaplain and then scored on an Acceptance Scale essentially identical to that used by Mason, *et al* (1969) (Figure 1). This was a consecutive series with random lapses only when the chaplain conducting the study was absent. Neither the patient nor the surgeons were aware of the rating score. The scores were withheld from the medical and nursing staff until the conclusion of the study. No attempt was made to give any special ministry to low-scoring patients. Chaplains' visits were made according to the normal hospital routine. Twenty-five of the patients were scored by one or more additional raters. In such cases, the score used was the average value of all the observations.

FIGURE 1
Acceptance Scale

Scales	Accepts Totally	Accepts Cautiously	Accepts with Reservations	Accepts with Resignation	Rejects
1. Reaction to Heart problem	Confronts directly	Shaken but goes on	Advances fearfully	Bogged Down	Trapped-Back-to-wall
2. Reaction to Surgeon	Trusts	Praises hopefully	Seeks reassurance	Submits	Suspects
3. Reaction to Surgery	Optimistic about results	Hopefully certain of success	Vacillates in expectation	Unwilling to hope	Pessimistic
4. Reaction to Chaplain	Seeks companionship in interpreting life	Seeks agreement for positive philosophy	Seeks consolation and avoids discussion of inner conflict	Seeks respect for virtue and wisdom of compliance	Perceives as alien force or expects him to mourn
5. Reaction to Others	Meets on equal terms	Acts as host	Is not sure how to react	Expects sympathy and concern	Gives sense that no response to him is adequate
6. Coping Ability	Confident he can cope	Hopeful he can cope	Ambivalent about coping ability	Doubtful he can cope	Convinced he cannot cope
7. Self-care Ability	Able to do things for self and be helpful	Tries to do things for self and cooperate	Torn between desire to do inability to do	Helpless and makes obvious display of it	Acts as if entitled to services

Figure 2, Continued

8. Self-Image	Accepts self and situation (without special concern)	Displays positive image (embarrassed by dependence)	Keeps things in check (ambivalent about dependence)	Self-pitying (recognizes dependence with pity)	Sulking or detached (angry over dependence)
9. Conversational	Willing to converse in depth	Pursues pleasant conversation	Caught between response and preoccupation	Talks mostly about affliction of self	Avoids open contacts with others
10. Philosophy	Accepts bad with good	Wonders how the bad fits	Seeks assurance this is not all bad	"What can you do?" (It's God's will.)	"It's a dirty trick."

The Acceptance Scale was scored by giving a numerical value for each of the 10 items that were evaluated by the rater. For each item, the score is five points if checked under "accepts totally" and declines by one point in each column to the right so that a check in the "rejects" column scores only one point. The scores of each category rated are added together, then divided by the number of items rated (10 or less). The highest possible score is five, the lowest, one.

The result of the patients' surgery was evaluated in two ways. First, six milestones of progress in the early postoperative period were selected and scored by the surgeons (Figure 2). A favorable or unfavorable mark was given in each category. The favorable marks were added, then the unfavorable marks subtracted from them. A hospital death is scored as -6. The best score is +6.

FIGURE 2
The Postoperative Score Sheet

	Yes	No
Survived Surgery		
Complications		
No narcotic injections after 3 days		
Regular diet in 48 hrs.		
Thinking disorder		
Home in 14 days		

The second measure of the surgical result was the change in the American Heart Association Classification (AHA Class) at three months postoperatively. This score was given by the cardiologist caring for the patient at that time. The best result was a +3 (from Class IV to Class I). The worst result was a -4 (from Class I to death).

The postoperative scores were compared to the preoperative acceptance ratings according to the scales shown in Figures 3 and 4.

FIGURE 3

Method of Correlating the Acceptance Rating
with the Postoperative Results

	High	**Middle**			**Low**
	High	**Upper Middle**	**Middle**	**Lower Middle**	**Low**
Postop Score	+6 +5 +4	+3 +2 +1	0	-1 -2 -3	-4 -5 -6
Acceptance Rating	5.0—4.1	4.0—3.1	3.0	2.9—2.0	1.9—1.0
Heart Assoc. Score	+3—+2	+1	0	-1	-2 -3 -4
	Excellent Result	Good Result	Unchanged Result	Poor Result	Catastrophic Result

FIGURE 4

Method of Using the Correlation Scale Shown in Figure 3
to Place Each Patient Studied into One of Five Categories

1. In the same column   On the nose
      Includes: Upper-middle, middle-middle
      lower-middle

2. In adjacent columns, either: Close
      High and upper middle, or
      Low and lower middle
      Includes: upper-middle, lower middle

3. Skipping from   Inconclusive
      Middle to high or from
      Middle to low

4. Skipping from   Off
      High to lower middle or from
      Low to upper middle

5. In the extreme end columns   Way off

RESULTS

The correlations between acceptance score and surgical result are shown in Table 1. For both the early and late postoperative evaluation, the significance is very strong ($p < .001$).

TABLE 1

Results of the Study Showing the Degree to which the Preoperative
Acceptance Rating is Predictive of the Postoperative Score
and of the AHA Class at three Months

	Acceptance vs postop score	Acceptance vs AHA Class at three months
On the nose	50	41
Close	38	41
Inconclusive	5	8
Off	6	8
Way off	1	2
Total	100	100

The relation between acceptance score and morbidity and mortality is even more striking (Table 2). The risks to a patient with an acceptance score of 2.9 or below are excessive. No such correlation exists between the preoperative AHA Class and risk. In the 19 Class IV patients, there was no postoperative mortality and the complication rate was practically the same as for the entire series (22%). The difference in mortality between the low-scoring patients and the AHA Class IV patients was evaluated by the modified T-test and is significant (p<.02).

TABLE 2
Relation between Acceptance Rating
and
Postoperative Morbidity and Mortality

No.patients	Acceptance Rating	Complications	Mortality
100	3.9(mean)	22%	9%(7 early, 2 late)
19(AHA Class 4)	3.5	21%	0
41	>4.1	12%	5%
51	4.0-3.0	26%	4%
8	<3.0	63%	40%

DISCUSSION

Our results confirm and extend the findings of Mason and his co-workers (1969). In open heart surgery, as in retinal detachment, there is a strong correlation between acceptance and healing. The Acceptance Scale is predictive of the result. We do not know why this is so. We do not imply any cause and effect relation. Nevertheless the predictive value is so strong that we recommend the use of the scale in any major surgical setting. In our opinion, further statistical validation of the instrument for each type of major operation or by each surgical specialty is not required.

What does remain to be done is to demonstrate that, for patients whose initial acceptance score is 2.9 or below, some rapid form of therapy is available that will improve the result. We know of only one investigation that has data suggesting that this is so (Florell, personal communication). "Crisis intervention" preoperatively in the orthopedic cases studied by Dr. Florell is shown to have improved the patients' early postoperative course. No data are given about the long-term result of the surgery.

Our plan is to focus on patients who score 2.9 or below. We will attempt to elevate their acceptance before the cardiac surgery is performed. We will follow these patients and determine if the surgical result is better than would be predicted by our initial series.

Summary

One hundred candidates for open heart surgery were rated preoperatively by means of an Acceptance Scale. The rating was found to have a strong correlation with the result of surgery. It is believed that the scale is sufficiently predictive to allow identification of a high-risk group of patients who should receive an intensive ministry before they are operated on. The scale is probably applicable to a very broad variety of surgical patients.

References

Mason, R., Clark, G., Reeves, R., & Wagner, B. (1969). Acceptance and Healing, *Journal of Religion and Health, 8,* 123-142. Florell, J. Personal communication.

Editor's Comments

This is the last of the "classical" articles reproduced here. Its results suggest that the concept of "acceptance" can be applied to open heart surgery patients.

As readers examine the reports which follow, they will notice an increased complexity in the statistical analysis. Those who are knowledgeable about statistics will welcome this complexity because it also represents an increased sophistication which produces clearer and stronger results. The tables in this article contain raw numbers or percentages (Table 2); most of the subsequent articles will increasingly report results of statistical tests which are conducted on such numbers. This represents the development in the field of statistics during the last two decades and strengthens our ability to more clearly describe results.

Spiritual Support in Life Threatening Illness

Bernard Spilka,
John D. Spangler,
Constance B. Nelson

ABSTRACT

This work evaluated the experiences of 45 parents of children with cancer and 101 cancer patients with their home pastors and hospital chaplains. The satisfactions and difficulties encountered in these interactions are detailed, and recommendations are offered to aid persons in acute distress. Individuals in these circumstances appear to desire spiritual support more than evident psychological aid, though the skillful use of the latter to understand the religious desires of the patients and parents is appreciated. It is also evident that pastors dealing with problems related to potential terminality are themselves under considerable stress.

Pastors probably face their most severe test when confronted with terminal patients and their families. Frequently, the cleric involved in such a crisis feels a number of personal shortcomings. Beliefs that one has not been adequately trained for this work are common; almost one out of every two pastors perceives this to be true (Spilka, Spangler, Rea, & Nelson, 1981). Anxiety about the pastor's own death may also be aroused along with its significance concerning guilt, loneliness, pain, isolation, and

Reproduced with permission of Plenum Publishing Co. from the *Journal of Religion and Health,* (1983), 22(2), 98-104.

failure (Spilka, Stout, Minton, & Sizemore, 1977). Finally, to paraphrase Bruder, one is "faced with the questions of ultimate, as well as immediate concern: meaning, purpose, value, faith, hope and love—the soul's destiny" (Bruder, 1962). The pressure of these burdens can never be borne lightly and, for many, may not be handled well at all.

Clergy are well aware of the rapid and dramatic development of efficacious psychological approaches to crisis management. Strunk (1957) has summarized the incorporation of such methodologies into the spiritual enterprise by observing that "theological interest led to the formation and proliferation of what is now called pastoral psychology". It has, however, been argued (Hume, 1970) that clergy may sometimes claim a reflected identity from the disciplines of psychology or psychiatry. In fact, Paul Johnson (1967) urged the profession to take seriously its "boundaries," and indicated that the task of clinical pastoral education is learning "to relate persons to resources of healing and spiritual growth" (emphasis added). This possible confusion between the psychological and the spiritual may be a source of difficulty, not only from the viewpoint of the pastor but possibly from that of the patient. Knowledge of what is helpful or distressing in these interactions has yet to be spelled out in detail.

In a continuing effort to resolve this problem, the present research is an extension of that reported earlier (Spilka, Spangler, & Rea, 1981). We now shift from the perspective of clergy to that of cancer patients and the parents of children with cancer. Our purpose has been to ascertain the kinds of activities and relationships that have proven helpful and meaningful, as well as those causing distress to these groups of patients and parents. Our earlier research suggested the following hypothesis: namely, when death threatens, greater satisfaction will attend measures regarded as spiritual support than those considered exclusively as psychological in nature.

For the purposes of this study, "psychological" will be understood as referring to issues of human relationships, working through the pain of grief and loss, enduring physical pain, and the emotional acceptance of unavoidable circumstances, all on the immediate human level. "Spiritual" refers to issues of life in terms of ultimate meanings, values, relationships with the Ultimate, and rationalizing the "non-manipulables" (Bernhardt, 1958) of life. Both psychological and spiritual are thus viewed as having their own vocabularies, literature, and prescribed (ritualistic) behavior patterns. Of course, there is considerable overlap; positive effects may result when spiritual strengths are skillfully brought to those who need them, and this skill may well be a function of psychological proficiencies.

METHOD

Sample

One hundred and one cancer patients and 45 parents of children with cancer participated in this study. Females were the majority in both groups, being 77 percent of the patients and 91 percent of the parents. The mean age of the patients was 52.5 years; mean age of the parents was 37.2 years. Prior to the development of cancer, 73.7 percent of the patients and 88.6 percent of the parents were church affiliated.

On a six-point scale of the importance of religion, prediagnosis importance and current importance were rated respectively at 4.5 and 4.9 or "quite important." We may, therefore, regard our sample as fairly, if not strongly, religious.

The distributions of religious affiliations were very similar for patients and parents. Thirty-one percent of the former were Catholic, while 26 percent of the latter were so identified. Respective percentages for Protestants were 58 and 57 percent, and in both groups 11 percent were Jews. About 3 to 5 percent of the respondents in each group considered themselves to be atheistic or agnostic. A wide range of Protestant religious bodies was represented with small numbers in each; so no real pattern distinguishing patients and parents was evident.

Twenty-eight different forms of cancer were present among the patients, with the largest subgroup being breast cancer (37 percent). Three other types were found among more than 5 percent of the patients: Hodgkins disease (9.0 percent), lymphosarcoma (7.7 percent) and granulocytic leukemia (6.4 percent).

Fourteen different kinds of cancer were represented in the children. Almost half (44.4 percent) had lymphocytic leukemia, while other forms of leukemia and a wide variety of tumors (Ewings, Wilms, medulloblastoma, etc.) make up the remainder of the conditions.

Tests and materials

A 55-item questionnaire was empirically developed with the aid of a number of cancer patients and medical personnel who had worked with children who had cancer. Six of the questions were of an open-ended nature, the remainder being objectively structured. In addition to demographic data, the first set of questions concerned the nature of the cancer, time since diagnosis, and religious activity.

A second set of questions focused on 10 identified activities of patients and parents with home pastors and hospital chaplains relative to home and hospital visits (Note 1). Third, both objective and subjective responses were gathered regarding sources of satisfaction or unhappiness with these contacts. Finally, opportunities for discussing current religious perspectives were also provided. Many respondents wrote at great length about their experiences with clergy, indicating in detail those activities of the pastors that were either gratifying or distressing.

Procedure

The data were gathered from a number of sources. In addition to personal contacts by the writers, help was secured through the American Cancer Society and a self-help group known as Cansurmount. Both a local chapter of Candlelighters and the national headquarters of this organization of parents offered their services and were extremely helpful in enlisting parents of children with cancer.

RESULTS AND DISCUSSION

Extent of contacts

To set the stage for understanding the nature of clergy-patient contacts, these need to be examined. Twenty-nine percent of the patients had visits in their homes by their pastor; 42 percent of the parents of children with cancer had similar meetings. The trend was reversed for hospital visits by one's home clergy; 66 percent of patients and 56 percent of parents reported such contacts. On the average, pastors made 2.5 visits to the patients and 2.8 visits to the home where a child had cancer. Fifty-six percent of the patients and the same proportion of the parents saw a hospital chaplain, the mean number of visits being respectively 2.5 and 2.7, essentially the same as with the home pastor.

Actions of clergy

Obviously there is a fair amount of pastor-patient and pastor-parent contact. With few exceptions, there is a religious quality in these interactions. Twenty-two to 47 percent of the patient contacts involved prayer; however, the clerical groups responded differently, with home pastors actually praying more with patients (46 percent) than with chaplains (22 percent). However, offers to pray for or with the patient are essentially equivalent. The greater familiarity of the patient with his or her pastor probably accounts for this. Such is also suggested by evidence that home pastors discuss family matters more with patients (47 versus 12 percent) and convey more of a sense of understanding than do hospital chaplains (44 versus 28 percent).

When a child has cancer, there are indications of greater anxiety and, we infer, stronger feelings of inadequacy among clergy than when an adult is ill. Forty-four to 58 percent of the parent-pastor interactions relate to prayer, with no meaningful differences existing between the home and hospital clerics. Heightened anxiety may be inferred in these circumstances, since the amount of reported talk about irrelevancies increased notably (21 to 34 percent for home pastors and 18 to 36 percent for chaplains). The fact that 16 percent more parents than patients perceived understanding by the hospital chaplain may imply greater efforts on his or her part when cancer strikes a child.

In general, prayer and talk about family matters were the activities most commonly noted by both patients and parents, these occurring between 40 and 50 percent of the time. Religious readings, talking about church affairs, counseling, and discussions of the future were present least frequently. About 15 percent of the time, patients and parents reported the clergyman as doing something "other" than one of the defined activities. The "other" activity frequently concerned the pastor or chaplain "simply being present"—a point that is not to be taken lightly.

When the pattern for pastors and chaplains is viewed comprehensively, regardless of content, fewer than half of the clergy engaged in any one behavior. Further, when patients and parents were asked if the cleric seemed to understand their feelings, again fewer than half were reported as doing so.

Hypothesis testing: patient and parent satisfaction

Our hypothesis suggested that patient satisfaction with clergy increases with the latter's willingness to engage in spiritual activities. To assess this possibility, correlations were run between satisfaction with clergy visits and the activities of the pastors and chaplains at these times. It should, however, be noted that the general level of satisfaction with clergy is high. On a four-point scale, the satisfaction means for patients and parents are 3.6 and 3.2, respectively, for home pastors and 3.5 and 2.8, respectively, for hospital chaplains.

The expectation of clerical spiritual involvement and patient and parent satisfaction was borne out. Consistently, for home pastors but not hospital chaplains, actually praying with patients and parents does result in favorable feelings. This difference between the two groups of clergy could be a function of familiarity with the patient and family. It is probable that increased ease with someone you know permits either the request or offer for prayer to be made with less reservation. Reading from scripture or other religious writings also affiliates with patient and parent satisfaction, the former only with home clergy, the latter with both chaplain and home pastor. Responses of a largely secular nature (e.g., talk about the family, irrelevancies, "other") are independent of felt satisfaction.

As might also have been expected, the perception that the cleric understands the problems of the patient or family is associated with positive feelings. It is also tied to three pastoral actions among the parents, namely, offering to pray for the family, actually praying with the family, and conducting religious readings. Such understanding also relates to a view of the cleric as counseling, talking about church affairs, the family, and the future. This can be seen as meaningful interaction on many levels: spiritual, immediate concerns and long-range problems.

One must always ask: what is spiritual support? For example, the simple fact of the visit—either in the home or the hospital—by their own clergy was the most frequently cited gratifying element in these contacts. The visit itself implied concern, interest, and understanding. Often the patients felt guilty that the visit might be an imposition on a busy pastor's time; however, they greatly appreciated this investment in them.

Visiting by home clergy to families where a child has cancer seems to be of much less significance than what takes place when the visit occurs. This might reflect the perceived greater seriousness of this situation.

When we consider what goes on at these times that makes for satisfaction, our hypothesis gains additional support. Spiritual concern and prayer dominate. Perceptions of sympathy or kindness shown by clergy are usually associated with prayer. In addition, what is seen by the patient as "just talking," when elaborated, resulted in such statements as, "He talked about how God didn't cause the illness, but he would help us get through it," or "helped resolve questions about life and faith." In other words, comments offered by patients and parents are literally infused with spiritual ideas and support further underlining the significance of such actions by clergy. Explicit citations of prayer and Bible reading often accompany images of understanding and helpfulness on the part of the pastor or hospital chaplain.

NEGATIVE REACTIONS OF PATIENTS AND PARENTS

Communication failure

Feelings seem sharper when negative responses are examined. Though a broad range of displeasing possibilities are enumerated, most revolve about what is termed "lack of communication, understanding, interest and concern." Visiting out of duty is associated with being mechanical and impersonal—a failure to appreciate the spiritual needs of the patients and parents. Representative of many comments is the appeal of a distressed mother who volunteered a three-page letter in which she stated: "I felt and I wanted him to verbalize about God's fairness, my fears of my child dying, and my helplessness to do anything about it...most importantly, I wanted him to help me pray with my husband...He never offered to pray or ask me if I wanted to pray with me." This need for prayer is repeated over and over again in the picture of a home pastor who held himself aloof from the family in a manner perhaps correlated with his own inability to deal with pain and impending death.

Extreme insensitivity

The main basis for dissatisfaction is the unfeeling tactlessness of some clergy. One mother stated that the minister would not baptize her child because she did not attend his church regularly, even though her husband did. Another claimed that the pastor told her "to pray for Jesus to take her little boy." This was repeated a number of times to the very great discomfort of the mother. Two efforts to effect apparent "deathbed conversions" were upsetting, particularly when one cleric "harangued" a patient to "change his pagan ways." Fortunately these incidents were relatively infrequent.

Clerical discomfort

More common are perceptions of the discomfort of the clergy. Patients and parents may be quite sensitive, even oversensitive, to the responses of home pastors and chaplains. Reference was made to some clergy "being nervous," "fidgeting," "concerned about his/her own comfort," resorting to cliches such as "God loves you" and "Make every day count." Another telling comment was, "He stood far away." A related problem is the perceived eagerness of clergy to end the visit with the patient or family. Frequently looking at one's watch conveys this message clearly. The necessity of making clergy aware of such habitual and possibly unconscious actions goes without saying.

"Doing nothing"

Of all patient or parent complaints, the most common is that the pastor or chaplain "did nothing." He or she was present, but no meaningful help was perceived, and no real contact or understanding took place. It would be helpful to have some assessment of the patients' or parents' expectations of the pastor or chaplain and to know in detail what "nothing" really means.

It will be recalled that satisfaction as well as complaints were expressed about relationships with clergy who "really did nothing." This seeming contradiction might suggest that those who were satisfied may be responding to the symbolic role and presence of the cleric; those dissatisfied might be reacting to a perceived passivity on the part of the cleric. Additional and "deeper" data are necessary for the resolution of this inconsistency.

"Will the real chaplain stand up?"

The second problem noted by 14 percent of patients and 12 percent of parents was that of identifying the chaplain. Casual everyday dress, sports clothes, lack of an identifying religious symbol, name, or position tag (or one too small to read), and, finally, simply not saying initially who one was were all cited by respondents as hindrances. This difficulty was not taken lightly by our sample. One patient stated that the chaplain "wore a regular suit. I couldn't understand his introduction or read his name tag because he stood by the door." Ease of identification and traditional clerical garb were invariably regarded positively.

SUMMARY

From this empirical study of patients and parents of children with cancer, one can conclude that the complexity and seriousness of the situation where life-threatening illness strikes cannot be overestimated. Our sample's many pages of comments and evaluations speak of the profound significance their religious faith has for them. The interaction between clergy and those in these extreme circumstances is, however, fraught with difficulties that relate to the sensitivity of patients and families and the skills, insights, training, and experience of the clerics themselves.

Our work over the past three years suggests considerable discrepancy between the views of those in the present study—recipients of ministry—and the clergy regarding success in dealing with critical life-threatening situations. Clergy seen to view themselves as more effective than do those receiving their aid. Better communication and understanding between the cleric and those to whom he or she provides help is obviously needed. One might suggest an action research program within hospitals to improve chaplain services. Working with home pastors would be more difficult, but additional continuing education workshops could be offered by the faculties of accredited clinical pastoral education and American Association of Pastoral Counselors' centers. Current training of future clergy, especially with internship opportunities, appears to be better than ever before in seminary curricula, but much remains to be accomplished. Still further evaluation of cleric-patient-family interactions is necessary. This should be aggressively pursued by churches and hospitals and possibly also by patient- and parent-advocate organizations such as the American Cancer Society, the Candlelighters, and other similar groups.

REFERENCES

Bernhardt, W. (1958). *A Functional Philosophy of Religion*. Denver: Criterion.
Bruder, E. (1962). Clinical Pastoral Training in Preparation for the Pastoral Ministry. *Journal of Pastoral Care, 16*, 25-34.
Hulme, W. (1970). *Pastoral Care Comes of Age*. Nashville: Abingdon.
Johnson, P. (1967). *Person and Counselor*. Nashville: Abingdon, p. 31.
Spilka, B., Spangler, J., & Rea, M. (1981). The Role of Theology in Pastoral Care for the Dying. *Theology Today, 38*, 16-29.
Spilka, B., Spangler, J., Rea, M., & Nelson, C. (1981). Religion and Death: The Clerical Perspective. *Journal of Religion and Health, 20*, 299-306.
Spilka, B., Stout, L., Minton, B., & Sizemore, D. (1977). Death and Personal Faith: A Psychometric Investigation. *Journal for the Scientific Study of Religion, 16*, 169-178.
Strunk, O. (1957). The Present Status of the Psychology of Religion. *Journal of Bible and Religion, 25*, 287-292.

NOTES

1. The eleven activities were as follows: offer to pray for, offer to pray with, actually pray with, religious reading, counsel, talk of irrelevancies, seem to understand, talk about church matters, talk about family, discuss future, and other. Detailed information on the sample, its characteristics and responses, and analyses of the data may be obtained on request from the first author.

EDITOR'S COMMENTS

The hypothesis is that "when death threatens, greater satisfaction will attend measures regarded as spiritual support than those considered exclusively as psychological in nature." The authors report that this hypothesis is confirmed. This is likely of interest to chaplains and parish pastors.

This reported confirmation must be placed within at least three limitations, however. First, as the authors acknowledge, most of these respondents were actively religious; they report that "prior to the development of cancer, 73.7 percent of patients and 88.6 percent of the parents were church affiliated." This suggests that the results are more relevant for parish pastors; hospital populations are typically not as actively religious and may create different results.

A second limitation is that the data were gathered on a new instrument whose reliability and validity characteristics are not reported. If, statistically speaking, the instrument was not reliable, then the results are compromised. More about the reliability of research instruments later.

A third limitation is that, while we are told that the hypothesis was supported, no numerical results are reported. They say that the correlations between the level of satisfaction and the presence of spiritual activities demonstrated this, but we do not know what they were or their level of statistical significance. The report would be stronger if the authors made a more effective use of the language of numbers.

5

Spirituality and Well-Being in Terminally Ill Hospitalized Adults

Pamela Reed

ABSTRACT

Initial research into the significance of spirituality among terminally ill adults was extended. Two hypotheses were examined using three groups of 100 adults matched on age, gender, education, and religious background: a) Terminally ill hospitalized adults indicate a greater spiritual perspective than nonterminally ill hospitalized adults and healthy nonhospitalized adults. b) Spiritual perspective is positively related to well-being among terminally ill hospitalized adults. All 300 participants completed the Spiritual Perspective Scale, Index of Well-Being, and other information. Planned comparison analysis results supported the first hypothesis: low but significant correlation lent support to the second hypothesis. Differences among groups on recent change in spiritual views also were examined; a significantly larger number of terminally ill adults indicated a change toward increased spirituality than did nonterminally ill or healthy adults.

I n an era of rapidly advancing technology that focuses on the generation and extension of human life, the need remains for greater understanding of human experiences associated with terminal illness

Reproduced with permission of John Wiley & Sons, Inc. from *Research in Nursing and Health*, (1987), 10, 335-344.

and dying. Dying is an inevitable and complex phase of human development with possibilities for both distress and growth (Germino & McCorkle, 1985; O'Hare, 1982). As a developmental phase, dying can be distinguished from other life phases by certain characteristics. Spirituality is postulated as one characteristic particularly salient during the dying phase. The study of spirituality may contribute to knowledge about significant experiences among terminally ill individuals. Thus, this study was designed to extend the initial research of Reed by examining the significance of spirituality among a larger number of terminally ill persons, residing in a different geographical region of the country and more acutely ill than those in an earlier study (1986b).

The idea of spirituality as potentially significant among terminally ill persons derives from the broader concept of transcendence as a human phenomenon associated with the end of life. Transcendence is defined as a level of awareness that exceeds ordinary, physical boundaries and limitations. Transcend means to cross over or climb beyond. It is reflective of the human capacity to extend the self beyond common boundaries of the immediate context and achieve new perspectives and experiences. The human propensity toward transcendence as the individual moves closer to death is depicted in nursing and life-span developmental models (Chinen, 1984; Labouvie-Vief, 1980; Neugarten, 1979; Newman, 1979; Parse, 1981; Rogers, 1970; Schaie, 1977; Stevenson, 1977). Moreover, transcendent perspectives accrued over the lifespan, particularly during the last phases of life, may help the individual maintain a sense of well-being when faced with the biological and perceptual losses associated with dying.

Spirituality is one empirical indicator of the human capacity for transcendence. Spirituality is defined in terms of personal views and behaviors that express a sense of relatedness to a transcendent dimension or to something greater than the self. Spiritual transcendence does not imply a detachment from other dimensions of one's life (Conrad, 1985; Kopas, 1981), but emphasizes an openness to a perceived environment that extends beyond spatial and temporal boundaries. Spiritual perspectives represent a way of defining one's conceptual boundaries such that concepts like prayer and a higher being are meaningful in the present life situation.

Spirituality is a broader concept than religion or religiosity. It may or may not incorporate religious rituals and behaviors, and does not necessarily involve participation in a religious organization (Granstrom, 1985). The term religiousness has been used in operationalizing spirituality (Reed, 1986b) and is congruent with the definition of spirituality in this study, although spirituality is more accurate. Indicators of spirituality include prayer, sense of meaning in life, reading and contemplation, sense of closeness to a higher being, interactions with others, and other experiences which reflect spiritual interaction or awareness (e.g. Conrad, 1985; Moberg, 1982; Ruffing-Rahal, 1984). Spirituality may vary according to developmental level and life events (Fowler, 1981; Feinstein, 1979).

Spirituality was cited as integral to the dying person's achievement of the developmental task of transcendence (Moberg, 1982) and need for a transcendent perspective (Highfield & Carson, 1983; Hine, 1982; Mudd, 1981). Research findings indicated that spiritual manifestations of transcendence are significant to the dying experience (Augustine & Kalish, 1975; Bascom, 1984; Hood & Morris, 1983; Klass & Gordon, 1978-79; Lifton, 1979). Spiritual behaviors were identified among the seven most common coping methods used by patients with a life-threatening health problem (Baldree, Murphy & Powers, 1982). Spiritual meaning was regarded as highly important among older adults facing death (Kemp, 1984). More recently, Reed (1986b) found that personal religiousness was manifested to a significantly greater degree among ambulatory terminally ill adults than among a comparison group of healthy adults.

These studies provide evidence to support spirituality as a significant human experience during terminal illness. Moreover, evidence from a small number of studies suggests that spirituality not only exists among dying or seriously ill individuals, but may function as a resource for them. Spiritual variables [have been found to be] significantly related to low death fear, low discomfort, decreased loneliness, emotional adjustment, and positive death perspectives among terminal cancer and other seriously ill patients (Gibbs & Achterberg-Lawlis, 1978; Miller, 1985; O'Brien, 1982; Reed, 1986a).

Continued research into spirituality among terminally ill individuals is warranted. Although nursing has for many years acknowledged the importance of the spiritual dimension of patient care, the need remains for a sound empirical base so that patients' spiritual resources can be fully integrated into nursing care. Specifically, two hypotheses were examined: a)Terminally ill hospitalized adults indicate significantly greater spiritual perspective than nonterminally ill hospitalized adults and healthy nonhospitalized adults, and b) There is a positive relationship between spiritual perspective and well-being among terminally ill hospitalized adults. In addition, a research question was explored regarding a comparison of the frequency and types of reported recent changes in spiritual views across the three groups of participants.

METHODS

Sample

The sample consisted of 300 adults from the same geographical location in the southeastern United States distributed into three groups of 100 each according to the following criteria: Group 1, terminally ill hospitalized cancer patients who were aware of the terminal nature of their illness; Group 2, nonterminally ill hospitalized patients; and Group 3, healthy nonhospitalized persons. The second group was built into the design to control for possible effects of hospitalization upon spiritual perspective. All hospitalized participants had to have been hospitalized at least one full day and night prior to the study to allow for adjustment to the environment. The three groups were match on four variables that may influence spiritual perspective: age, gender, years of education, and religious background.

Group 1 participants had been hospitalized for the occurrence or recurrence of incurable cancer. Group 2 individuals were hospitalized for problems that were typically not life threatening. On the average, individuals in Group 1 had been hospitalized for six days and those in Group 2 five days. Group 3 participants were relatively healthy and free of any serious illnesses and were selected from community-center, neighborhood, and shopping-mall settings. All participants were mentally alert and literate in English.

The groups were comparable on the matching variables with no significant differences. The mean age of participants in Group 1 was 61.1 years (SD=14.56, range = 20 to 85 years), in Group 2 60.23 years (SD= 13.56, range = 20 to 85 years), and in Group 3, 60.54 years (SD= 10.85, range =23 to 82 years). There were 45 men and 55 women in each group. The average number of years of education was 12.63 (SD=3.77) in Group 1, 12.55 (SD=3.24) in Group 2, and 13.09 (SD=2.40) in Group 3. Of the participants in each group, 51% claimed a Protestant background, 30% to 31% Catholic, 4% Jewish, 6% to 7% checked other, and 8% indicated they had no religious background.

Most participants in each group were white (81%), and a small number were black (3% to 4%), Hispanic (12% to 13%), and American Indian or Asian American (2% to 3%). For each group, 55% to 66% were retired although three times as many Group 2 as Group 1 participants were employed. The lower employment rate in Group 1 was due to disabilities attributable to their terminal illness. Marital status was similar across groups in terms of those who were married and widowed. Fewer in Group 3 were divorced or single in comparison to Groups 1 and 2, but this difference was not significant.

Instruments

The *Spiritual Perspective Scale* (SPS) formerly called the "Religious Perspective Scale" (Reed, 1986b), was used to measure the saliency of spirituality in each group. Minor modifications were made in the instrument based on analyses from the 1986 study. The 10-item SPS measures persons' perspectives on the extent to which spirituality permeates their lives and they engage in spiritually-related interactions. Participants respond to the items based on their personal understanding of spirituality.

Acceptable reliability and validity of the SPS has been demonstrated in previous research on terminally ill and healthy adults (Reed, 1986b) as it has in the current study. Reliability of the SPS in this study was measured by Cronbach's alpha as an estimate of internal consistency. Alpha coefficients ranged from .93 in Group 2 to .95 in Groups 1 and 3. Inter-item analysis indicated that one item concerning prayer was redundant. No inter-item correlations fell below .41; average inter-correlations ranged from .57 to .68 across the groups. Evidence for construct validity was found in this study sample, as in previous research, in that women and those who reported having a religious background scored higher on the SPS. Qualitative data generated by open-ended questions also indicated the validity of the SPS for participants in this study. The psychometric properties of the instrument have remained adequate in research on adults of various health conditions, including terminally ill, healthy, and non-seriously ill.

The SPS is administered in either a structured interview or questionnaire format. Responses to each item are selected using a scale of 1 to 6. Descriptive words correspond to each number. Examples of the items are:
1.In talking with your family or friends, how often do you mention spiritual matters?
> 1.Not at all
> 2.Less than once a year
> 3.About once a year
> 4.About once a month
> 5.About once a week
> 6.About once a day

2.My spirituality is especially important to me because it answers many questions about the meaning of life.
> 1.Strongly Disagree
> 2.Disagree
> 3.Disagree more than agree
> 4.Agree more than disagree

                              5.Agree
                              6.Strongly Agree
    The SPS is scored by calculating the arithmetic mean across all items.
Possible scores range from 1 to 6, with 6 indicating greater spiritual perspective.

The Index of Well-Being

    (IWB) was used to measure participants' satisfaction with life as it was
currently experienced. The IWB was constructed by Campbell, Converse, and
Rogers (1976) who claimed that the index taps both cognitive and affective
dimensions of general well-being. It consists of nine items; the first eight are
in the form of semantic differentials and the last is a rating of overall life
satisfaction.
    Reliability and validity of the IWB have been examined in previous
research on samples of 2160 (Campbell *et.al.*, 1976) and 114 (Reed, 1986b).
Alpha coefficients were above .89 and item-scale correlations were .67 and
above. Concurrent validity has also been estimated to be moderate by a Pearson
correlation of .35 found between well-being and two variables, self-esteem and
self-competence (Campbell *et.al.,* 1976). Internal consistency of the IWB
estimated by Cronbach's alpha coefficient was .90 or above in each of the three
groups in the current study. Item analysis revealed no redundancies or
inconsistencies among the items. Average inter-item correlations ranged from
.51 to .61.
    Responses to the nine items are made on a 6-point Likert-type scale with
6 indicating greatest life satisfaction. Examples of the items are:
    1.My present life is:
           Rewarding__:__:__:__:__:__ Disappointing
                   1 2 3 4 5 6
    2.My present life is:

           Discouraging__:__:__:__:__:__Hopeful
                   1   2 3 4 5 6
    The IWB is scored as a weighted sum of two scores: a) the score on the
overall life satisfaction item weighted 1.1, and b) the mean score of the eight
semantic differentials, weighted 1.0. Potential score range from 2.1 to 12.6.
    In addition to these instruments, two items were used to elicit other data.
A perceived health rating from 1 for poor health to 5 for excellent health was
used to validate the participants' understanding of their health status. Second,
an open-ended question about changes, if any, that had occurred in spiritual
views during recent months or years was appended to the SPS.

Procedure

Procedures for data collection and management ensured informed consent and protection of the human rights of participants. Those in Group 1 were obtained from the same two hospital settings as those in Group 2, although the in-patient units varied. Hospital charts were reviewed and the primary nurse was interviewed to determine that criteria were met.

Each participant provided general background information and completed the SPS and IWB independently, with the exception of some in Groups 1 and 2 who requested assistance in reading the items or in recording their response. In these instances, special attention was given to maintaining consistency across participants; items were read by the data collector verbatim to the participant and no interpretations were provided. The open-ended question on change in spiritual views was addressed following completion of the SPS. To complete all of the questions, 20 to 60 minutes were required and, for some, to discuss issues raised by the SPS. Terminally ill participants were particularly interested in expressing their views on spirituality at the end of the study.

RESULTS

Hypothesis 1

(Namely that) terminally ill hospitalized adults (Group 1) indicate greater spiritual perspective than either nonterminally ill hospitalized adults (Group 2) or healthy nonhospitalized adults (Group 3), was supported. Planned comparisons were used to test the hypothesis since the expected outcome was defined *a priori*. The assumptions of normal distribution of scores and homogeneity of variance were examined first. Variances in the SPS scores were homogeneous across the three groups (Cochran's C $(3,99) = .35$, p=.88). The distributions of scores were similar across groups and were close to normal but positively skewed. The mean score on the SPS for Group 1 was 4.530 (SD=1.38), for Group 2, 4.157 (SD=1.27), and for Group 3, 4.160 (SD=1.36). Individual SPS scores ranged from 1 to 6.

Two orthogonal comparisons were designed to test the hypothesis. The first comparison contrasted the mean SPS score of Group 1 with the combined averages of Group 2 and Group 3 since there was no theoretical base in this study to postulate a significant difference between Group 2 and Group 3 in spiritual perspectives. A significant difference between Group 1 and the average of Group 2 and Group 3 SPS scores, coupled with a lack of difference between Group 2 and Group 3 SPS scores was needed to support the hypothesis. This was found, as Table 1 indicates. The first comparison was significant (F (1,297)=5.16, p=.02), whereas there was no difference between Group 2 and Group 3 mean SPS scores.

TABLE 1

Planned Comparisons of Spiritual Perspective Scores Between Terminally Ill, Nonterminally Ill, and Healthy Groups

Source	SS	df	MS	F
Between				
	9.25	2		
Comparison:				
Terminally Ill with				
Nonterminally Ill and Healthy	9.24	1	9.24	5.16*
Nonterminally Ill and Healthy	.00	1	.00	
Error (within)	532.38	297	1.79	
Totals				
	541.63	299		

*p=.02

Hypothesis 2

(Which stated that) there is a positive relationship between spiritual perspective and well-being in the terminally ill hospitalized group (Group 1), also was supported. The Pearson product moment correlation was .22 (p<.02). This relationship was not significant either in Group 2 (r=.09), or Group 3 (r=-.02).

Additional Analysis

Further analyses of the IWB scores across groups were done. The IWB scores were examined for significant differences across the three groups and none were found (F (2,297) =.186). IWB scores were highly similar; ranging from 10.30 to 10.40 (possible range of 2.10 to 12.60) indicating a moderately high degree of well-being. The means and standard deviations on the IWB for each group are listed in Table 2.

Perceived health means and standard deviations also are displayed in Table 2. As expected, Group 1 participants rated their health lower than did Group 2 who, in turn, rated their health lower than Group 3. Analysis of variance followed by *post hoc* comparisons (Scheffe) revealed that each of these differences was significant.

TABLE 2

Means, Standard Deviations, and Pearson Correlations
on Well-Being and Perceived Health

Comparison Group	Well-Being		Perceived Health		
	M	SD	M	SD	Pearson r
Terminally ill (n=100)	10.36	2.27	1.76	1.02	.32***
Nonterminally ill (n=100)	10.38	2.17	2.88	1.29	.44**
Healthy (n=100)	10.27	1.68	3.69	.94	.23*

*=p<.05; **=p.01; ***=p<.001

Significant correlations between IWB and perceived health were found in all groups (Table 2). For Group 1, IWB also correlated significantly, but weakly, with age (r=.18, p<.05). This relationship was not found in either Group 2 or Group 3, with correlations below .09. Thus, the results indicated that well-being was positively related to age only among the terminally ill.

The frequency and types of reported recent changes in spiritual views (as elicited from the open-ended question appended to the SPS) were compared across the three groups. Those who indicated a change were queried further about the way their views had changed. Approximately the same number of individuals in Group 1 (n=44) as in Group 2 (n=42) stated that they had changed their spiritual views. Somewhat fewer in Group 3 (n=28) indicated change. Chi-square analysis of the frequency of change in spiritual views across the three groups was not significant ($X^2(2)$ =4.0).

The content of responses concerning the type of change in spiritual views among those who initially indicated a change had occurred were analyzed and are summarized in Table 3. Of the 44 who indicated change in spiritual views in Group 1, 39 (88.6%) clearly indicated that the change represented movement toward greater spirituality; for example, experiencing a stronger faith or more meaningful prayer. Relatively few participants in Group 1, 2 (4.5%) stated that they had eschewed specific religious teachings and rituals of childhood. The remaining 3 (6.8%) expressed that change had occurred in terms of more questions and doubts about their spiritual beliefs.

TABLE 3
Description of Changes in Spiritual Views

Responses	N	%
Group 1-Terminally ill, hospitalized (n=44)		
Stronger faith or reliance upon God; felt closer to God	23	52.3a
Prayer is more frequent, more personal, more meaningful	12	27.3a
Experienced spiritual gain from life's misfortunes	4	9.0a
More questions and doubts about beliefs	3	6.8
Eschewed certain religious teachings/ practices of childhood	2	4.5
Group 2-Nonterminally ill, hospitalized (n=420)		
Stronger faith, stronger beliefs	19	45.2a
Lost faith, more critical of organized religion	6	14.3
Eschewed certain religious teachings/ practices of childhood	5	11.9
Pray more often	4	9.5a
(Table 3, Continued)		
More doubts and questions about life and death	4	9.5
Changed denominations	4	9.5
Group 3-Healthy, nonhospitalized (n=28)		
More personal, stronger faith; pray more often	16	57.1a
Eschewed certain religious teachings/ practices of childhood	5	17.8
Lost faith, critical of organized religion	4	14.3
Changed denominations	3	10.7

a=The sum of these figures for each group is the percentage of individuals who changed toward increased spirituality.

In Group 2, 23 (54.7%) of the 42 who identified some change in spiritual views indicated that the change was in the direction of a stronger faith or more frequent prayer (Table 3). Death of a family member, aging, illness, and other crises were frequently mentioned as reasons for this change. A larger number of those in Group 2, 10 (23.8%), than in Group 1, 3 (6.8%), described the change in terms of more doubt or lost faith.

Finally, among the 28 Group-3 participants who indicated a change in spiritual views, 16 (57.1%) described an increase in spiritual beliefs or behaviors (Table 3). As in Group 2, Group-3 participants frequently mentioned their own aging or death of a family member or spouse as influencing their increased spirituality. The same percentage of participants in Group 3 as in Group 2 stated that their spiritual beliefs had waned (14.3%) which was over twice the percentage in Group 1 (6.8%). Group 3 had the largest percentage of participants who indicated that they had eschewed certain religious teachings and rituals of their childhood (17.8%), with fewer in Group 2 (11.9%), and even fewer in Group 1 (4.5%) who stated this. As one moves from Group 3 to Group 1, then, there is a diminishing incidence of reference to loss of faith or disregard of childhood religious beliefs and an increasing percentage of statements about a strengthened spirituality. A significantly greater number of terminally ill adults indicated change toward increased spirituality than did nonterminally ill or healthy adults; chi-square analysis comparing all three groups on change toward increased spirituality was significant ($X^2 = 10.70$, p<.01) with no difference found between the nonterminally ill and healthy ($X^2(1) = 1.29$). In addition, change in spiritual views was found to correlate positively with SPS scores in each group; Group 1 had the highest and most significant correlation at .44 (p<.001), for Group 2, r=.22 (p<.05) and Group 3, r=.16 (p<.05).

DISCUSSION

The results of this study provide support for viewing spirituality as a potentially significant variable in the dying process. As hypothesized, hospitalized terminally ill adults indicated greater spirituality than both the hospitalized nonterminally ill group and healthy group of adults. Findings of this study support findings of other research (Reed, 1986b) in which terminally ill out-patients facing the end of their lives indicated a significantly greater degree of spirituality than did a matched group of healthy adults who did not perceive the end of their lifespan to be near.

Research on adults who because of their health status likely had an increased awareness of personal mortality also supports the findings here. For example, a notable level of spirituality was found among hemodialysis patients (Baldree *et.al.*, 1982; O'Brien, 1982). Critically ill hospitalized patients reported a greater sense of purpose in life than either a noncritically ill hospitalized or a well group (Thomas & Weiner, 1974). Significantly higher levels of spiritual well-being were found in a chronically ill group than were found in a healthy group (Miller, 1985), although interpretation of the results was limited by a lack of control on age and gender.

It is unlikely that the difference in spirituality identified in the current study can be attributed to differences in age, gender, years of education, or religious background across the groups since these variables were controlled at the outset. In addition, the experience of hospitalization seemed to have had little influence on SPS scores, given the similarity in SPS scores between Group 2 and Group 3. Other variables not accounted for in this nonrandom sample may have influenced increased spirituality in the Group 1. For example, it was noted from the qualitative data that those in Group 2 (hospitalized) and Group 3 (healthy) identified prior death involvements as influencing positive changes in their focus on spirituality. Those in Group 1 commented on how their own terminal illness had positively influenced their attitudes toward spirituality. Whether association with other death-related events is similar to experiencing one's own dying in effecting greater spirituality is open for investigation.

The significant though small relationship between spirituality and well-being among the terminally ill was consistent with findings of other researchers who identified relationships of similar magnitude between spiritual variables and positive emotional states among the terminally ill (Gibbs & Achterberg-Lawlis, 1978; Moberg, 1982). No relationship between spirituality and well-being was found among the other two groups of participants. Individuals who are ambulatory and perceive more time left to live are able to avail themselves of other resources that may correlate with well-being. Alternatively, the biological and psychosocial losses associated with dying may render terminally ill persons more open to spirituality as a way to maintain well-being. However, the somewhat weak relationship between spirituality and well-being in the terminally ill indicated that other factors related to their well-being as well. Nevertheless, the similarity in well-being scores across all groups suggested that dying individuals have the potential for well-being as much as their nonseriously ill and healthy cohorts.

Age was found to relate significantly although weakly to well-being in the terminally ill group, such that younger terminally ill individuals had lower well-being than did older terminally ill persons. This finding supports Reed's (1986b) previous findings and Neugarten's (1979) timing-of-events theory; dying is more timely among older persons and, thus, may be more easily integrated among the older terminally ill individuals.

Findings from the open-ended question concerning recent change in spiritual views showed that, among those who indicated a change in each group, the terminally ill group had the largest percentage who reported change toward an increase in spiritual beliefs and behaviors. Analysis of these qualitative responses along with the significant positive correlations found between change in spiritual views and SPS scores suggest that when a change in spiritual views did occur it was almost always associated with greater spirituality, particularly in Group 1.

Underlying the conceptual framework of this study was the assumption that dying, like other developmental phases, is accompanied by characteristic changes. Increased spirituality was put forth as accompanying dying. The findings of this study provide only indirect support for increased spirituality as a developmental change evident in the dying phase. Inferences regarding spiritual change as influenced by crises and life-threatening experiences have been drawn from other cross-sectional and longitudinal studies (Hall, 1986; McGlaughlin & Malony, 1984; O'Brien, 1982). Although indirect evidence about change may be generated by cross-sectional designs, the validity of these interpretations is questionable (Achenback, 1978; Hultsch & Deutsch, 1982). Research methods which combine cross-sectional with longitudinal strategies would provide more valid evidence of the significant changes theorized to occur as a person moves across the dying trajectory. The findings to date may be useful in planning more costly but more powerful designs for studying spirituality as a developmentally based resource of dying individuals.

The outcomes of this study have contributed to a better understanding of spirituality among the terminally ill. Admittedly, there are dimensions of spirituality that are ineffable. However, the participants' spirituality was not so "transcendent" that it could not, at least in part, be expressed and measured. Item analysis of the SPS scores and examination of qualitative responses indicated that certain symbols such as God, prayer, and forgiveness were frequently used in expressing what is spiritual to an individual faced with a health crisis. Others also have found this in their clinical work and research (Conwill, 1986; Miller, 1985; Todd, 1985). Continued research in this area may ultimately provide the empirical knowledge base needed for purposeful integration of spiritual dimensions in care of terminally ill individuals.

REFERENCES

Achenbach, T.M. (1978). *Research in developmental psychology: Concepts, strategies, methods.* New York: The Free Press.

Augustine, M.J., & Kalish, R. A. (1975). Religion, transcendence, and appropriate death. *Journal of Transpersonal Psychology, 7*(1), 1-13.

Baldree, K.S., Murphy, S. P., & Powers, J. J. (1982). Stress identification and coping patterns in patients on hemodialysis. *Nursing Research, 31*, 109-111.

Bascom, G.S. (1984). Physical, emotional, and cognitive care of dying patients. *Bulletin of the Menninger Clinic, 48*, 351-356.

Campbell, A., Converse, P.E., & Rodgers, W. (1976). *The quality of American Life: Perceptions, evaluations, and satisfactions.* New York: Russell Sage Foundation.

Chinen, A.B. (1984). Modal logic: A new paradigm of development and late-life potential. *Human Development, 27*, 42-56.

Conrad, N.L. (1985). Spiritual support for the dying. *Nursing Clinics of North America, 20*, 415-426.

Conwill, W.L. (1986). Chronic pain conceptualization and religious interpretation. *Journal of Religion and Health, 25*, 46-50.

Feinstein, A. (1979). Personal mythology as a paradigm for a holistic public psychology. *American Journal of Orthopsychiatry, 49*, 198-217.

Fowler, J.W. (1981). *Stages of faith: The psychology of human development and the quest for meaning.* San Francisco: Harper & Row.

Germino, B., & McCorkle, R. (1985). Acknowledged awareness of lifethreatening illness. *International Journal of Nursing Studies, 22*, 33-44.

Gibbs, H.W., & Achterberg-Lawlis, J. (1978). Spiritual values and death anxiety: Implications for counseling with terminal cancer patients. *Journal of Counseling Psychology, 25*, 563-569.

Granstrom, S.L. (1985). Spiritual care for oncology patients. *Topics in Clinical Nursing, 7, 39-45.*

Hall, C.M. (1986). Crisis as opportunity for spiritual growth. *Journal of Religion and Health, 25*, 8-17.

Highfield, M.F., & Carson, C. (1983). Spiritual needs of patients: Are they recognized? *Cancer Nursing, 6*, 187-192.

Hine, V.H. (1982). Holistic dying: The role of the nurse clinician. *Topics in Clinical Nursing, 4*, 45-54.

Hood, R.W., Jr., & Morris, R. (1983). Toward a theory of death transcendence. *Journal for the Scientific Study of Religion, 22*, 353-365.

Hulsich, D.F., & Deutsch, F. (1981). *Adult development and aging:A life-span perspective*. New York: McGraw-Hill.

Kemp, J.T. (1984). Learning from clients: Counseling the frail and dying elderly. *Personnel and Guidance Journal, 62*, 270-272.

Klass, D., & Gordon, A. (1978-79). Varieties of transcending experience at death: A videotape-based study. *Omega, 9*, 19-36.

Kopas, J. (1981). Jung and Assagioli in religious perspective. *Journal of Psychology and Theology, 9*, 216-223.

Labouvie-Vief, G. (1980). Adaptive dimensions of adult cognition. In N. Datan, & N. Lohmann (Ed.), *Transitions of aging* (pp.3-26). San Francisco: Academic Press.

Lifton, R.J. (1979). *The broken connection*. New York: Simon & Schuster.

McLaughlin, S.A., & Malony, H. (1984). Near-death experience and religion: A further investigation. *Journal of Religion and Health, 23*, 149-159.

Miller, J.F. (1985). Assessment of loneliness and spiritual well-being in chronically ill and healthy adults. *Journal of Professional Nursing, 1*, 79-85.

Moberg, D.O. (1982). Spiritual well-being of the dying. In G. Lesnoff-Caravaglia (Ed.), *Aging and the human condition* (pp.139-155). New York: Human Sciences Press.

Mudd, E.R. (1981). Spiritual needs of terminally ill patients. *Bulletin of the American Protestant Hospital Association, 45* (3), 1-5.

Neugarten, B.L. (1979). Time, age, and the life cycle. *The American Journal of Psychiatry, 136*, 887-894.

Newman, M. (1979). *Theory development in nursing*. Philadelphia: F.A. Davis.

O'Brien, M.E. (1982). Religious faith and adjustment to long-term hemodialysis. *Journal of Religion and Health, 21*, 68-80.

O'Hare, D.G. (1982). The experience of dying. In G. Lesnoff-C a r a v a g l i a (Ed.), *Aging and the human condition*. New York: Human Sciences Press.

Parse, R.R. (1981). *Man-living-health: A theory of nursing*. New York: John Wiley and Sons.

Reed, P.G. (1986a). Death perspectives and temporal variables in terminally ill and healthy adults. *Death Studies, 10*, 443-454.

Reed, P.G. (1986b). Religiousness in terminally ill and healthy adults. *Research in Nursing & Health, 9*, 35-41.

Rogers, M.E. (1970). *An introduction to the theoretical basis of nursing*. Philadelphia: F.A. Davis, Co.

Ruffing-Rahal, M.A. (1984). The spiritual dimension and well-being Implications for the elderly. *Home Healthcare Nurse, 2*(2), 12-13, 16.

Schaie, K.W. (1977). Toward a stage theory of adult development. *International Journal of Aging and Human Development, 8*, 129-138.

Stevenson, J.S. (1979). *Issues and crises during middlescnce.* New York: Appleton-Century-Crofts.

Thomas, J.M., Jr., & Weiner, E.A. (1974). Psychological differences among groups of critically ill hospitalized patients, noncritically ill hospitalized patients, and well controls. *Journal of Consulting and Clinical Psychology, 42*, 274-279.

Todd, E. (1985).The value of confession and forgiveness according to Jung. *Journal of Religion and Health, 24*, 39-48.

EDITOR'S COMMENTS

This is an important study because it demonstrates a foundation from which hospital chaplains can argue that pastoral care to hospitalized terminally ill patients is important. As the author says, the results suggest that spirituality is "a potentially significant variable in the dying process." The limitations of the study are important to note, however. She states that it is "potentially" significant because the study only demonstrates that the hospitalized terminally ill create higher SPS scores and report changes which are toward increased spirituality. That is not the same as demonstrating that they need or benefit from pastoral care. And, her findings do not inevitably lead to a conclusion that chaplains are necessary. The critic might argue that the higher SPS scores do not imply that support of that spirituality is necessary. Or, if it is necessary, family members or parish clergy can provide it. The challenge becomes more substantial if the critic suggests that chaplains demonstrate that the need for support of this spirituality exists or that a benefit ensues when pastoral care is given.

⑥

Positive Therapeutic Effects of Intercessory Prayer in a Coronary Care Unit Population

Randolph C. Byrd

Abstract

The therapeutic effects of intercessory prayer (IP) to the Judeo-Christian God, one of the oldest forms of therapy, has had little attention in the medical literature. To evaluate the effects of IP in a coronary care unit (CCU) population, a prospective randomized double-blind protocol was followed. Over ten months, 393 patients admitted to the CCU were randomized, after signing informed consent, to an intercessory prayer group (192 patients) or to a control group (201 patients). While hospitalized, the first group received IP by participating Christians praying outside the hospital; the control group did not. At entry, chi-square and stepwise logistic analysis revealed no statistical difference between the groups. After entry, all patients had follow-up for the remainder of the admission. The IP group subsequently had a significantly lower severity score based on the hospital course after entry (P < .01). Multivariant analysis separated the groups on the basis of the outcome variables (P < .0001). The control patients required ventilatory assistance, antibiotics, and diuretics more frequently than patients in the IP group. These data suggest that intercessory prayer to the Judeo-Christian God has a beneficial therapeutic effect in patients admitted to a CCU.

Reproduced with permission of the *Southern Medical Journal*, (1988), 81(7), 826-829.

Who has not, during a time of illness or pain, cried out to a higher being for help and healing (Spivak, 1917)? Praying for help and healing is a fundamental concept in practically all societies, though the object to which these prayers are directed varies among the religions of the world (Spivak, 1917). In western culture, the idea of praying for the benefit of others (intercessory prayer) to the Judeo-Christian God is widely accepted and practiced. However, the medical literature contains no scientific evidence either confirming or negating the healing effectiveness of intercessory prayer. In only a few studies have scientific methods been used to attempt to determine whether or not prayer is therapeutically effective (Galton, 1872; Galton, 1883; Joyce & Welldon, 1965; Collipp, 1969), and these studies have been inconclusive (Rosner, 1975).

My study concerning prayer and patients in a general hospital coronary care unit was designed to answer two questions: (1) Does intercessory prayer to the Judeo-Christian God have any effect on the patient's medical condition and recovery while in the hospital? (2) How are these effects characterized, if present?

METHODS

Between August 1982 and May 1983, 393 patients were entered into a prospective double-blind randomized protocol to assess the therapeutic effects of intercessory prayer. All patients admitted to the coronary care unit at San Francisco General Hospital were eligible for entry into the study; 57 patients refused for personal reasons, religious convictions, and/or unwillingness to sign the informed consent. Before entry, the nature of the project was fully explained to each patient and informed consent was obtained. Patients were randomly assigned (using a computer-generated list) either to receive or not to receive intercessory prayer. The patients, the staff and doctors in the unit, and I remained "blinded" throughout the study. As a precaution against biasing the study, the patients were not contacted again. It was assumed that some of the patients in both groups would be prayed for by people not associated with the study; this was not controlled for. Thus some of the patients in the control group would be prayed for, whereas all of the patients in the prayer group would be (i.e., by both nonassociated people and by the designated intercessors of the study).

For the purposes of this study, intercessors were chosen on the following basis. They were "born again" Christians (according to the Gospel of John 3:3) with an active Christian life as manifested by daily devotional prayer and active Christian fellowship with a local church. Members of several protestant churches and the Roman Catholic Church were represented among the intercessors.

Patients and intercessors were not matched by religion or denomination. After randomization, each patient was assigned to three to seven intercessors. The patients' first name, diagnosis, and general condition, along with pertinent updates in their condition, were given to the intercessors. The intercessory prayer was done outside of the hospital daily until the patient was discharged from the hospital. Under the direction of a coordinator, each intercessor was asked to pray daily for a rapid recovery and for prevention of complications and death, in addition to other areas of prayer they believed to be beneficial to the patient.

DATA ANALYSIS

I collected the information on each patient in a blinded manner, without knowledge of the spiritual status, condition, or ideas of the entrants during the study. Data were subsequently collated and entered into a PDP-11 computer for analysis, using the Biomedical Data Processing (BMDP) statistical package (Dixon, 1981). The data were analyzed with an unpaired t-test for interval data and a chi-square test (or Fisher's exact test when necessary) for categorical data. A stepwise logistic regression (Dixon, 1981) was used for the multivariant analysis (Press & Wilson, 1978; Lee, 1980). Interval data were expressed as the mean $\pm$ one standard deviation.

RESULTS

Data collected on each patient as he entered into the study (Table 1) revealed the condition of the patient groups at the time informed consent was signed. The 109 patients with acute myocardial infarction had the following Killip's classification: class I, 16% (prayer group) vs 16% (control group); class II 8% vs 10%; class III, 1% vs 1%; and class IV, 2% vs 2% (p=NS). Univariant and multivariant analysis showed no statistical differences between the two groups at entry. Thus it was concluded that the two groups were statistically inseparable and that results from the analysis of the effects of intercessory prayer would be valid.

TABLE 1

Patients' Status on Entry

	Intercessory Prayer Group (n=192)	Control Group (n=201)	P
Age (mean + SD)	58.2 + 14.8	60.1 + 15.0	NS
Sex:Female	65	63	NS
Male	127	138	NS
Time (days, mean + SD)*	0.9 + 1.2	0.9 + 1.1	NS
Primary Cardiac Diagnosis	% (No.)	% (No.)	P
Congestive heart failure	33 (63)	33 (66)	NS
Cardiomegaly	32 (62)	32 (64)	NS
Prior myocardial infarction	30 (57)	26 (50)	NS
Acute myocardial infarction	27 (51)	29 (58)	NS
Unstable angina	25 (48)	30 (61)	NS
Chest pain, cause unknown	19 (36)	15 (31)	NS
Acute pulmonary edema	13 (25)	13 (27)	NS
syncope	11 (21)	6 (12)	NS
Cardiomyopathy	8 (16)	9 (17)	NS
Supraventricular tachyrhythmia	8 (15)	12 (24)	NS
VT/VF	8 (14)	9 (17)	NS
Intubation/ventilation	6 (11)	10 (19)	NS
Valvular heart disease	5 (8)	8 (15)	NS
Hypotension (systolic <90 torr)	4 (8)	5 (10)	NS
Cardiopulmonary arrest	4 (8)	6 (12)	NS
Third-degree heart block	2 (3)	1 (1)	NS
Primary Noncardiac Diagnosis			
Diabetes mellitus	8 (16)	9 (18)	NS
COPD	8 (15)	10 (19)	NS
Gastrointestinal bleeding	5 (10)	2 (3)	NS
Severe hypertension	5 (10)	7 (13)	NS
Pneumonia	5 (9)	4 (7)	NS
Chronic renal failure	4 (8)	4 (8)	NS
Trauma	4 (7)	3 (6)	NS
Cerebrovascular accident	4 (7)	2 (4)	NS
Drug overdoes	3 (5)	3 (5)	NS
Sepsis	2 (3)	2 (4)	NS
Cirrhosis of the liver	2 (3)	1 (2)	NS

(Table 1 continued)

Pulmonary emboli	1 (2)	1 (1)	NS
Systemic emboli	1 (2)	0 (0)	NS
Hepatitis	0 (0)	1 (2)	NS

NS=P>.05. VT/VF =ventricular tachycardia/ventricular fibrillation; COPD = chronic obstructive pulmonary disease.
*Time from admission to the coronary care unit to randomization.

After entry, all patients had follow-up for the remainder of the hospitalization. New problems, new diagnoses, and new therapeutic interventions that occurred after entry into the study were recorded and are summarized in Table 2. Of the multiple variables measured, congestive heart failure, cardiopulmonary arrest, pneumonia, diuretics, antibiotics, and intubation/ ventilation were seen less frequently in the prayer group.

TABLE 2
Results of Intercessory Prayer

Study Variables	Intercessory Prayer	Control Group	P
Days in CCU after entry	2.0 + 2.5	2.4 + 4.1	NS
Days in hospital after entry	7.6 + 8.9	7.6 + 8.7	NS
Number of discharge medications	3.7 + 2.2	4.0 + 2.4	NS
New Problems, Diagnoses, and Therapeutic Events After Entry	% (No.)	% (No.)	P
Antianginal agents	11 (21)	10 (19)	NS
unstable angina	10 (20)	9 (18)	NS
Antiarrhythmics	9 (17)	13 (27)	NS
Coronary angiography	9 (17)	11 (21)	NS
VT/VF	7 (14)	9 (17)	NS
Readmissions to CCU	7 (14)	7 (14)	NS
Mortality	7 (13)	9 (17)	NS
Congestive heart failure	4 (8)	10 (20)	<0.03
Inotropic agents	4 (8)	8 (16)	NS
Vasodilators	4 (8)	6 (12)	NS
Supraventricular tachyrhythmia	4 (8)	8 (15)	NS
Arterial pressure monitoring	4 (8)	8 (15)	NS
Central pressure monitoring	3 (6)	7 (15)	NS

(Table 2 continued)

Diuretics	3 (5)	8 (15)	<0.0
Major surgery before discharge	3 (5)	7 (14)	NS
Temporary pacemaker	2 (4)	1 (1)	NS
Sepsis	2 (4)	4 (7)	NS
Cardiopulmonary arrest	2 (3)	7 (14)	<0.02
Third-degree heart block	2 (3)	1 (2)	NS
Pneumonia	2 (3)	7 (13)	<0.03
Hypotension (systolic <90 torr)	2 (3)	4 (7)	NS
Extension of infarction	2 (3)	3 (6)	NS
Antibiotics	2 (3)	9 (17)	<0.005
Permanent pacemaker	2 (3)	1 (1)	NS
Gastrointestinal bleeding	1 (1)	2 (3)	NS
Intubation/ventilation	0 (0)	6 (12)	<0.002

NS = $p > .05$; VT/VF = ventricular tachycardia or ventricular fibrillation.

Multivariant analysis of the data using the variables listed in Table 2 revealed a significant difference ($P<.0001$) between the two groups based on events that occurred after entry into the study. Fewer patients in the prayer group required ventilatory support, antibiotics, or diuretics.

The hospital course after entry was graded *good, intermediate*, or *bad*, based on the following criteria. The course was considered to be good if no new diagnoses, problems, or therapies were recorded for the patient or if events occurred that only minimally increased the patient's morbidity or risk of death. The course was considered intermediate if there were higher levels of morbidity and a moderate risk of death. The course of patients who had the highest morbidity and risk of death or who died during the study was graded as bad. The grades were assigned on the basis of the hospital course alone, and no correlation was made as to the condition of the patient at the time of entry. That is, even a patient whose condition was severely critical at the time of entry received a grade of good if no new problems or diagnoses developed after entry, and if the patient recovered without new therapeutic interventions and was discharged home. In patients who had minor problems on entry but subsequently had severe life-threatening complications and prolonged hospitalization, the hospital course received a grade of bad.

The scoring used for the three levels is summarized in Table 3. In the prayer group 85% were considered to have a good hospital course after entry vs 73% in the control group. An intermediate grade was given in 1% of the prayer group vs 5% of the controls. A bad hospital course was observed in

14% of the prayer group vs 22% of the controls. A two by three chi-square analysis of these data gave a P value of <.01.

TABLE 3

Results of Scoring the Postentry Hospital Course

Score	Prayer Group (n=192)	Control Group (n=201)	P
Good	163	147	
Intermediate	2	10	
Bad	27	44	
			<0.01

DISCUSSION

In reviewing the social and scientific literature on the efficacy of prayer to the Judeo-Christian God there seems to be no end to articles discussing it but very few articles that actually test for the effects of prayer. The Bible records examples of the effectiveness of prayer in healing in the book of Genesis 20:17,18; Numbers 12:13; and Acts 28:8.

Roland (1970) believed that a work on the effectiveness of prayer by Galton in 1872 represents one of the first applications of statistics to science and one of the first objective studies of prayer. Galton (1883), on reporting the effects of prayer in the clergy, found no salutary effects. He cited (1872) a previous work by Guy from which he concluded that prayer for sovereigns in England did not make them live longer than other prominent people of the time. Though perhaps a unique approach for his time, the study suffered greatly in design, as retrospective studies are prone to do. Galton also believed that prayer seemed to be a perfectly reasonable subject for research. But the literature remained silent after this, probably as a result of the furor his comments created at the time.

In 1965 a double-blind clinical trial of the effects of prayer on rheumatic patients was reported by Joyce and Welldon (1965), who studied 19 matched pairs of patients over 18 months, with a crossover between the control group and the prayer group at six months. During the first half of the study the prayer group did better but in the second half the control group did better. Their results showed no significant differences as a result of prayer. Subsequently, in 1969 Collipp reported the results of a triple-blind study of the efficacy of prayer on

18 leukemic children. In a randomized trial, his data suggested that prayer had a beneficial effect, but it did not reach significance because the number of patients was small and the initial randomization did not produce matching groups, thus nullifying any suggested benefit for the prayer group.

I approached the study of the efficacy of prayer in the following manner suggested by Galton (1872):

> There are two lines of research, by either of which we may pursue this inquiry. The one that promises the most trustworthy results is to examine large classes of cases, and to be guided by broad averages; the other, which I will not employ in these pages, is to deal with isolated instances.

Several points concerning the present study should be mentioned. First, prayer by and for the control group (by persons not in conjunction with this study) could not be accounted for. Nor was there any attempt to limit prayer among the controls. Such action would certainly be unethical and probably impossible to achieve. Therefore, "pure" groups were not attained in this study— all of one group and part of the other had access to the intervention under study. This may have resulted in smaller differences observed between the two groups. How God acted in this situation is unknown; ie, were the groups treated by God as a whole or were individual prayers alone answered?

Second, whether patients prayed of themselves and to what degree they held religious convictions was not determined. Because many of the patients were seriously ill, it was not possible to obtain an interview extensive enough to answer these two questions. Furthermore, it was thought that discussions concerning the patients' relationship to God might be emotionally disturbing to a significant number of patients at the time of admission to the coronary care unit, though it was generally noted that almost all patients in the study expressed the belief that prayer probably helped and certainly could not hurt.

The data presented in this report show that the initial randomization resulted in two statistically similar groups as judged by the results of univariant and multivariant analysis. Prayers to the Judeo-Christian God were made on behalf of the patients in the prayer group by "born again" believers in Jesus Christ. Analysis of events after entry into the study showed the prayer group had less congestive heart failure, required less diuretic and antibiotic therapy, had fewer episodes of pneumonia, had fewer cardiac arrests, and were less frequently intubated and ventilated. Even though for these variables the P values were $<.05$, they could not be considered statistically significant because of the large number of variables examined. I used two methods to overcome this statistical limitation: incorporation of the outcome variable into a severity score, and multivariant analysis. Both of these methods produced statistically significant results in favor of the prayer group. The severity score showed that the prayer group had an overall better outcome (P<.01), and the multivariant analysis produced a P value of < .0001 on the basis of the prayer group's lesser requirements for antibiotics, diuretics, and intubation/ventilation.

In this study I have attempted to determine whether intercessory prayer to the Judeo-Christian God has any effect on the medical condition and recovery of hospitalized patients. I further have attempted to measure any effects, if present, of those prayers. Based on these data there seemed to be an effect, and that effect was presumed to be beneficial.

REFERENCES

Biomedical Data Processing Statistical Software. (1981). Dixon WJ (e d) . Berkeley, University of California Press.

Collipp, P. (1969). The efficacy of prayer: a triple blind study. *Medical Times, 97*, 201-204.

Galton, F. (1872). Statistical inquiries into the efficacy of prayer. *Fortnightly Review, 12*, 125-135.

Galton, F. (1883). *Inquiries into Human Faculty and Its Development.*London: Macmillan Co, 277-294.

Joyce, C., & Welldon, R. (1965). The efficacy of prayer: a double-blind clinical trial. *Journal of Chronic Diseases, 18*, 367-377.

Lee, E. (1980). *Statistical Methods for Survival Data Analysis.* Belmont, Lifetime LearningPublications, pp 338-365.

Press, J., & Wilson, S. (1978). Choosing between logistic regression and discriminant analysis. *Journal of the American Statistical Association, 73*, 699-705.

Roland, C. (1970). Does prayer preserve? *Archives of Internal Medicine, 125*, 580-587.

Rosner, F. (1975). The efficacy of prayer: scientific vs religious evidence. *Journal of Religion and Health, 14*, 294-298.

Spivak, C. (1917). Hebrew prayers for the sick. *Ann Med Hist 1*, 83-85.

SCORING SYSTEM

Good

Only one of the following: left heart catherization; mild unstable angina pectoris of less than 6 hours' duration; self-limiting ventricular tachycardia within the first 72 hours of myocardial infarction; supraventricular tachyrhythmia; uncomplicated third-degree heart block requiring temporary pacemaker; mild congestive heart failure without pulmonary edema; no complications at all.

Intermediate

Moderate to severe unstable angina pectoris without infarction, congestive heart failure with pulmonary edema, noncardiac surgery, third-degree heart block requiring permanent pacemaker, pneumonia without congestive heart failure, combination of any two events from the **good** category.

Bad

Nonelective cardiac surgery, readmission to the CCU after a myocardial infarction with unstable angina, extension of initial infarction, cerebrovascular accident, cardiopulmonary arrest, need for artificial ventilator, severe congestive heart failure with pulmonary edema and pneumonia, hemodynamic shock due to sepsis or left ventricular failure, death.

EDITOR'S COMMENTS

Like Florell's work reproduced earlier in this volume, this is an intervention study. One group of patients was prayed for and another group was not--at least not by those who were recruited to pray as part of the research study. The results are strongerbecause the author used multivariant analysis, a sophisticated statistical process. Readers who wish to understand this process more fully should refer to my comments following the article by Pargament in which I discussion the characteristics of multiple regression analysis.

A popular maxim states that "prayer changes things." The results of this study suggest that it is, in fact, true. Results suggested that "fewer patients in the prayer group required ventilatory support, antibiotics, or diuretics." Behind this study, of course are assumptions that God responds to prayer by altering physical reality. This assumption is not likely held by all readers; some believe that the "things" prayer changes are the personal anxiety and fear which pervade the CCU experience. This relief, in turn, affects many physical functions such as those studied here. Thus it becomes clear that theological assumption directly influence research design.

It is important to take this study seriously, but also to be critical of it (as we must be with all research). What is required is a second and third study to determine if these results can be reproduced. If not, we should assume that they were random findings. If these results are demonstrated again, it certainly would not be the first instance in which research outcomes inform religious and theological assumptions.

7

God Help Me:(I): Religious Coping Efforts as Predictors of the Outcomes to Significant Negative Life Events

Kenneth I. Pargament
David S. Ensing
Kathryn Falgout
Hannah Olsen
Barbara Reilly
Kimberly Van Haitsma
Richard Warren

ABSTRACT

Examined the role various religious coping efforts serve in dealing with negative events among a sample of 586 members of Christian churches who turn to religion in coping. Participants described the most serious negative event they had experienced in the past year and then indicated how they coped with it through both religious and nonreligious means. The religious variables were significant predictors of three measures of the outcome of the event. Beliefs in a just benevolent God, the experience of God as a supportive partner in coping, involvement in religious rituals, and the search for support through religion were associated with more positive outcomes. The religious coping variables predicted outcomes

Reproduced with permission of the Plenum Publishing Co. from the *American Journal of Community Psychology*, (1990), 18(6), 793-824.

beyond the effects of traditional dispositional religious variables and nonreligious coping variables. These findings underscore the need for an integration of the religious dimension into the coping literature.

How helpful are religious coping efforts in response to negative events? This paper focuses on the relationship between several forms of religious coping efforts and the outcomes of negative events among those who involve religion in the coping process. Although personal narratives and anecdotal reports have provided dramatic and immediate accounts of helpful and detrimental religious involvement in the process of coping, relatively few systematic studies of religion and coping have been conducted. However, the results of this small body of work indicate that religious beliefs and practices are commonly involved in coping. Bulman and Wortman (1977) studied 29 victims of accidents resulting in paraplegia. The most common responses to the question "Why me?" were religious, with the accident viewed as part of God's will for the individual. Koenig, George, and Siegler (1988) asked a random sample of 100 older adults living in the community to describe the coping behaviors they used to deal with three stressful events. Religious coping behaviors were most popular, cited by 45% of the sample. The most frequently mentioned of these activities were trust and faith in God, prayer, and help and strength from God. Social church-related activities were less commonly noted. McRae (1984) asked a community sample of 255 men and women to check the coping mechanisms they used to deal with a previously reported stressful event. The use of faith was one of the most common coping mechanisms, reported by 75% of the sample dealing with a loss and 72% of the sample facing a threatening event. O'Brien (1982) interviewed 126 chronic dialysis patients; 74% reported that their religious or ethical beliefs affected their coping with the disease and the treatment regime.

These studies highlight the frequent use of religion in coping with negative events. They also highlight the need for a more comprehensive assessment of religiousness and greater specification of its role in coping. For example, the finding that many people cope through prayer raises questions about the nature of prayer. Clark (1958) distinguished among several kinds of prayer, including prayers of petition, confession, communion, intercession, and thanksgiving. He suggested that different kinds of prayer serve different functions for the individual. Similarly, the finding that many people turn to their faith as a means of coping (McRae, 1984) raises questions about the nature of that faith. While McRae categorized faith as a passive form of coping, others have defined more active and interactive forms of faith (Pargament et al., 1988).

Unfortunately, within the general coping literature, religion has not been examined at close range or in much detail. Typically, it is defined as a generic dispositional variable and measured within a general population by a few indicators (e.g., frequency of prayer, frequency of church attendance, faith in God). Furthermore, these indicators are often combined into measures of more general coping dimensions making it impossible to sort out specific religious effects (e.g., Cleary & Houts, 1984; Folkman & Lazarus, 1988; Gil, Abrams, Phillips, & Keefe, 1989). This approach is inconsistent with a large body of literature suggesting that religiousness is a multidimensional construct involving ideological, intellectual, ritualistic, experiential, and consequential dimensions (for review see Spilka, Hood, & Gorsuch, 1985). In short, a more comprehensive assessment, sensitive to the complex nature of religiousness, is needed to clarify and specify the role of religion in coping. However, this assessment must be conceptually based.

A Conceptual Framework of Religion and Coping

A Framework of Coping

Coping is generally viewed as a process through which individuals try to understand and deal with significant personal or situational demands in their lives (Lazarus & Folkman, 1984; Moos, 1986; Tyler, 1978). While theorists describe the coping process as highly interactive and dynamic, several key elements of the process have been articulated:

Life situations or events may take a variety of forms: singular, multiple, or cumulative, positive or negative, novel or familiar, predictable or unpredictable, personal or interpersonal, and major or minor (DeLongis, Coyne, Dakof, Folkman, & Lazarus, 1982; Eckenrode, 1984). But research indicates that life events are not strong predictors of physical and mental health (Rabkin & Streuning, 1978; Thoits, 1983).

Appraisals of the situation in terms of its cause (causal), the degree to which it is seen as harmful, threatening, or challenging (primary), and the individual's ability and options to handle it (secondary) have been examined as important cognitions mediating the relationship between the situation and the response (Folkman, Schaefer, & Lazarus, 1979).

Coping activities aimed at dealing with the problem represent another key element affecting the response to life events. Researchers have distinguished among a variety of coping activities (e.g., problem-focused, emotion-focused, rational action, seeking help, positive thinking, withdrawal, self-blame, social comparison) (Billings & Moos, 1984; McRae, 1984; Taylor, 1983).

The *outcomes* of the coping process are multidimensional: immediate, short-term, and long-term; situational, interpersonal, psychological, and physical; positive, negative, and mixed (Lazarus & Folkman, 1984).

The process of coping is affected by the *personal and social resources and constraints* of the individual. These resources and constraints include the individual's level of competence, personality characteristics, attitudes and beliefs, financial status, physical health status, and social networks (Heller & Swindle, 1983; Tyler, 1978).

Guiding the coping process are several kinds of *purpose*. Within the psychological domain, theorists have articulated a number of important purposes served by religion: self-esteem, control, meaning, growth, hope, intimacy and belonging, emotional release, personal identity, emotional restraint, and comfort (Erikson, 1963; Frankl, 1963; Maslow, 1970; Taylor, 1983).

Religion and Coping

Pargament (1990) described three ways in which religion can be involved in coping. First, it can be a part of each of the elements of the coping process. Many life events are, at least in part, religious in nature (e.g., baptism, Bar Mitzvah, marriage, divorce, funeral, mystical experience, joining/leaving a congregation). Religious appraisals are also available as a source of explanation for life events. For example, tragedies can be evaluated as part of God's plan, a punishment from God, or unintended by God (Cook & Wimberly, 1983; Jenkins & Pargament, 1988; Kushner, 1981). Religious coping activities can also be articulated such as confession, support from clergy and congregation members, anger towards God, a focus on the world-to-come, praying for a miracle, or looking to God for emotional strength. The outcomes of the coping process may be religious (e.g., increased religious commitment or congregational involvement). Various religious orientations and belief systems, norms, and congregation types can serve as either resources or constraints in coping. Finally, coping may be guided by a spiritual function, the desire for a closer relationship with God.

Second, religion can *contribute* to the coping process. For example, researchers have found that religious involvement decreases the likelihood of some important life events including drug abuse, alcohol abuse, and non-marital sexual activity (Spilka, Hood, & Gorsuch, 1985). Wright, Pratt, and Schmall (1985) studied 240 caregivers of Alzheimer's patients and found that spiritually oriented caregivers reframed their situation more positively than less spiritually oriented caregivers.

Finally, religion can be a *product* of the coping process. For instance, Pargament and Hahn (1986) examined the religious responses of college students to four types of imagined life events: positive, negative, just world, and unjust world. They found that unjust world events were more likely to trigger attributions to God's will. Positive outcome events were attributed most often to God's love. Negative outcome events triggered attributions to God's anger. A national survey of adults examined the kinds of life events associated with reports of increased faith (Princeton Religion Research Center, 1987). Increased faith reportedly followed the birth of a child, loneliness, emotional difficulties, and work promotions.

THE PRESENT STUDY

The framework of religion and coping raises a number of questions for empirical study. Perhaps the most basic of these questions concerns the relationship between religious forms of coping and the outcome of the coping process.

Theoretical literature suggests that religious coping can affect the outcomes of negative events. Talcott Parsons wrote "religion has its greatest relevance to the points of maximum strain and tension in human life as well as to positive affirmations of faith in life, often in the face of these strains" (in Fichter, 1981, p. 21). Religious appraisals, coping activities, and resources and constraints may serve a number of functions important to the resolution of problems (Pargament, 1990). For example, Spilka, Shaver, and Kirkpatrick (1985) illustrated how prayer, religious rituals, and faith can affect feelings of control and self-esteem. They also noted that religious beliefs offer a variety of meaningful explanations for key events. Others have described religion as a source of hope in the face of stress (Kahoe, 1982), a source of comfort and/or challenge (Glock, Ringer & Babbie, 1967), a basis for defining and resolving problems (Newman & Pargament, 1990), and a means of promoting personal identity and intimacy with others (Greeley, 1972; Hammond, 1988). Religious systems can also contribute to the regulations of emotions. They may stimulate emotional release as illustrated by black fundamentalist congregations in which emotional expression is encouraged (Griffith, Young, & Smith, 1984), or aid emotional/behavioral restraint as illustrated by groups such as Alcoholics Anonymous that integrate religious themes into their work.

Empirical evidence of the efficacy of religion is sparse. There are, however, a few exceptions. Gibbs and Achterberg-Lawlis (1978) interviewed 16 patients close to death. They found that fear of death was negatively associated with reported religious faith, and that sleep disturbance was negatively associated with identification of the church as a major source of support. Jenkins and Pargament (1988) found that cancer patients who reported God to be in control of their lives were rated by their nurses as significantly less upset, and reported greater self-esteem. In an interview study of patients with advanced cancer, reports of religious beliefs and activities were associated with lower levels of reported pain and greater happiness (Yates, Chalmer, St. James, Follansbee, & McKegney, 1981). Grevengoed and Pargament (1987) studied college students who had recently experienced the death of a family member or close friend. Students who attributed the death to God's will or God's love reported more favorable evaluations of their coping with the death. In a national survey of a black adult population, prayer was reported most frequently (44% of the sample) as the coping response of greatest efficacy in dealing with serious personal problems (Neighbors, Jackson, Bowman, & Gurin, 1983). Maton and Rappaport (1984) conducted an intensive prospective analysis of a nondenominational Christian fellowship. Interpersonal change toward the ideals of the fellowship was predicted by the experience of a life crisis, commitment to an intimate relationship with God and the congregation, and a belief in God's primary role in affecting the outcomes of events. Working with members of three different mutual support groups, Maton (1989) found that a measure of spiritual support related negatively to depression and positively to self-esteem above and beyond the effects of general social support. Gilbert (1989) interviewed 27 couples following the death of their children regarding the relationship between religion and bereavement: 56% reported that their religion had been a source of support throughout their trauma, 22% felt their religion had not been helpful to them, and 22% reported that their religion was irrelevant to their ordeal.

In sum, there is theoretical support and limited empirical evidence to suggest a relationship between religious coping and the outcomes of negative life events. This study, the first in a series of empirical investigations on religion and coping, takes a closer look at the helpfulness of various religious coping efforts among those who turn to religion in dealing with negative life events. More specifically, it focuses on several unanswered questions.

What kinds of religious coping efforts are helpful, harmful, or irrelevant to people dealing with significant negative events? When religion has been examined in studies of coping, it has generally been measured by a few items. A more comprehensive assessment of religiousness is needed to identify elements that may be helpful, harmful, or irrelevant to the coping process.

Do the concepts and measures of religious coping increase our ability to understand and predict outcomes of coping over and above the contributions of traditional dispositional religious constructs and measures? Gorsuch (1984) noted that new measures and constructs in the psychology of religion must demonstrate their contributions beyond those of existing methods. Traditionally, researchers have defined and measured religiousness dispositionally in terms of generalized beliefs (e.g., doctrinal orthodoxy, concepts of God), orientations (e.g., intrinsic, extrinsic, and quest), or generalized behaviors (e.g., average frequency of church attendance) rather than as a response to specific events (Batson & Ventis, 1982; Spilka, Hood, & Gorsuch, 1985). Most commonly, these constructs have been related to personological measures of mental health or adaptation rather than to measures of the outcome to a specific event. In contrast, several key elements of the religious coping process (e.g., appraisals, coping activities, purposes, and outcomes) are situationally based. Because the religious coping constructs have been developed within a conceptual framework purposefully linked to outcome and because they operate at the same event-specific level of analysis as the concept of outcome, we would expect religious coping to predict outcomes above and beyond the effects of traditional measures of religiousness.

Do concepts and measures of religious coping increase our ability to understand and predict outcomes of coping over and above the contributions of traditional nonreligious coping constructs and measures? While religious coping measures may be predictive of the outcomes of coping, they may be redundant functionally to traditional nonreligious coping measures. For example, prayer as a coping strategy may be functionally equivalent to passive avoidant coping strategies such as daydreaming, accepting fate, or wishful thinking. If this were the case, there would be no need to identify and measure prayer as a special form of coping. However, several theorists suggest that religion may offer unique contributions to coping with negative events. For example, Spilka, Shaver, and Kirkpatrick (1985) assert that religious concepts with a focus on orderliness, benevolence, and justice in the universe offer particularly compelling ways of coming to grips with negative events. Further, Pargament (1990) suggests that religious beliefs may be especially efficacious in dealing with aspects of situations that cannot be personally controlled and are not amenable to problem solving.

It is important to stress that this study does not consider the question, what is more effective religious or nonreligious coping? A study pitting those who use religion in coping against those who use nonreligious coping strategies exclusively may overstate a religious—secular dichotomy, for both forms of coping appear to be commonly involved in dealing with negative events. Perhaps more importantly, the question of "which is better" overlooks the diversity within religious and nonreligious coping approaches. This study takes a closer look into the religious world. It focuses on the more basic questions of the additive contributions of religious coping efforts over traditional approaches and of the kinds of religious coping efforts more and less helpful to people. To examine these questions, we sought a population in the religious world; one involved in a variety of forms of religious coping.

METHODS

Sample

The sample was selected from 10 Midwestern churches representing a range of denominations: Lutheran (Missouri Synod and ELCA), Presbyterian, Episcopalian, American Baptist, Roman Catholic, and nondenominational groups. These congregations were drawn from rural, urban, and suburban areas, and varied in size, age, and stability. Within each church, the membership was stratified into groups of more and less frequent attenders of religious services. Those who attended services on the average of once a month or more were designated more active and those who attended services less than once a month were designated less active. Participants were drawn systematically and proportionately from each group. Since this study was part of a larger evaluation of congregation life, the number of members selected from each congregation varied according to the size of the church, from approximately 75 to 150. Those selected were asked to complete a survey anonymously in their respective church as part of a broad examination of congregational and religious life. Approximately 65% of those who agreed to come to their church to complete the survey did so. Schedule conflicts and illness were most frequently cited as reasons for not participating in the study.

The sample in this study consisted of 586 members. It represents a subset of the larger sample of 792 participants who completed their surveys. Participants who indicated that religion was not involved in dealing with the most serious negative event they had experienced in the past year were dropped (n = 174). Further, the 32 members who endorsed more than two items on the MMPI Lie scale were excluded.

The sample was 66% female, 96% white, 38% college educated, and 64% married. Thirty percent of the sample had an average family income of less than $24,999 a year, 38% had an income between $25,000 and $49,999, and 32% had an income of $50,000 or more. The average age in the sample was 46. The sample generally endorsed mainline Christian beliefs; 87% reported a belief in the existence of a just and merciful personal God and 84% strongly endorsed a belief in life after death.

The characteristics of the sample were compared with the characteristics of the church population as estimated by the clergy and/or leaders. The sample was representative of the church population with respect to the age of the members and the number of years they had belonged to the congregation. However, the sample consisted of a smaller proportion of males (34%) than the estimated church population (45%). In addition, a smaller proportion of the sample reportedly attended religious services less than once a month (16%) than the congregation population (38%). The underrepresentation of the less active member (and males who tend to be less active) is a common problem in religious research (Roozen & Carroll, 1989), reflective of the difficulty in gathering the responses of those who are less involved in the life of the organization as well as the possible overreporting of church attendance in survey research (Pargament et al., 1987).

Although the sample was more representative of the participating churchgoer and mainline Christian beliefs, it was, by no means, completely homogenous in religious beliefs and practices. For example, 15% of the sample reported reading the Bible one or more times a day; another 14% reported never reading the Bible. Twenty-two percent of the sample strongly disagreed that "There is a physical Hell where people are punished after death for the sins of their lives"; 28% of the sample strongly agreed with this statement. While 21% of the sample was involved in three or more church programs, 19% had no involvement in church activities. Thirty-eight percent spent one hour or less a week in church; 14% spent five hours or more in the congregation.

Measures

The participants completed a lengthy battery of measures to assess negative events, religious involvement in coping, nonreligious coping activities, and outcomes. These scales are described briefly below. With the exception of the newly developed scales of religious involvement in coping, these measures have demonstrated evidence of reliability and validity in other studies.

Negative Events

The most serious negative events reported in the past year were sorted into categories. The most commonly reported negative events were serious problems of friend or family members such as illness or injury (25%), death of a family member or close friend (18%), interpersonal conflicts such as a separation or divorce (14%), work-related problems such as being laid off or fired (8%), or personal illness or injury (8%).

Appraisals

The participants were then asked to report their reaction to the event at the time it had occurred. Using a 5-point Likert scale ranging from *not at all a reaction* (1) to *a strong reaction* (5), they responded to several items dealing with religious appraisals and nonreligious appraisals adapted from Pargament and Hahn (1986) and Stone and Neale (1984). Appraisals that the negative event reflected God's Will (M = 2.52) were endorsed more strongly than appraisals involving the other loci of responsibility—God's Punishment (M = 1.14), Self (M = 1.69), or Chance (M = 2.03). The sample reported greater Threat to the Well-Being of Others (M = 2.73) than Threat to Personal Health (M = 1.99) or Threat to Spiritual Well-Being (M = 1.85). Most strongly endorsed were appraisals that the individual had to Accept the Situation (M = 4.07), that the situation was a Challenge to Face (M = 4.03), and that the event offered an Opportunity to Grow as a person (M = 3.40). Mean scores for the other appraisals were Harm/Loss (M = 2.41), Can Change the Situation (M = 2.55), and Cannot Handle the Situation (M = 2.44).

Coping Activities (Religious)

A list of 31 religious coping activities was generated through interviews with clergy and other adults on their uses of religion in coping, the empirical literature, and the written personal accounts of those who turned to religion in times of stress. Our intent was to tap into the diverse array of religious coping activities as efficiently as possible. Thus items dealt with several dimensions of religious coping: interpersonal, spiritual, cognitive, emotional, behavioral, social, avoidance, passive, and collaborative.

The sample responded to this list of items in terms of the degree to which each was involved in coping with their events on a 4-point Likert scale (ranging from *not at all* to *a great deal*). Their responses to the 31 items were entered into a principal factors analysis with SMCs in the diagonal and a Varimax rotation. Using a scree plot in conjunction with interpretability to select the solution, a five-factor solution was chosen which accounted for almost 100% of the common variance in the sample (note 1). Final communality estimates for this solution ranged from .05 to .70 with a median of .47. The solution is presented in Table 1. As can be seen, the first factor, labeled Spiritually Based, stresses the individual's personal loving relationship with God throughout the coping process. Spiritually based coping takes the form of emotional reassurance, positive framing of problems, acceptance of the limits of personal control, and guidance in problem solving. What these cognitive, emotional, and behavioral activities share is an emphasis on the intimate partnership between the individual and God in coping. In the second factor, Good Deeds, the response to the negative event shifts from the event itself to a focus on living a better, more religiously integrated life. Discontent, the third factor, incorporates items that express anger or distance from God and the church, and questions about one's faith. The fourth factor, Interpersonal Religious Support, involves support from the clergy and other members of the church. Plead, the fifth factor, includes pleas for a miracle, bargaining with God, and questions to God about why the event happened.

Items loading most highly on their respective factors and with loadings of greater than .40 were summed to create scales of religious coping.

TABLE 1
Psychometric Characteristics of Religious Coping Activities Scales

	α	M	SD	Factor loading
Spiritually based	.92	2.64	0.70	
Trusted that God would not let anything terrible happen to me		2.65	1.09	.45
Experienced God's love and care		2.97	0.92	.70
Realized that God was trying to strengthen me		2.62	1.05	.57
In dealing with the problem I was guided by God		2.78	0.96	.72
Realized that I didn't have to suffer since Jesus suffered for me		2.07	1.09	.51
Used Christ as an example of how I should live		2.44	0.99	.61
Took control over what I could, and gave the rest up to God		2.93	0.98	.63
My faith showed me different ways to handle the problem		2.53	0.85	.59
Accepted that the situation was not in my hands but in the hands of God		2.85	1.07	.55
Found the lesson from God in the event		2.34	1.00	.64
God showed me how to deal with the situation		2.65	0.94	.80
Used my faith to help me decide how to cope with the situation		2.99	0.89	.75
Good deeds	.82	2.22	0.72	
Tried to be less sinful		2.22	1.01	.69
Confessed my sins		2.33	1.09	.64
Led a more loving life		2.44	0.96	.47
Attended religious services or participated in religious rituals		2.69	1.09	.52
Participated in church groups (support groups, prayer groups, Bible)		1.85	1.08	.48
Provided help to other church members		1.80	0.84	.54
Discontent	.68	1.37	0.60	
Felt angry with or distant from God		1.38	0.72	.48
Felt angry with or distant from the members of the church		1.36	0.80	.62

(Table 1, Continued)

Questioned my religious beliefs and faith		1.44 0.80	.66
Religious support	.78	2.02 1.01	
Received support from clergy		1.89 1.08	.71
Received support from other members of the church		2.31 1.18	.68
Plead	.61	1.75 0.74	
Asked for a miracle		1.96 1.18	.50
Bargained with God to make things better		1.33 0.68	.50
Asked God why it happened		2.09 1.10	.48
Religious avoidance	.61	2.01 0.74	
Focused on the world-to-come rather than the problems of this world		1.81 0.99	
I let God solve my problems for me		2.09 1.00	
Prayed or read the Bible to keep my mind off of my problems		2.15 1.03	

Two items involving religious avoidance of problems did not enter into these factors. However, the concept of religious avoidance is theoretically interesting. To explore this concept, a sixth scale was developed from three items. They include coping activities that divert the individual's attention from problem through reading the Bible or focusing on the afterlife. The absolute values of the Pearson correlations among the six scales ranged from .01 to .70 with a median of .27.

Table 1 also presents the scale means and standard deviations, item means, and internal consistency estimates for each of the six religious coping scales. The scale and items means indicated that Spiritually Based activities were most involved in coping and Discontent was least involved. Many of the other religious coping activities were commonly used by our sample. The alphas for the religious coping scales are moderately high-to-low. Lower alphas are likely due to the smaller numbers of items and diverse nature of the items in the coping scales. If the scales generally yield meaningful results, a revision of the shorter scales would be in order.

Coping Activities (Nonreligious)

Nonreligious coping activities were measured by 19 items adapted from Moos, Cronkite, Billings, and Finney (1984) and McRae (1984). Participants responded to the items on a 4-point Likert scale *not at all* to *a great deal*. Once again, items were selected to measure diverse nonreligious coping activities (e.g., passive, active, avoidance, cognitive, emotional, behavioral, interpersonal) as efficiently as possible.

The sample responded to these items using the same response format as the religious coping activities items. The items were entered into a principal factors analysis with SMCs in the diagonal and a Varimax rotation. Using the same criteria as in the previous analysis, a four-factor solution emerged accounting for almost 100% of the common variance in the sample. Final communality estimates ranged from .08 to .64 with a median of .25. Shown in Table 2, the factors are labeled Focus Positive, Problem Solving, Avoidance, and Interpersonal Support. Scales were created from these analyses with the items which loaded most highly on their respective factors and with loadings of greater than .30. These scales show moderate-to-low internal consistency. The lower reliabilities likely reflect the diversity of items as well as some restriction.of range on items in the Avoidance and Interpersonal Support scales. The absolute values of the Pearson correlations ranged from .01 to .60 with a median of .13.

TABLE 2

Psychometric Characteristics of Nonreligious Coping Scales

	α	M	SD	Factor loading
Focus positive	.78	2.73	0.80	
Thought about the good side of the situation		2.65	1.10	.65
Tried to look on the bright side of things		2.86	0.98	.69
Realized in looking at the situation that things could be worse		2.84	1.02	.49
Tried to get something positive from the situation		2.64	0.97	.47
Problem solving	.70	2.48	0.73	
Considered several ways to handle the event		2.76	0.97	.50
Made a plan of action and followed it		2.3	1.02	.59
Tried to see the event as having something to teach me		2.62	1.01	.56
Tried to step back from the situation and be more objective		2.26	0.91	.53
Avoidance	.49	2.04	0.60	
Tried not to think about it		2.03	0.90	.41
Kept my feelings to myself		2.10	0.93	.33
Avoided being with other people		1.46	0.75	.43
Wished the situation would go away		2.60	1.22	.48
Support	.42	2.15	0.87	
Received support from friends or co-workers (not members of church)		2.54	1.08	.50
Received support from professionals (not clergy)		1.77	1.13	.43

Purposes of Religion in Coping

Participants were asked to indicate what they were seeking or aiming for through their religion as they dealt with their events. They responded to 11 items representing 11 purposes on a 4-point Likert scale ranging from *not at all* to *a great deal*. These items were then entered into a principal components analysis with a Varimax rotation (note 2). A scree plot pointed to a five-factor solution. The five factors accounted for 78% of the total variance in the sample. Final communality estimates ranged from .71 to .86 with a median of .77. The factors are shown in Table 3: Self-development made up of self-esteem, control, and self-actualization purposes; Spiritual incorporating meaning and hope purposes with the spiritual desire for personal closeness with God; Resolve in which religion is looked to for a resolution to the problem and emotional resolution; Sharing involving desires for help in expressing feelings to others and for intimacy with others; and Restraint focusing on religious help in restraining emotions and behaviors.

TABLE 3
Psychometric Characteristics of Purposes of Religion Scales

	α	M	SD	Factor loading
Self-development	.85	2.54	0.93	
Help in feeling good about myself		2.45	1.07	.81
Feeling more in control of my life		2.61	1.06	.81
Help in improving myself as a person		2.59	1.07	.63
Spiritual	.73	2.85	0.80	
Personal closeness with God		2.77	1.01	.72
A sense of meaning and purpose in life		2.69	1.08	.62
Feeling of hope about the future		3.09	0.95	.69
Resolve	.71	2.94	0.87	
Help in solving my problems		2.80	1.09	.72
A sense of peace and comfort		3.10	0.91	.73
Sharing	.68	2.65	0.88	
Help in expressing my feelings		2.71	0.97	.79
A sense of closeness and belonging with other people		2.61	1.05	.77
Restraint	—	2.74	0.98	
Help in keeping my emotions or actions under control		2.74	0.98	.83

Items loading most highly on their respective factors and with loadings of greater than .50 were summed to create scales. The internal consistencies of these scales are shown in Table 3. The correlations among these scales were moderately high, ranging from .40 to .60 with a median of .55.

Outcomes

We distinguished among three kinds of outcomes of the event: the recent mental health status of the individual, the general outcome of the event, and the religious outcome of the event. Recent mental health status was assessed by the General Health Questionnaire (GHQ; Goldberg, 1978). This 12-item instrument focuses on recent increases or decreases in mood, self-confidence, sleeping, tension, and concentration. In this sample, the GHQ evidenced moderate internal consistency (alpha = .79). To be consistent with the scoring of the other outcome measures, higher scores on the GHQ indicate better recent mental health status. The General Outcome of the event was measured by five items adapted from Aldwin and Revenson (1987) and Grevengoed and Pargament (1987). The sample was asked to evaluate how much they learned from the event, how well they handled their feelings, how well they handled the event itself, and whether they felt stronger and better about themselves. The five items formed a scale with moderately high internal consistency (alpha = .79). Religious Outcome was measured by three items focusing on perceived changes in closeness to God, closeness to the church, and spiritual growth in response to the event (alpha = .87).

Resources and Constraints

We conceptualized the dispositional religious variables as resources and constraints that shape the coping process. Factor analytic studies of religiousness have pointed to the multidimensional nature of religious beliefs, practices, and orientations (King & Hunt, 1975). These diverse dimensions of the individual's approach to religion were assessed by the following scales: Loving Images of God (Benson & Spilka, 1973); Intrinsic (Hoge, 1972); Extrinsic (Feagin, 1964), and Quest (Batson and Ventis, 1982) orientations; Doctrinal Orthodoxy made up of items from Batson (1976), King and Hunt (1975), and Putney and Middleton (1961); Collaborative, Deferring, and Self-Directed coping styles (Pargament *et al.*, 1988); and Religious Experience made up of items from Benson and Williams (1982) and King and Hunt (1975). In addition, the sample reported its frequency of church attendance, prayer, and Bible reading. Each of these scales demonstrated acceptable internal consistency (alpha > .70) in this sample, with the exception of the measure of Quest (alpha = .60).

To control, at least in part, for response bias in this self-report study, the participants completed a measure of Indiscriminate Proreligiousness (Pro-P) that taps into evaluations of religious beliefs and practices in an undifferentiated uncritical manner (alpha = .74) (Pargament *et al.*, 1987). As noted earlier, individuals who endorsed more than two items on the MMPI Lie scale were dropped from further analyses.

Finally, demographic variables of age, gender, marital status, education level, and income were assessed.

RESULTS

Religious Variables and the Prediction of Outcomes

The measure of Indiscriminate Proreligiousness (Pro-P) and demographic variables were entered into multiple regression equations as predictors of each of the three outcome measures in order to partial out their effects. Pro-P emerged as the only significant predictor of the GHQ (R^2 = .03, p < .001). General Outcome was predicted by Pro-P, gender, and age (R^2 = .10, p < .001). Religious Outcome was predicted by Pro-P, gender, age, and income (R^2 = .20, p < .001). More favorable outcomes were reported by more indiscriminately proreligious, women, poorer, and older members. To standardize the subsequent analyses, the same four significant predictors, Pro-P, gender, age, and income, were entered first into the hierarchical regressions for each of the outcome variables.

In order to determine how well the religious variables predict outcomes of the coping process, multiple regression equations were developed for each of the three outcomes measures with all of the religious variables (religious dispositional variables, religious appraisals, religious coping activities, and religious purposes) serving as predictors (and the effects of the four control variables removed). The religious variables were significant predictors of each of the three outcomes measures: GHQ (R^2 = .12, p < .001), General Outcome (R^2 = .30, p < .001), and Religious Outcome (R^2 = .37, p < .001). Thus, the religious variables account for modest to moderately large amounts of variance in the outcomes of coping. The religious variables predict religious and general outcome most strongly and recent mental health status least strongly.

Pearson correlations were calculated on the relationship between the religious dimensions and outcome measures. These correlations are presented in Table 4. Separate multiple regression analyses were also conducted for the four classes of religious predictors: religious appraisals, religious purposes, religious coping activities, and religious dispositional variables. Each of the three outcome measures was regressed on to each of the four classes of religious predictors, yielding a total of 12 regression equations. The resulting R^2 reflect the incremental contributions of the religious predictors beyond the effects of the four control variables. These results are shown in Table 4. We also examined the unique contributions of each religious variable by looking at the significance of the beta weight in a fully simultaneous model containing all the variables in that class. Significant unique contributors to the prediction of outcome are underlined in Table 4.

TABLE 4

Correlations and Regression Analyses of Religious Variables and Outcome Measures

	Outcome Measures[a]		
	General Health Questionnaire (n=568)	General outcome (n=537)	Religious outcome (n=547)
Religious appraisals			
God's will	ns	.19[e]	.16 [e]
God's punishment	-.17[e]	-.16[e]	ns
Threat to spiritual well-being	-.17[e]	-.17[e]	-.09[e]
Incremental R^{2b}	.02[d]	.05[e]	.02[d]
Religious coping activites	.25[e]	.51[e]	.65[e]
Good deeds	.13[c]	.32[e]	.55[e]
Religious support	.10[c]	.32[e]	.51[e]
Discontent	-.22[e]	-.13[d]	-.12[d]
Plead	-.11[c]	ns	.17[e]
Religious avoidance	.10[c]	.28[e]	.48[e]
Incremental R^2	.08[e]	.17[e]	.32[e]
Religious purposes			
Self development	ns	.32[e]	.30[e]
Spiritual	.08[c]	.30[e]	.48[e]
Sharing	ns	.14[e]	.35[e]
Restraint	ns	.15[e]	.24[e]
Resolve	ns	.21[e]	.41[e]
Incremental R^2	ns	.10[e]	.16[e]
Religious dispositional variables			
Deferring	.12[d]	.25[e]	.42[e]
Collaborative	.14[d]	.25[e]	.46[e]
Self directed	-.10[c]	-.16[d]	-.30[e]

(Table 4, Continued)

Intrinsic	$\underline{.11}^{c}$	$.19^{e}$	$\underline{.41}^{e}$
Extrinsic	ns	$.15^{d}$	$.22^{d}$
DOS	ns	$.18^{e}$	$.31^{e}$
Quest	ns	ns	ns
Loving images of God	$.10^{c}$	$\underline{.11}^{e}$	$.13^{d}$
Religious experience	$\underline{.18}^{e}$	$\underline{.28}^{e}$	$\underline{.43}^{e}$
Attendance	ns	$.12^{d}$	$\underline{.36}^{e}$
Frequency of prayer	ns	$.14^{d}$	$.30^{e}$
Incremental R^2	$.03^{e}$	$.04^{e}$	$.16^{e}$

[a]Underlined correlations indicate variables which are significant predictors when entered last into the regression equation for that class of variables. Sample size varies slightly across the regression analyses for the three outcome measures due to missing values.
[b]The incremental R^2 reflect the effects of the predictors above and beyond those of the control variables: Pro-P, age, gender, and income.
[c]$p<.05$
[d]$p<.001$
[e]$p<.0001$

Religious coping activities predicted the outcomes more strongly than the other classes of religious predictors. Within the class of religious coping activities, spiritually based coping activities related most strongly and consistently to positive outcomes, contributing unique variance to the prediction of each of the outcome scales. Good Deeds, Religious Support, and Religious Avoidance were also associated with positive outcomes. Discontent related to poorer outcomes, adding unique variance to the prediction of the GHQ and Religious Outcome. While Plead was associated with a positive Religious Outcome, it also related to a more negative GHQ.

Religious appraisals to God's Will were associated with positive General Outcome and Religious Outcome. Appraisals that the events represented God's Punishment and a Threat to Spiritual Well-Being added independent variance to the prediction of poorer GHQ and General Outcome.

The five religious purpose variables were positively associated with General Outcome and Religious Outcome. The Spiritual purpose contributed independently to the prediction of these two outcomes and was the only religious purpose associated with the GHQ.

Within the class of religious dispositional variables, five scales were associated consistently with positive outcomes: Deferring, Collaborative, Intrinsic, Loving Image of God, and Religious Experience. The Self-directing religious coping style related consistently to poorer outcomes. General Outcome and Religious Outcome were also correlated positively with Extrinsic, Doctrinal Orthodoxy, Church Attendance, and Frequency of Prayer.

Religious Coping and Religious Dispositions

To compare the contributions of the religious coping measures to those of the religious dispositional measures, we conducted hierarchical multiple regression analyses for each outcome variable. First, the control variables (Pro-P, gender, age, and income) were entered into the analysis. Second, the religious dispositional measures were entered. The religious coping measures were then entered into the equation. Incremental R^2 were calculated and tested for statistical significance. The results of these analyses are presented in Table 5. In support of our prediction we find that the religious coping measures add unique variance to the prediction of the three outcome measures: GHQ (R^2 = .09, p < .001). General Outcome (R^2 = .26, p < .001), and Religious Outcome (R^2 = .21, p < .001) (note 3).

TABLE 5

Hierarchical Regression Analyses Predicting
Outcomes from Control Variables,
Religious Dispositional Variables and Religious Coping Variables

	R^2 control variables	Incremental R^2 with religious dispositional variables added	Incremental R^2 with religious coping variables added	R^2 cumulative[a]
GHQ	.03	.03	.09	.15
General outcome	.10	.04	.26	.40
Religious outcome	.20	.16	.21	.57

[a]R^2 > .02, p<.01

Religious Coping and Nonreligious Coping

Pearson correlations and multiple regression analyses were conducted on the relationship between nonreligious appraisals, nonreligious coping activities, and the outcome measures. Once again, the control variables were entered first into the analysis and the incremental R^2 associated with the added contributions of the nonreligious variables were calculated. The results of these analyses are presented in Table 6.

TABLE 6

Correlations and Regression Analyses of Nonreligious Variables and Outcome Measures

	Outcome Measures[a]		
	General Health Questionnaire (n=568)	General outcome (n=537)	Religious outcome (n=547)
Nonreligious appraisals			
Caused by self	-.11[c]	ns	ns
Caused by chance	ns	ns	ns
Threat to personal health	-.13[d]	.10[c]	.11[c]
Threat to others	ns	-.10[c]	ns
Harm/loss	-.11[d]	ns	ns
Opportunity to grow	.12[d]	.36[e]	.32[e]
Challenge to face	ns	.27[cw]	.16[e]
Accept the situation	ns	.10[c]	ns
Can change	ns	.23[e]	ns
Cannot handle	-.23[e]	-.08[c]	ns
Incremental R^2[b]	.07[e]	.16[e]	.12[e]
Nonreligious coping activites			
Focus on positive	.22[e]	.41[e]	.28[e]
Problem solving	.20[e]	.44[e]	.24[e]
Avoidance	-.22[e]	-.12[d]	ns
Interpersonal support	ns	.21[e]	.19[e]
Incremental R^2	.09[e]	.20[e]	.06[e]

[a]Underlined correlations indicate those variables which are significant predictors when entered last into the regression equation for that class of (Table 6 continued) variables. Sample size varies slightly across the regression analyses for the three outcome measures due to missing values.

[b]The incremental R^2 reflect the effects of the predictors above and beyond those of the control variables: Pro-P, age, gender, and income.

[c]$p<.01$

[d]$p<.001$

[e]$p<.0001$

The class of nonreligious appraisals and coping activities accounted for small to modest amounts of variance in the prediction of outcomes (incremental R^2 from .06 to .20). Appraisals of the event as an Opportunity to Grow were consistently associated with positive outcomes. The appraisal of Challenge to Face was related to positive General Outcome and Religious Outcome. The appraisal of Cannot Handle was the strongest predictor of poorer GHQ, and was associated with poorer General Outcome.

Within the nonreligious coping activities, Focus on Positive was a consistent unique contributor to the prediction of positive outcomes. Problem

Solving was consistently related to better outcomes, and Interpersonal Support related positively and uniquely to General Outcome and Religious Outcome. Avoidance was tied to poorer General Outcome and GHQ.

To test the contributions of religious coping measures over those of nonreligious coping measures, we focused on the coping activities dimension, since this class of variables had greater predictive power than other classes. Paralleling the analyses above, we conducted hierarchical multiple regression analyses for each of the outcome measures. The control variables were entered into the analysis, followed by the nonreligious coping activities scales, and then followed by the religious coping activities scales. Once again, incremental R^2 were calculated and tested for statistical significance. The results are shown in Table 7. The religious coping activities scales added modest amounts of unique variance to the prediction of General Outcome ($R^2 = .07$, p < .001) and the GHQ ($R^2 = .03$, p < .001) and larger independent variance to the prediction of Religious Outcome ($R^2 = .26$, p < .001).

TABLE 7

Hierarchical Regression Analyses Predicting
Outcomes from Control Variables,
Nonreligious Coping Variables and Religious Coping Variables

	R^2 control variables	Incremental R^2 with nonreligious coping variables added	Incremental R^2 with religious coping activities variables added	R^2 cumulative[a]
GHQ	.03	.09	.03	.15
General outcome	.10	.20	.07	.37
Religious outcome	.20	.06	.26	.52

[a]$R^2 > .02$, p<.01

Finally, correlations were conducted to assess the relationship among religious and nonreligious coping activities scales. As can be seen in Table 8, Focus on Positive was tied to religious coping activities involving Spiritually Based coping, Good Deeds, Religious Avoidance, Religious Support, and lower levels of Discontent and Pleading. Problem Solving was correlated with Spiritually Based, Good Deeds, Religious Avoidance, and Religious Support. Nonreligious Avoidance related to Religious Avoidance, Good Deeds, Discontent, Pleading, and lower levels of Religious Support. Nonreligious Interpersonal Support was associated with Spiritually Based coping, Good Deeds, Religious Avoidance, Religious Support and Pleading.

TABLE 8

Pearson Correlations of Religious and Nonreligious Coping Activites

| | Nonreligious coping activities | | | |
Religious coping activities	Focus on positive	Problem solving	Avoidance	Support
Spiritually based	.45[c]	.39[c]	ns	.21[c]
Good deeds	.29[c]	.31[c]	.14[b]	.18
Religious avoidance	.22[c]	.19[c]	.08[a]	.13[b]
Discontent	-.13[c]	ns	.35[c]	ns
Religious support	.18[c]	.08[a]	-.10[b]	.30[c]
Plead	-.11[b]	ns	.28[c]	.14[b]

[a]$p<.05$
[b]$p<.001$
[c]$p<.0001$

Discussion and Conclusions

These findings highlight the important role religious beliefs, practices, and motivations play among church members who turn to religion in coping with significant negative events ranging from death, illness, and injury to divorce, separation, and work-related problems. Consistent with the results of studies of community members (McRae, 1984), the elderly (Koenig *et al.*, 1988), accident victims (Bulman & Wortman, 1977), and the ill (O'Brien, 1982), a large proportion of the sample (78%) reported that their religion was involved in some way in understanding or dealing with their significant negative event. It appears that religious involvement in coping with significant negative events is commonplace rather than unusual.

Whether this involvement is predictive of the outcomes of the coping process is less clear. Our findings indicate that, at least in some groups, religious practices and beliefs are significantly associated with outcomes. After controlling for the effects of demographic variables and indiscriminate proreligiousness, religious appraisals, religious coping activities, religious functions, and the religious dispositions accounted for 37% of the explained variance of Religious Outcome. The religious variables were also significant predictors of the nonreligious outcome measures, accounting for 30% of the variance of the General Outcome measure and 12% of the variance of the GHQ. Thus, it seems that religious involvement in coping has implications for outcomes that are not limited to the religious realm; rather, the implications extend to the resolution of the problem and the mental health status of the individual.

What Kinds of Religiousness Are More and Less Helpful in Coping?

In this study we attempted to go beyond the basic question of whether religion is helpful to examine more comprehensively the kinds of religiousness that are more and less helpful in coping. Toward this end, we included a number of measures of religiousness tied to the coping framework: religious appraisals, religious coping activities, religious purposes, and religious outcomes. The factor analyses of the religious coping activities and religious purposes dimensions reveal that religious involvement in coping can take a variety of forms: interactional: interpersonal relations with others (Religious Support) or with God (Spiritually Based coping activities); behavioral: changes in life-style, requests for divine intercession, or participation in religious services and rites (Good Deeds, Plead, Religious Avoidance); emotional: feelings of love or anger (Discontent) to God; or motivational: a religiously based search for spiritual development (Spiritual purpose), personal growth (Self-Development), the resolution of problems (Resolve), closeness with others (Sharing), and emotional/behavioral control (Restraint). Thus, religious coping efforts, like more general religious dispositions, appear to be multidimensional.

In reviewing the efficacy of these diverse religious approaches as predictors of outcomes of negative events, four key themes emerge.

1. A belief in a just, loving God appears to be predictive of more positive outcomes to negative events. Appraisals of events as reflective of God's will, images of a loving God, and orthodox beliefs in a just and merciful personal God were generally associated with positive outcomes. In contrast, appraisals of the event as a punishment from God or as a threat were related to poorer outcomes, as were feelings of anger and distance from God and church members (Discontent).

Why should beliefs in a just, benevolent God be more helpful in coping than beliefs in a punitive or distant God? As noted earlier, religious beliefs and practices may serve a number of psychological functions. Spilka, Shaver, and Kirkpatrick (1985) assert that to the extent religious concepts are well-integrated, emphasize the orderliness of the universe, and view the world as fair, they offer a source of meaning and answers to seemingly unanswerable questions. To the extent that God is viewed as a benevolent Being, religious beliefs also offer a basis for self-esteem, (*e.g.*, God loves me and He doesn't make dirt) (Benson & Spilka, 1973). And to the extent that God is just and benevolent, religion offers an external framework of control more benign than other external frameworks such as beliefs in powerful others or chance (Pargament, Sullivan, Tyler, & Steele, 1982). In contrast, beliefs in an angry unfair God can pose a threat to the sense of meaning, self-esteem, and control in life.

2. The experience of God as a supportive partner in the coping process appears to be another important correlate of positive outcomes. The most potent predictor of outcomes in this study was Spiritually Based coping activities. Central to these activities is the individual's relationship with God. As the items on the scale indicate, this relationship is not abstract or impersonal, but intimate (*e.g.*, "experienced God's love and care"), emotion-focused (*e.g.*, "realized that I didn't have to suffer since Jesus suffered for me"), and problem-focused (*e.g.*, "My faith showed me different ways to handle the problem"). For the individual this relationship involves both personal effort (*e.g.*, "Used my faith to help me decide how to cope with the situation") and a recognition of the limits of personal agency (*e.g.*, "Took control over what I could and gave the rest up to God"). The positive correlations between Religious Experience, Collaborative, and Deferring religious coping styles, and outcomes were consistent with the effects of spiritually based coping for each of these measures reflects a facet of the spiritual coping construct.

In this sample of church members who turn to religion in coping, some form of supportive relationship with God seems more helpful than a more autonomous stance in coping. Self-directed coping efforts in which God's role is consciously minimized and the individual alone takes the responsibility for problem solving were inconsistent both with the experience of God as a partner in coping and with positive outcomes.

Many psychologists have contrasted God-centered with person-centered views of the world (Ellis, 1960; Freud, 1949; Fromm, 1960). These results highlight the importance of a third perspective—the relational—in which the interaction between individual and God is the crucial theme (Maton, 1989; Pargament *et al.*, 1988; Pollner, 1989), and the individual's role in the relationship is neither simply active nor simply passive. From this perspective, God can be viewed as another member of a social network who, like other network members, can at times offer help in the coping process (Cohen & Willis, 1985; Coyne & DeLongis, 1986). As a "member" of the network, God can serve functions similar to other members including emotional, instrumental and informational support (Tardy, 1985). God may also play special roles in the network. For example, the relationship with God may be particularly supportive to the individual faced with the limits of personal control through the knowledge that the deity will be there to make events endurable. Further studies are needed to specify the qualities of the individual's relationship with God of greatest significance to the coping process.

3. Involvement in religious rituals was also associated with more positive outcomes. These rituals were of several different forms: attendance at religious services, prayer, efforts to avoid the negative event through rituals such as

reading the Bible or a focus on the afterlife, attempts to live a less sinful, more loving life, and support from the clergy and other church members. Religious rituals have long been a focus of study for social scientists, particularly anthropologists and sociologists. They suggest that rituals serve a variety of functions: emotional release and maintenance (Malinowski, 1925), as basis for meaning (Geertz, 1966), and social integration and personal identity (Durkheim, 1915). Religious rituals can also contribute to the sense of controllability and predictability in life (Frazer, 1925). For example, the individual may attempt to influence the outcomes of events indirectly through prayer to God or through efforts to live a more decent life. By underscoring God's benevolence and justice, rituals can also encourage a suspension of the need for personal control through the knowledge that the problem is in the hands of God (Spilka, Shaver, & Kirkpatrick, 1985).

4. Among these churchgoers, the search for spiritual and personal support through religion was, in itself, associated with more positive outcomes in coping. This finding underscores the significance of religious motivations in the coping process. Individuals did not perceive their approach to religion in their times of trouble as simply a response to psychological need. Many reported that they looked to God for closeness and to their religion as a guiding force in dealing with problems; for them religion represents what Allport (1950) has described as "a master motive" (p. 81). And consistent with Allport's perspective, this intrinsic spiritually oriented approach was, in itself, associated with positive outcomes. Our findings are also consistent with empirical studies in which intrinsic religiousness has been associated with some related personological constructs—an internal locus of control, purpose in life, lower trait anxiety, and lower death anxiety (see Donahue, 1985, for review).

But our findings depart from the general theory and literature on extrinsic religiousness. Allport (1950) contrasted intrinsic religious motivation in which the individual "lives his religion" with extrinsic religious motivation in which the person "uses his religion...an interest held because it serves other more ultimate interests" (Allport & Ross, 1967, p. 434). Extrinsic religiousness has been positively associated with prejudice, dogmatism, and fear of death; reviewing this literature Donahue (1985) commented: "Extrinsic religiousness...does a good job of measuring the sort of religion that gives religion a bad name" (p. 416).

Here, however, extrinsic religiousness and utilitarian approaches to religion (Self-Development, Sharing, Restraint, and Resolve) were associated with more positive general and religious outcomes. Perhaps the simplest explanation of this apparent discrepancy is that while extrinsically oriented individuals may be more prejudiced, dogmatic, and anxious, their "use" of religion can still be helpful to them in dealing with negative events. Alternatively, our results may point to the need to distinguish more sharply among kinds of uses of religion as Kirkpatrick (1989) has done in factor analytic studies of extrinsic religiousness. For example, the search for self-development, intimacy, and emotional sustenance may have very different implications from the search for social status or instrumental gain through religion (Pargament, 1990). Some of these uses of religion may not necessarily be inconsistent with a spiritual motivation. In fact, in this study the Spiritual purpose scale was significantly related to each of the other purpose scales (*rs* from .33 to .60). Thus, for many people religion may be both lived and used (Echemendia & Pargament, 1982). How religion is used and the implications of these different uses for the coping process represent important questions for further research.

These findings then begin to specify more clearly the kinds of religious beliefs, behaviors, and motivations more and less helpful to those who involve religion in the coping process. They suggest the need to move beyond single-item measures of religiousness in studies of coping to a more complete and differentiated approach.

The Additive Contributions of the Religious Coping Constructs

We turn now to the question of what additional contributions, if any, the religious coping constructs make to our understanding of the coping process. We examined whether measures of religious coping predict outcomes above and beyond the contributions of standard religious dispositional measures. Clearly they do. In fact, the religious coping measures were considerably stronger independent predictors of outcome than the traditional measures of religiousness. It is likely that this finding reflects the development of our religious coping constructs and measures within a more general coping framework, one purposefully linked to outcome. From the perspective of this framework, general religious dispositions translate into specific coping efforts in the face of critical life situations. These concrete efforts can be conceptualized as intervening variables, bridging the relationship between the general resources of religion and the outcomes of specific events. If this is true then the measures of outcome should relate more strongly to the measures of religious coping than to the dispositional measures (as we have found). Furthermore, the dispositional measures should relate more strongly to the measures of religious coping than to the measures of outcome. Analyses of the relationship between religious dispositional and religious coping variables will be the focus of another paper.

The measures of religious coping and outcome operate at a similar event-specific level. In contrast, the religious dispositional measures deal with generalized beliefs, motivations, and practice; not their applications to specific events. Here as in other studies, the constructs operationalized at more commensurate levels were more predictive of each other (Fishbein & Ajzen, 1975). It follows that in studies of particular situations, religious measures tailored to the situation will have greater predictive power than generalized dispositional measures. For example, the specific religious responses of victims to tragedy should relate to outcomes more strongly than their general image of God or average annual church attendance.

We also examined whether the concepts and measures of religious coping add to our understanding above and beyond the contributions of general concepts and measures of coping. Looking at the relationship between religious coping activities and nonreligious coping activities, we found that the two kinds of coping activities were modestly to moderately associated with each other. For example, the nonreligious coping activity of focusing on the positive was significantly associated with spiritually based coping, good deeds, religious avoidance, religious support, and lower levels of discontent and pleading. But while they were related, religious and nonreligious coping activities were not redundant.

Had we focused only on the nonreligious coping activities here, the coping process of this sample would have looked similar to that of other samples. As with other groups, appraisals of the negative event as an opportunity to grow and a challenge rather than as a threat, a loss, or beyond one's ability to cope were associated with better outcomes. Coping activities involving a focus on the positive, problem solving, and interpersonal support also had more positive implications than those involving avoidance. But for these church-affiliated members, the religious coping activities offer something to the coping process that goes beyond the contributions of nonreligious activities.

What is that something? Theorists have suggested that religion provides a unique framework for coming to grips with the limits of personal knowledge, control, and resources in coping (Bakan, 1968; Pruyser, 1968; Tillich, 1952), limits that may be more apparent in the face of serious negative events. A comparison of religious avoidance and nonreligious avoidance provides an interesting case in point. The two types of avoidance are related to each other in a small but statistically significant fashion. However, religious avoidance relates to better outcomes, whereas nonreligious avoidance relates to poorer outcomes. In comparing the items in the scales, both involve efforts to avoid painful feelings and thoughts. However, the religious avoidance items offer an external support to the individual in this process (*e.g.*, God, the Bible, the world-to-come). The nonreligious avoidance items do not (*e.g.*, "tried not to think about it," "wished the situation would go away"). Thus, unlike generally avoidant activities, the external support associated with religious avoidance may provide stability, meaning, and comfort to the individual in coping.

In sum, religious coping activities represent an important element of the coping process, at least among the religiously involved. These findings underscore the need for an integration of the religious dimension into the coping literature. The word integration is crucial, for these findings also point to the dangers of drawing too sharp a line between religious and nonreligious coping activities. Both religious and nonreligious processes appear to be commonly involved and interrelated in coping. While comparisons could be drawn between those who make use of religion in coping with those who do not, these "competitive" studies might overlook the variety of forms both religious and nonreligious coping efforts can take and the diverse implications of these forms for outcome. Perhaps the more important question has to do with the comparative efficacy of different patterns of religious/nonreligious coping.

Limitations

This study attempts to provide some correction to a bias in the general coping literature. When it has been studied at all, religion has been examined from an "outside" perspective (Dittes, 1969); a generic background variable measured by a few simple indicators within a general population. In this study, we move religion more to the foreground, taking a closer "inside" look by differentiating more finely among religious phenomena within different religiously oriented groups. It is important to note that neither inside nor outside perspective can offer a complete picture of religion and coping. From each vantage point some features are apparent and some are hidden. Thus, the outside views of religion from the general coping literature cannot be generalized to the inside (i.e., the members of particular religious groups). Similarly, the inside perspectives of religious participants cannot be generalized to the outside (*e.g.*, the generic role of religion within the larger society).

These findings, in particular, are most representative of the perspectives of mainstream, church-affiliated, and participating Christians. Of course these groups represent a large proportion of Americans (Gallup Report, 1985; Jacquet, 1988). Furthermore, these church members are not homogeneous. They report a range of religious views and practices. Nevertheless, other groups are not represented in this study including those who define themselves as religious but are not affiliated with a church, those who define themselves as nonreligious, and members of other religious institutions (*e.g.*, Jews, Muslims, and sects).

We might expect different religious groups to use different kinds of religious coping efforts. For example, Ebaugh, Richman, and Chafetz (1984) interviewed members of Catholic Charismatic, Bahai, and Christian Scientist groups about their ways of responding to crisis. Charismatics looked to their group for emotional support; Christian Scientists focused more on positive thinking; and Bahais coped more intellectually through reading of religious materials. These coping approaches may also vary in their effectiveness for different groups. For example, within Judaism, a religion that emphasizes the importance of efforts to live by a moral code, good deeds may play a more important role in the resolution of negative events than within mainstream Christianity. Similarly, in a recent study of women who had experienced pregnancy loss, Lasker, Lohmann, and Toedter (1989) found stronger correlations between religious coping variables and perinatal grief among those who considered themselves "religious" or "very religious." With their limitations in mind, other "inside" studies are needed to examine the coping process within other religious groups.

This study is also limited by its cross-sectional design. While the measures of coping with the stressful event direct the participants to consider their efforts prior to the outcomes, both classes of measures were obtained at the same point in time. Thus, it is possible that the perceptions of the outcome influenced the individual's reconstruction of his/her coping efforts (*e.g.*, the event turned out well so God must have helped me). The concurrent reports of these variables could have also been affected by other variables that preceded these reports. For example, both religious coping efforts and outcomes may grow out of a more general set of personal and social resources (*e.g.*, mental health, personality, social networks) brought to the coping process. Although efforts were made to control for some potentially confounding factors—social desirability, indiscriminate proreligiousness, and demographic variables—longitudinal studies are clearly needed to delineate more sharply the impact of religious coping on the outcomes of serious events. Two recent investigations represent promising steps in this direction, and suggest that our results are not simply attributable to the cross-sectional design. In a study of high school students in transition to college, a measure of spiritual support obtained in high school predicted the adjustment of students to college under conditions of high stress, but not for those experiencing less stress (Maton, 1989). In a set of 2-month prospective studies of college students, a higher intrinsic orientation predicted a decline in depression while a lower intrinsic orientation predicted an increase in depression among Protestant but not Catholic students faced with uncontrollable negative events (Parks, Cohen, & Herb, in press).

The reliability of three of the shorter scales derived through factor analyses (Plead, Avoidance, and Interpersonal Support) and a fourth developed for exploratory purposes (Religious Avoidance) was limited, possibly reducing the magnitude of some of our findings. However, each of these scales was significantly tied to the outcome measures. Although these findings offer some support for the validity of these scales, further development of these instruments is needed. The religious purpose scales also require additional work. Made up of a modest number of items, these scales yielded somewhat different dimensions across factor analytic methods.

Several important questions have not been addressed in this study. One set of questions deals with the ecology of religious coping. What personal, situational, and contextual factors are associated with religious involvement in the coping process? How stable are religious coping activities over time and situations? Other questions focus more on the complexities of the relationships among religious coping and outcome variables. For example, there is some literature to suggest that these relationships may be moderated by the nature of the event (Maton, 1989), demographic characteristics of the individual such as gender or age, or the salience of religion to the person (see Pargament, 1990, for review). Questions also arise about the definition and measurement of outcome in this study. Can these self-reports of outcome be buttressed by behavioral measurement or reports from significant others? Are these outcomes sustained over time? Do some of the religious coping methods (*e.g.*, pleading, religious avoidance) offer short-term relief but longer term problems (*e.g.*, reduced competence) in dealing with negative events? Do other religious coping methods (*e.g.*, discontent) lead to short-term distress but longer term well-being? These represent important questions for further study; the ecology of religious coping and the impact of religious coping over a 2-year period in this sample will be examined in subsequent papers in this "God Help Me" series.

In spite of these limitations, it seems clear that, at least among some groups, the constructs of religious coping enhance our ability to understand the process of coping with significant negative events. These findings highlight the important role the religious component can play in coping and the need for a more complete integration of religious constructs into the general coping literature. With a clearer understanding of the role of religion in coping, the psychologist should be better equipped to approach the religious community as a site for prevention, promotion, and collaboration.

REFERENCES

Aldwin, C.M., & Revenson, T.A. (1987). Does coping help? A reexamination of the relation between coping and mental health. *Journal of Personality and Social Psychology, 53,* 337-348.

Allport, G. (1950). *The individual and his religion: A psychological interpretation.* New York: MacMillan.

Allport, G.W. & Ross, J.M. (1967). Personal religious orientation and prejudice. *Journal of Personality and Social Psychology, 5,* 432-443.

Bakan, D. (1968). *Disease, pain and sacrifice: Toward a psychology of suffering.* Chicago: University of Chicago Press.

Batson, C.D. (1976). Religion as prosocial: Agent or double agent. *Journal for the Scientific Study of Religion, 15,* 29-45.

Batson, C., & Ventis, W. (1982). *The religious experience: A social-psychological perspective.* New York: Oxford University Press.

Benson, P., & Spilka, B. (1973). God image as a function of self-esteem and locus of control. *Journal for the Scientific Study of Religion, 12,* 297-310.

Benson, P.L., & Williams, D.L. (1982). *Religion on Capitol Hill: Myths and realities.* New York: Harper and Row.

Billings, A.G., & Moos, R.H. (1984). Coping, stress and social resources among adults with unipolar depression. *Journal of Personality and Social Psychology, 46,* 877-891.

Bulman, J., & Wortman, C. (1977). Attributions of blame and coping in the "real world": Severe accident victims react to their lot. *Journal of Personality and Social Psychology, 35,* 351-363.

Clark, W. (1958). *The psychology of religion.* New York: MacMillan.

Cleary, P.D., & Houts, P.S. (1984). The psychological impact of the Three Mile Incident. *Journal of Human Stress,* Spring, 28-34.

Cohen, S., & Willis, T. (1985). Stress, social support, and the buffering hypothesis. *Psychological Bulletin, 98,* 310-357.

Cook, J.A., & Wimberly, D. (1983). If I should die before I wake: Religious commitment and adjustment to the death of a child. *Journal for the Scientific Study of Religion, 22,* 222-238.

Coyne, J.C. & DeLongis, A. (1986). Going beyond social support: The role of social relationships in adaptation. *Journal of Consulting and Clinical Psychology, 54,* 454-460.

DeLongis, A., Coyne, J., Dakof, G., Folkman, S., & Lazarus, R. (1982). Relationship of daily hassles, uplifts, and major life events to health status. *Health Psychology, 1,* 119-136.

Dittes, J.E. (1969). Psychology of religion. In G. Lindzey & E. Aronson (Eds.), *The handbook of social psychology* (2nd ed., Vol. 5, pp. 602-659). Reading, MA: Addison-Wesley.

Donahue, M.J. (1985). Intrinsic and extrinsic religiousness: Review and meta-analysis. *Journal of Personality and Social Psychology, 48,* 400-419.

Durkheim, E. (1915). *The elementary forms of the religious life.* New York: Free Press.

Ebaugh, H., Richman, K., & Chafetz, J. (1984). Life crises among the religiously committed: Do sectarian differences matter? *Journal for the Scientific Study of Religion, 23,* 19-31.

Echemendia, R. & Pargament, K.I. (1982). The psychosocial functions of religion: Reconceptualization and measurement. Paper presented at the meeting of the American Psychological Association, Washington, D.C.

Ellis, A. (1960). There is no place for the concept of sin in psychotherapy. *Journal of Counseling Psychology, 7,* 188-192.

Eckenrode, J. (1984). Impact of chronic and acute stressors on daily reports of mood. *Journal of Personality and Social Psychology, 46,* 907-918.

Erikson, E. (1963). *Childhood and society.* New York: Norton.

Feagin, J. (1964). Prejudice and religious types: A focused study of Southern Fundamentalists. *Journal for the Scientific Study of Religion, 4,* 3-13.

Fichter, J.H. (1981). *Religion and pain: The spiritual dimensions of health care.* New York: Crossroad.

Fishbein, M., & Ajzen, I., (1975). *Belief, attitude, intention, and behavior: An introduction to theory and research.* Reading MA: Addison-Wesley.

Folkman, S., & Lazarus, R.S. (1988). Coping as a mediator of emotion. *Journal of personality and social psychology, 54,* 466-475.

Folkman, S., Schaefer, C., & Lazarus, R.S. (1979). Cognitive processes as mediators of stress and coping. In V. Hamilton & D.M. Warburton (Eds.), *Human stress and cognition: An information-processing approach.* London: Wiley.

Frankl, V.E. (1963). *Man's search for meaning.* New York: Washington Square Press.

Frazer, J.G. (1925). *The golden bough.* New York: MacMillan.

Freud, S. (1949). *The future of an illusion.* New York: Liveright Publishing Corporation.

Fromm, E. (1960). *Psychoanalysis and religion.* New York: Rinehart and Winston.

Gallup Report. (1985, May). No. 236. Princeton, NJ: Author.

Geertz, C. (1966). Religion as a cultural system. In M. Banton (ed.), *Anthropological approaches to the study of religion* (pp. 1-46) London: Tavistock.

Gibbs, H.W. & Achterberg-Lawlis, J. (1978). Spiritual values and death anxiety: Implications for counseling with terminal cancer patients. *Journal of Counseling Psychology, 25,* 563-569.

Gil, K.M., Abrams, M.R., Phillips, G., & Keefe, F.J. (1989). Sickle cell disease pain: Relation of coping strategies to adjustment. *Journal of Consulting and Clinical Psychology, 57,* 725-731.

Gilbert, K.R. (1989). *Religion as a resource for bereaved parents as they cope with the death of their child.* Paper presented at the annual meeting of the National Council on Family Relations, New Orleans.

Glock, C.Y., Ringer, B.B., & Babbie, R. (1967). *To comfort and to challenge: A dilemma of the contemporary church.* Berkeley: University of California Press.

Goldberg, D. (1978). *Manual of the General Health Questionnaire.* Windsor, Ontario: National Foundation for Educational Research.

Gorsuch, R. (1984). Measurement: The boon and bane of investigating religion. *American Psychologist, 39,* 228-236.

Grevengoed, N., & Pargament, K. (1987). *Attributions for death: An examination of the role of religion and the relationship between attributions and mental health.* Paper presented at the annual meeting of the Society for the Scientific Study of Religion, Louisville, KY.

Greeley, A.M. (1972). *The denominational society.* Glenview, IL: Scott, Foresman.

Griffith, E., Young, J., & Smith, D. (1984). An analysis of the therapeutic elements in a black church service. *Hospital and Community Psychiatry, 35,* 464-469.

Hammond, P. (1988). Religion and the persistence of identity. *Journal for the Scientific Study of Religion, 27,* 1-11.

Heller, K., & Swindle, R. (1983). Social networks, perceived social support, and coping with stress. In R.D. Felner, L. Jason, J. Moritsugu, & S. Farber (Eds.), *Preventive psychology: Theory, research, and practice* (pp. 87-103). New York: Pergamon.

Hoge, D. (1972). A validated intrinsic religious motivation scale. *Journal for the Scientific Study of Religion, 11,* 396-497.

Jenkins, R., & Pargament, K. (1988). Cognitive appraisals in cancer patients. *Social Science and Medicine, 26,* 625-633.

Kahoe, R.D. (1982). *The power of religious hope.* Paper presented at the annual meeting of the American Psychological Association, Washington, D.C.

King, M. & Hunt, R. (1975). Measuring the religious variable: National replication. *Journal for the Scientific Study of Religion, 14,* 13-22.

Kirpatrick, L.A. (1989). A psychometric analysis of the Allport-Ross and Feagin measures of intrinsic-extrinsic religious orientation. In *Research in the Social Scientific Study of Religion, 1,* 1-30.

Koenig, H., George, L., & Siegler, J. (1988). The use of religion and other emotion-regulating coping strategies among older adults. *Gerontologist, 28,* 303-310.

Kushner, H.S. (1981). *When bad things happen to good people.* New York: Schocken.

Lasker, J.N., Lohmann, J., & Toedter, L. (1989). *The role of religion in bereavement: The case of pregnancy loss.* Paper presented at the Society for the Scientific Study of Religion, Salt Lake City, UT.

Lazarus, R., & Folkman, S. (1984). *Stress, appraisal and coping.* New York: Springer.

Malinowski, B. (1925). Magic, science, and religion. In J. Needham (Ed.), *Science, religion, and reality.* New York: Macmillan.

Maslow, A.H. (1970). *Motivation and personality.* New York: Harper and Row.

Maton, K. (1989). The stress-buffering role of spiritual support:Cross-sectional and prospective investigations. *Journal for the Scientific Study of Religion, 28,* 310-323.

Maton, K., & Rappaport, J. (1984). Empowerment in a religious setting: A multivariate investigation. *Prevention in Human Services, 3,* 37-72.

McCrae, R.R. (1984). Situational determinants of coping responses: Loss, threat and challenge. *Journal of Personality and Social Psychology, 46,* 919-928.

Moos, R.H. (1986). *Coping with life crises: An integrated approach.* New York: Plenum Press.

Moos, R., Cronkite, R., Billings, A., & Finney, J. (1984). *Health and daily living form manual.* Palo Alto, CA: Social Ecology Laboratory.

Neighbors, H.W., Jackson, J.S., Bowman, P.J., & Gurin, G. (1983). S t r e s s , coping, and black mental health: Preliminary findings from a national study, *Prevention in Human Services,* 5-29.

Newman, J., & Pargament, K. (1990). The role of religion in problem solving. *Review of Religious Research, 31,* 390-404.

O'Brien, M.E. (1982). Religious faith and adjustment to long-term dialysis. *Journal of Religion and Health, 21*(1), 68-80.

Pargament, K. (1990). God help me. Toward a theoretical framework of coping for the psychology of religion. *Research in the Social Scientific Study of Religion, 2,* 195-224.

Pargament K., Brannick, M., Adamakos, H., Ensing, D., Keleman, M., Warren, R., Falgout, K., Cook, P., & Myers, J. (1987). Indiscriminate proreligiousness: Conceptualization and measurement. *Journal for the Scientific Study of Religion, 26,* 182-200.

Pargament, K.I., & Hahn, J. (1986). God and the just world: Causal and coping attributions in health situations. *Journal for the Scientific Study of Religion, 25,* 193-207.

Pargament, K., Kennell, J., Hathaway, W., Grevengoed, N., Newman, J., & Jones, W. (1988). Religion and the problem solving process: Three styles of coping. *Journal for the Scientific Study of Religion, 27,* 90-104.

Pargament, K.I., Sullivan, M.S., Tyler, F.B., & Steele, R.E. (1982). Patterns of attribution of control and individual psychosocial competence. *Psychological Reports, 51,* 1243-1252.

Park, C., Cohen, L.H., & Herb, L. (in press). Intrinsic religiousness and religious coping as life stress moderators for Catholics versus Protestants. *Journal of Personality and Social Psychology.*

Pollner, M. (1989). Divine relations, social relations, and well-being. *Journal of Health and Social Behavior, 30,* 92-104.

Princeton Religion Research Center (1987). *Faith development and your ministry.* Princeton, NJ: Author.

Pruyser, P.W. (1968). *A dynamic psychology of religion.* New York: Harper and Row.

Putney, S., & Middleton, R. (1961). Dimensions and correlates of religious ideologies. *Social Forces, 39,* 285-290.

Rabkin, J., & Struening, E. (1976). Life events, stress and illness. *Science, 194,* 1013-1020.

Roozen, D.A. & Carroll, J.W. (1989). Methodological issues in denominational surveys of congregations. *Review of Religious Research, 31*(2), 115-131.

Snook, S., & Gorsuch, R.L. (1989). Component analysis versus common factor analysis: A Monte Carlo study. *Psychological Bulletin, 106,* 148-154.

Spilka, B., Hood, R., & Gorsuch, L. (1985). *The psychology of religion: An empirical approach.* Englewood Cliffs, NJ: Prentice-Hall.

Spilka, B., Shaver, P., & Kirkpatrick, L. (1985). A general attribution theory for the psychology of religion. *Journal for the Scientific Study of Religion, 224,* 1-20.

Stone, A.A., & Neale, J.M. (1984). New measures of daily coping: Development and preliminary results. *Journal of Personality and Social Psychology, 46,* 892-906.

Tardy, C.H. (1985). Social support measurement. *American Journal of Community Psychology, 13,* 187-202.

Taylor, S.E. (1983). Adjustment to threatening events: A theory of cognitive adaptation. *American Psychologist, 38,* 1161-1174.

Thoits, P.A. (1983). Dimensions of life events that influence psychological distress: An evaluation and synthesis of the literature. In H.B. Kaplan (Ed.), *Psychosocial stress: Trends in theory and research* (pp. 33-103). New York: Academic Press.

Tyler, F. (1978). Individual psychosocial competence: A personality configuration. *Education and Psychological Measurement, 38,* 309-323.

Wright, S. Pratt, C., & Schmall, V. (1985). Spiritual support for caregivers of dementia patients. *Journal of Religion and Health, 24*(1), 31-38.

Yates, J., Chalmer, B., St. James, P., Follensbee, M., & McKegney, F. (1981). Religion in patients with advanced cancer. *Medical and Pediatric Oncology, 9,* 121-128.

NOTES

1. Complete statistical results of the factor analyses, a complete correlation matrix of the variables in the study, and a copy of these instruments are available from the first author upon request.

2. Following the recommendation of Snook and Gorsuch (1989), principal factors analyses were conducted on the religious coping activities, nonreligious coping activities, and religious purposes scales. However, in the case of the purposes of religion items, the principal factors analysis yielded a somewhat less interpretable solution than the principal components analysis. In particular, the "personal closeness with God" item loaded more cleanly on the Spiritual factor in the principal components analysis. We chose to use the principal component analysis finding, emphasizing interpretability here at some cost of consistency among analyses and statistical preferability.

3. To assess the independent contribution of the religious dispositional variables to the prediction of outcome, we conducted a similar set of hierarchical regression analyses in which the religious dispositional measures were added last into the equation after control and religious coping variables. The incremental R^2 for the religious dispositional measures were smaller than those

associated with the religious coping measures: GHQ (.01, ns), General Outcome (.03,p<.001), and Religious Outcome (.03, p<.001).

EDITOR'S COMMENTS

This is a rich report but also the most statistically complicated of those in this volume. Its richness consists of an extensive literature review with many references. Readers who are interested in the role of religious resources in the coping process will find these citations helpful.

The logic behind this project was to determine if the use of religious/spiritual resources in coping with negative life events produced better outcomes than if they were not used. A strength of the project was that a theoretical framework was developed at the beginning and the research was intended to determine whether empirical evidence would support it.

The most pressing question for readers who are not trained in statistics is how to understand all the analyses. The design is found in Figure 1.

FIGURE 1

Independent Variables	Outcome Measures*		
	GHQ	General Outcome	Religious Outcome
age	X	X	X
gender	X	X	X
marital status	X	X	X
education level	X	X	X
income	X	X	X
frequency of church attendance	X	X	X
frequency of prayer and Bible reading	X	X	X
indiscriminately pro-religious	X	X	X
MMPI lie scale	X	X	X
Items concerning religious appraisal of the event	X	X	X
Items concerning non-religious appraisal of the event	X	X	X
Religious coping items (Table 1)	X	X	X
Non-religious coping items (Table 2)	X	X	X
Purposes of religious coping (Table 3)	X	X	X
Dispositional religious variables:			
Loving images of God	X	X	X
Intrinsic, extrinsic, & quest religious orientations	X	X	X
Doctrinal orthodoxy	X	X	X
Collaborative, deferring & self-directed coping styles	X	X	X
Religious experience scale	X	X	X

*Outcome measures are the response variables in this design.

The analysis moves step by step to answer the research question. The authors report factor analysis, item mean scores and standard deviations for the coping (Tables 1 & 2) and purpose scales (Table 3). Reporting these results is necessary because, as the authors acknowledge, these scales were new, built from a number of sources. The factor structure clustered items and the authors then examined the relationships of these clusters to the outcome measures.

The secret to outcome research is to demonstrate that some persons or interventions produce better results, better outcomes, than others. The "long-hand" methodology for such a project would be to test subjects at a beginning point, wait for a negative life event to happen, and then, at a designated time after the event, to test them again. This would be practically impossible to carry out. A more economical method, both in terms of time and money, is frequently used and it is demonstrated in this project. All data, including outcome measures, were gathered at the same time. A statistical test (hierarchical multiple regression) was then used to determine which of the independent variables explained the most variance in the data of the response variables. This is, in effect, determining by statistical means which independent variables make the largest contribution to the data of the response variables.

But it is a bit more complicated than that. The research question was whether religious coping scores explained variance in the outcome measures beyond that explained by the non-religious coping scores. But how can the influence on the outcome variables of all those other independent variables be controlled? Suppose that religious coping efforts did show a strong influence on the outcome scores. Trustworthy results would require that a clear indication that this influence was not due to a unique contribution of age or gender or any other variable. The way to manage this is to first of all conduct regression analyses for these variables so that their relationship to the outcome measures is known. In this data set, age, gender, income, and indiscriminately pro-religious scores were significantly influential and the reader will note that the authors state this clearly early in the Result section.

Now the next step. The multiple regression process can determine the influence of a number of variables at one time on the outcome data. Thus, such a command might look like this:

Determine the influence of age, gender, income, indiscriminately pro-religious, non-religious coping, and religious coping on the outcome variables.

The important feature here is that when the influence of age is identified by the computer program, it also removes it from further influence in the analysis of the remaining variables. Thus, when the influence of gender was calculated, the effects of age were no longer present. This process continued so that when the last variable was considered, the influence of all previous variables in the command had been removed. Thus, the reader will find that the authors in this report sometimes describe the order in which the variables were listed in the computer command. And, although they may not say so directly, the most important variable, in this case that of religious coping, was placed last in the command so that all identified influences from other variables was removed by the time it was considered.

This study is a strong step forward in the study of religious coping and its results are important for chaplains and pastors. The results suggest the important role played by religion and spirituality in the process of recovery.

8

Religious Belief, Depression, and Ambulation Status in Elderly Women with Broken Hips

Peter Pressman
John S. Lyons
David B. Larson
James J. Strain

ABSTRACT

The authors studied the relationship between religious belief and psychiatric and medical status in 30 elderly women recovering from the surgical repair of broken hips. Religious belief was associated with lower levels of depressive symptoms and better ambulation status.

The topic of religious belief appears to be gaining recognition as a focus for research in psychiatry. Bergin (1983), Larson *et.al.* (1986), and Kroll and Sheehan (1989) have observed the relative neglect of the psychiatric study of religion and called for inclusion of measures of religious and spiritual variables in the study of mental health.

There is evidence that religious belief is related to health and well-being, particularly among older adults (Koenig, Moberg, & Kvale, 1988). Sherrill

Reproduced with permission of the American Psychiatric Association from the *American Journal of Psychiatry*, (1990), 147 (6), 758-760.

and Larson (1988) found an association between religious belief and coping among burn patients and emphasized the importance of understanding the relationship between patients' religious commitment and their ability to recover from the stress of traumatic injury.   Gutmann (1987) described the role of spiritual systems cross-culturally in helping older adults renew themselves "despite the attritions, insults, and stigmata of aging" (p.227). Cassem (1988) has asserted that religious commitment appears to offer stability and strength to medical patients.   And Peterson and Roy (1985) have included religious belief among a set of "comfort beliefs" that aid individuals during difficult periods.

The definition and measurement of the personal importance of religion offer a complication to empirical study. Willets and Crider (1988) suggested that the two most relevant dimensions of religious commitment were belief and practice/ritual. Belief refers to the acceptance of a benevolent Deity and is associated with the hope that problems will be mastered. Practice is defined by frequency of church attendance and implies an individual's identification with social support networks. Caplan (1981) proposed that the value of religious practice was in a particular type of social support which buffered those who experienced stressful life events. Kroll and Sheehan (1989), on the other hand, documented that religious practices tend to lag behind religious beliefs and emphasized the importance of beliefs in enhancing well-being.

The present study attempted to examine the relationship between religion and physical and mental well-being by studying a set of older adults with broken hips.

METHOD

The subjects were 30 female patients recruited on the orthopedic units of a large midwestern teaching hospital. Recognition of the possible importance of religion in this sample was stimulated by spontaneous comments of a number of subjects during routine psychiatric assessments. Subjects were 65 years or older and had no psychiatric history and were not currently cognitively impaired (Mini-Mental State examination scores greater than 19). A total of 50 consecutively admitted patients were asked to participate in the study. Eight refused, and 11 had scores below 20 on the Mini-Mental State. Of the remaining 31 subjects, only one was male, and he was therefore eliminated for purposes of sample homogeneity. All had sustained hip fractures in the pertrochanteric area and had undergone surgical repair with a sliding fixation device. Subjects were routinely assessed twice during their hospital stay: within 48 hours of surgery and not less than 24 hours before discharge from the hospital. Each discharge assessment employed three instruments: the Geriatric Depression Scale (Lyon, Strain, Hammer *et al.*, 1989), the Index of Religiousness (Zuckerman, Kasl & Ostfeld, 1984), and a measure of ambulation status that included assistance required and linear distance walked at discharge. The Geriatric Depression Scale was also administered during the postsurgical assessment. Ambulation status was assessed by the patients' physical therapist as a routine part of the discharge note. This assessment was missing for two subjects. Each patient's severity of illness was assessed with the Horn system (1983).

The Index of Religiousness is a three-item measure of the personal importance of religion. The first item asks about attendance at religious services. The second item requests subjects to rate their perceived religiousness. The third item asked to what degree religion (and/or God) is a source of strength and comfort. A total score was obtained by standardizing each item and adding the items together.

RESULTS

The Index of Religiousness total scores were correlated with initial and discharge Geriatric Depression Scale scores and meters walked at discharge. The Index of Religiousness total scores were not correlated with initial depression scale scores ($r=-.30$, $df=29$, ns) but were significantly associated with discharge depression scale scores ($r=-.61$,, $df=29$, $p<0.01$). Patients with stronger religious beliefs and practices were less depressed at discharge. This relationship remained significant even when severity of illness was controlled in a hierarchical regression ($F=9.97$, $df=1,28$, $p<0.004$).

The Index of Religiousness total scores were also significantly correlated with meters walked at discharge ($r=0.45$, $df=27$, $p<0.05$). Patients with stronger religious beliefs and practices had better ambulation status at discharge. This association remained significant after severity of illness was controlled in a hierarchical regression ($F=12.15$, $df=1,26$, $p<0.002$).

In order to determine whether the relationship between the Index of Religiousness total score and ambulation status was mediated by depression, a hierarchical regression model was used in which meters walked at discharge were predicted in an equation, with discharge depression entered first, followed by the patient's Index of Religiousness total score. In this model, there was a trend for the Index of Religiousness score to be related to ambulation status even when depression was controlled ($F=3.50$, $df=1,26$, $p<0.08$). This indicates that after depression was controlled, the Index of Religiousness score was no longer significantly associated with ambulation status, although this association might have remained significant with a larger sample.

Next, the individual items of the Index of Religiousness were correlated with both measures of depression and the discharge ambulation status. Only the item regarding God as a source of strength and comfort was associated with initial depression (r=-0.39, df=29, p<0.05). Both this item (r=-0.52, df=29, p<0.05) and attendance at religious services (r=-0.62, df=29, p<0.05) were significantly associated with discharge depression. Finally, ambulation status was associated with church attendance (r=0.50, df=29, p<0.05).

DISCUSSION

The results of the present study offer support for the notion that religious belief is associated with lower levels of depression and better ambulation status in elderly patients with broken hips. The relationship between religiousness and these measures did not appear to be explained by severity of illness. That is, patients with strong religious beliefs were less likely to be depressed and more likely to walk further at discharge independent of their severity of illness.

Given that the Index of Religiousness score was not significantly correlated with ambulation status independent of depression, it is possible that the relationship between religiousness and meters walked at discharge is at least partially explained by depression. That is, it is consistent with the data that the more religious patients were less depressed and thus responded better to the physical therapy.

The complex association among physical, psychiatric, and religious variables supports an integrated approach to the delivery of psychiatric, social work, and chaplain services in the general hospital (Lyons, Hammer, Larson *et al.*, 1987). Collaborative relationships between consultation/liaison psychiatrists, social workers, and chaplains should enhance each discipline's awareness of what the others can offer for patient care.

This study contributes to a growing body of literature demonstrating the importance of considering religious beliefs and practices in studying psychosocial aspects of medical care. Particularly when studying older adults, psychiatric researchers should overcome the historical neglect of these variables (Larson, Pattison, Blazer, *et al.*, 1986) in order to appreciate the complex and multidimensional nature of psychiatric adjustments in elderly medical/surgical patients.

REFERENCES

Bergin, A. (1983). Religiosity and mental health: a critical reevaluation and meta-analysis. *Professional Psychology: Research and Practice, 14*, 170-184.

Caplan, G. (1981). Mastery of stress: psychosocial aspects. *American Journal of Psychiatry, 138*, 413-420.

Cassem E. (1988). The person confronting death. In A. Nicholi (ed.). *The New Harvard Guide to Psychiatry*. Cambridge, Mass: Harvard University Press.

Gutmann, D. (1987). *Reclaimed Powers: Toward a New Psychology of Men and Women in Later Life*. New York: Basic Books.

Horn, D., Sharkey, P., & Bertram, D. (1983). Measuring the severity of illness: homogeneous case-mix groups. *Medical Care, 21*, 14-27.

Koenig, H., Moberg, D., & Kvale J. (1988). Religious activities and attitudes of older adults in a geriatric assessment clinic. *Journal of the American Geriatric Society, 36*, 362-374.

Kroll, J., & Sheehan, W. (1989). Religious beliefs and practices among 52 psychiatric inpatients in Minnesota. *American Journal of Psychiatry, 146*, 67-72.

Larson, D., Pattison, E., Blazer, D. *et al.* (1986). Systematic analysis of research on religious variables in four major psychiatric journals, 1978-1982. *American Journal of Psychiatry, 143*, 329-334.

Lyons, J., Hammer, J., Larson, D. *et al.* (1987). The impact of a prospective payment system on psychosocial service delivery in the general hospital. *Medical Care, 25*, 140-147.

Lyons, J., Strain, J., Hammer, J., *et al.* (1989). Reliability, validity, and temporal stability of the Geriatric Depression Scale in hospitalized elderly. *International Journal of Psychiatry in Medicine, 19*, 203-209.

Peterson, L., & Roy, A. (1985). Religiosity, anxiety, and meaning and purpose: religion's consequences for psychological wellbeing. *Review of Religious Research, 27*, 49-62.

Sherrill, K., & Larson, D. (1988). Adult burn patients: the role of religion in recovery. *Southern Medical Journal, 81*, 821-829.

Willets, F., & Crider, D. (1988). Religion and well-being: men and women in the middle years. *Review of Religious Research, 29*, 281-292.

Zuckerman, D., Kasl, S., & Ostfeld, A. (1984). Psychosocial predictors of mortality among the elderly poor. *American Journal of Epidemiology, 119*, 410-422.

Organ Donation and Hospital Chaplains Attitudes, Beliefs, and Concerns

William R. DeLong

ABSTRACT

The attitudes, religious issues, and participation level of 110 practicing hospital chaplains concerning cadaver-organ donation are considered. Chaplains are identifying with the emotional aspects of organ donation, in particular the grief and emotional trauma of the grieving family. Donor rates of minority groups are discussed from the perspective of religious traditions and myths. Religious questions of next of kin are investigated, and recommendations are made for a comprehensive approach to cadaver-organ procurement.

In the United States there are currently over 140 institutions performing transplantations that rely on the good will and generosity of others. Because of public-policy decisions such as "required request," organ-donation protocol is now common in medical institutions in this country. The prospect of medical-caregivers becoming involved in an organ donation situation is no longer remote.

Medical personnel in trauma centers and ICUs are critically important in identifying and referring potential organ donors (Prottas & Batten, 1988). Among medical personnel, nurses constitute the professional group most likely

Reproduced with permission of Williams and Wilkins from *Transplantation*, (1990), 50(1), 25-29.

to fulfill "required request" policies in hospitals (DeLong, 1989). Consequently, it has been health-care providers in the ICU who have been surveyed about their attitudes concerning organ donation and transplantation (Prottas & Batten, 1988; Youngner, Landefeld, Coulton, Juknialis, & Leary, 1989). Nurses and medical doctors, however, often are not the first professional group to establish rapport with the family of potentially brain-dead patients. Because of the medical staff's role in lifesaving intervention, it is much more likely that a social worker or hospital chaplain will be first to contact the family of brain-dead patients. This is significant given the fact that it is the family that is the locus of medical decision making, including giving permission for organ donation, despite a patient's preference noted on a donor card or driver's license (Prottas, 1989).

Little has been done to investigate the attitudes of hospital chaplains concerning organ donation. This is surprising since in many institutions hospital chaplains are the primary grief and crisis counselors, and many families still look to the clergy in times of crisis and stress. Further, religious concerns have been highlighted in studies that indicate minority groups do not donate organs because of religious beliefs and cultural myths (Perez, Schulman, Davis, Olson, Tellis, Matas, 1989). In many instances then, hospital chaplains may be the first member of the medical-care team to work with families of brain-dead patients.

This study addresses one primary question: What are the attitudes of hospital chaplains concerning organ donation? Subsequent questions then arise: What are the questions most often asked them by families of potential organ donors? How do they see their role in a process of gift giving that by definition occurs in the midst of sudden loss and death?

MATERIALS AND METHODS

Hospital chaplains were randomly selected from the current membership list of the College of Chaplains, the certifying agency for the profession. The population was divided between chaplains serving at university-based hospitals and at other settings such as priviate or community hospitals throughout the continental United States. The membership listing of the College of Chaplains does not specify if the hospital in which the chaplain is serving is a designated trauma center. Working under the assumption that a trauma center will have more serious head traumas, and thus the potential for more brain-dead patients, the population was divided to account for the possibility of more trauma centers existing at teaching institutions.

A five-item survey was mailed to 55 chaplains from each group (Table 1). The response for each group clustered at 28, a return rate of 50%.

TABLE 1

Primary Survey of Hospital Chaplains

Please indicate the most appropriate response

1.   In the event of a brain-dead patient, how likely are you to participate in the process of organ donation?

100%_____0% (please specify)

2.   In your organ-donation experience, what was the most important religious/theological concern voiced by the next-of-kin?

a.   Respect of the donor
b.   Authority or permission of the religious body
c.   Resurrection of the body at the end of time
d.   Keeping the body intact, as one entity
e.   Suffering of the patient
Comments?

3.   What issue in organ donation concerns you most from a religious or theological perspective?

a.   Respect of the donor
b.   Authority or permission of the religious body
c.   Resurrection of the body at the end of time
d.   Keeping the body intact, as one entity
e.   Suffering of the patient
Comments?

4.   What issue in organ donation concerns you most from a personal or professional perspective (as separate from religious or theological)?

a.   Timing of the asking for donation
b.   Ethical concerns
c.   Potential for coercion in the decision making
d.   Public education about donation
Comments?

5.   In your opinion, should hospital chaplain participate in asking for organ donors?

a.   Yes
b.   No
c.   Consultant only
d.   Undecided
Comments?

Because religious concerns can be so varied, a preliminary survey to facilitate the formulation of meaningful categories for the actual survey was sent to a limited group of chaplains selected in the same way (n=55). The preliminary survey consisted of "open-ended" questions regarding various aspects of the donation process. Based on this survey various responses were created for each question of the primary survey. The preliminary survey had a response rate of 45% (n=24). The respondents of the preliminary survey were not considered a part of the sample group for the second.

RESULTS

Chaplain participation in organ donation.

The likelihood of the chaplains surveyed to "participate in the organ-donation process in the event of a brain-dead patient" in both groups hovered around 50%, with university-based chaplains representing a slightly lesser involvement. The level of participation was defined by the respondent and left open to a range of participation. Thus participation could include simply saying a prayer with the family of a brain-dead patient, to more extensive counseling and grief management.

In some instances, chaplains said that policy dictated they be informed, at all times, when a patient in their institution was declared brain-dead (n=3). Others indicated that they would become involved only if the family or medical staff specifically asked for their consultation (n=7).

Reasons for the differences in the percentage of participation were not clear. However, some chaplains from the university group indicated that the occurrence of brain-dead patients was fairly common in their institutions, a more-routine experience. Conversely, some chaplains in the non-university group indicated that this was a rare incident, and thus the medical staff desired chaplain participation more frequently in these situations. The difference in chaplain participation may be a result of the medical staff's comfort with organ donation and brain-dead patients. Further research would be needed to substantiate this point.

Religious concerns of next of kin

Given their level of involvement in organ donation, the chaplains were then asked, "What was the most-often-voiced religious/theological concern of next of kin?" (Table 2).

TABLE 2
Chaplain Report of Religious Concerns of Next-of-Kin

	Univ(n=28)		NonUniv (n=28)	
	(n)	%	(n)	%
Resurrection of body	9	32	4	14.0
Suffering of patient	7	25	11	39.2
Authority/permission	6	21.4	7	25.0
Respect donor wishes	4	14.2	2	7.1
Integrity of body	2	7.1	4	14.2

The two main concerns expressed to chaplains by family members were the suffering of the patient and the theological belief in the resurrection of the body at the end of time. Here chaplains reported family members saying that their loved ones "had suffered enough." Several family members said, "Hasn't he been through enough, can't they just leave him alone?"

The belief in the resurrection of the body at the Second Coming of Jesus Christ proved to be a significant factor for family members approached for organ donation. According to the chaplains, this was usually voiced as a question, that is, wondering whether organ donation would affect bodily resurrection. Two chaplains responded that the donation was prevented because of this theological concern. Finally, the issue of the integrity of the body was raised by families of Jewish patients whose faith emphasizes the body remain intact. Permission was an issue for those members of religious denominations that have made prepared statements relating to these concerns. Thus, many Catholic families inquired about the permissibility of organ donation from the standpoint of the church. This was also the case for Jehovah's Witnesses.

Religious concerns of chaplains

These questions and issues reflect what chaplains are hearing from families of brain-dead patients; what they themselves feel about organ donation is very different. Chaplains were asked what concerns they have with organ donation from a religious or theological perspective.

TABLE 3

Chaplains' Religious/Theological Concerns

	Univ(n=28)		Nonunit(n=28)	
	(n)	**%**	**(n)**	**%**
Respect of donor	17	60.7	12	42.8
Authority/Permission	6	21.4	5	17.8
Resurrection of body	2	7.1	6	21.4
Integrity of body	2	7.1	1	3.5
Suffering	1	3.5	4	14.2

Most important to chaplains in both groups was that the donor be respected. Many commented that even though the patient was brain dead, "he should still be treated with dignity and respect." Others stated they did not want the medical team to simply view the donor as a means to an end but rather that he or she be seen as "fully a person." Finally, many commented on the religious theme of giving one's life for another. The gift-giving quality of the donation was viewed by most chaplains as consistent with religious values. Donation was seen by many of the chaplains as a fitting response for a person of faith when confronted with this kind of tragedy.

The second most salient issue for hospital chaplains was their concern that religious beliefs be respected. Some chaplains felt that medical staff would see the decision of a family member who wished not to donate on religious grounds as superfluous or unimportant. Some chaplains saw their role as protecting the "rights" of the family to decline on religious grounds (n=14).

Professional concerns of chaplains

When asked about organ donation from a professional perspective, that is, as apart from a religious or theological viewpoint, chaplains said they worried about family members being manipulated or coerced in the decision-making process. Many saw the demand for organs as additional pressure to the medical staff even in those institutions that do not have transplant programs. Again, chaplains saw their role as advocates for the patient in this difficult time of grief and loss.

TABLE 4

Chaplains' Profession Concerns

	Univ(n=28)		Nonunit(n=28)	
	(n)	**%**	**(n)**	**%**
Coercion	11	39.2	9	32.1
Education	8	28.5	7	25.0
Time	5	17.8	7	25.0
Ethical	4	14.2	5	17.8

The sensitivity to coercion is an issue only slightly more important than feeling that organ donation is not getting the kind of public education it deserves. Many chaplains found themselves having to initiate conversations between medical personnel and families in order to explain brain death in a much detailed manner. One chaplain remarked, "The conversation I facilitated in the ICU should have taken place at the family table at home." The need for public education is seen as important for both groups of chaplains.

The third most important concern among hospital chaplains is the timing of the medical team in asking a family about organ donation. Many chaplains felt that the medical staff approached the family too soon after brain death had been declared. Some chaplains thought that families were not given enough time to come to terms with brain death as a concept, and then with the fact that their loved one had died. One respondent said, "In one meeting with the family, the surgeon explained brain death, told the family that their son had died, and asked about organ donation." In this instance, the chaplain felt that too much was expected of the family in too short a time.

Finally, about 15% of each group was concerned with various ethical consideration. One chaplain said, "The entire process of organ donation is built on the premise that someone else can give away my organs. I'm not sure this is right." In another instance a chaplain indicated his discomfort with the determination of brain death. "It is not clear that brain death is agreed upon by any two physicians. There is nothing quite like having two physicians argue about a person's life-and-death status." Other ethical concerns were voiced by chaplains, but no two were alike.

Should chaplains participate in asking for organ donation?

The final item on the survey simply asked if chaplains felt that they, as a professional group, should ask families about organ donation.

TABLE 5
Should Chaplains' Participate in Organ Donation Request?

	Univ(n=28)		Nonunit(n=28)	
	(n)	**%**	**(n)**	**%**
Yes	15	53.5	10	35.7
No	4	14.2	8	28.5
Consultant only	9	32.1	10	35.7
Undecided	0	0	0	0

Both groups indicated deep concern about their roles in organ donation. Many felt that it was the role of the medical staff to actually ask the family. However, most chaplains felt they should be present because of the difficulty of the decision and the grief the family would be experiencing. Therefore, many chaplains felt that they should take only a supportive role in the donation process. This belief, however, did not predominate in the university group. Here, chaplains felt they could take a more active role in the actually process of donation. Several chaplains in the university group had responses similar to this: "I see donation as a good thing. If the family had a religious faith, and I was asked, I would counsel toward donation."

The overwhelming opinion on this question, however, was that chaplains could play an important role in the donation process because of their training in grief and crisis counseling. For this reason 35 of the 54 respondents indicated that chaplains should be part of the asking, while 19 believed they should have some form of involvement, primarily in grief support.

DISCUSSION

Families that have participated in the donation process report several issues that make the donation experience more difficult. These problem areas fall into three groups: "problems with the timing of the process, communication problems with the staff, and complaints about administrative activities in the post-donation period" (Batten & Prottas, 1987). Two of these issues, timing and communication, were also concerns of the chaplains surveyed.

The single most-reported complaint about the donation process is that the family is "approached for permission too soon" (Batten & Prottas, 1987). Chaplains in this study also feel that families are asked to assimilate too much too quickly. In our experience at the University of Arizona Health Sciences Center, we have found that many families benefit by the chaplain acting in concert with the medical staff. One of the roles of the chaplain at our center is to help the family understand what the medical staff may be asking them in the immediate future, preparing them for the fact that the medical staff "may be coming to ask you about organ donation." This advance warning functions in much the same way as anticipatory grief. Instead of the medical staff asking the family this crucial question in what feels like a rushed and abrupt manner, the question is already anticipated by the family, and its effect is thereby softened.

The second issue that families feel is problematic is the communication of the concept of brain death and the feeling that "they are not being treated with the empathy they would like" (Batten & Prottas, 1987). Chaplains in this study clearly indicate that they are attending to the emotional needs of the grieving family. In fact, some feel that they should not be a part of the asking because it may hamper this role of grief support. Chaplains are empathizing with families of brain-dead patients. Further, chaplains are helping the medical staff ensure that families understand the concept of brain death. Again at our center, the chaplain functions as a sounding board, carefully listening to see if the family has integrated into its own understanding the concept of brain death. If not, another meeting with members of the medical team is set.

Chaplains, although working with the grief of the family, also see themselves as advocates for the family. The concern that family members not be coerced, either because of the emotional drama or because of statements made by the medial team, is very important to the hospital chaplains surveyed.

Chaplains feel that brain-dead patients need to be treated with the utmost respect. This is expressed primarily in terms of personhood and the dignity of the body. One chaplain indicated that "we must remember that this was a life lived, not just a body in the ICU ready to be used to save another's life." This concern has also been voiced in *The New England Journal of Medicine*, where Stuart Younger and others (1985) describe the need to "establish new rituals and practices appropriate for this new class of brain-dead patients." Chaplains feel that it is important for family members to understand that the medical staff respected the life, and hence the body, of their brain-dead loved one. Chaplains feel very strongly that the medical staff continue to treat brain-dead patients with the same manner and respect accorded any human being.

Finally, chaplains are hearing religious questions from the next of kin of brain-dead patients. This is important given the role that religion plays in the lives of many people. Recent studies indicate that religion is an important factor in the decision of minorities against organ donation (Perez *et.al.*, 1989).

Investigating the reasons for low donation rates among non-whites, Callender notes that blacks have deep-seated fears resulting from religion, myth, and superstition (Callender, Bayton, & Clark, 1982). These same fears were shown to have significant roles in the lower donor rate among Latino families

(Perez *et.al.*, 1989). Chaplains report in this study that families of brain-dead patients are very concerned with the disposition of the body at the time of resurrection, a traditional Christian doctrine often misinterpreted and in need of further elaboration.

In the same way, 25% of the chaplains in the nonuniversity group (21.4% in the university group) responded that denomination permission was the concern most often asked of them by families of brain-dead patients. In particular, families of Catholic faith believed that permission was an important part of the donation process. This is consistent with the Gallup poll finding that "...30% of Latinos thought that the reason 'Hispanics' tend to donate organs less frequently was religious belief..."(Perez *et.al.*, 1989). Because no means was provided in this survey for chaplains to designate the ethnic groups upon which their responses were based, correlations between religious views and ethnicity are not possible. Because of the importance of religious thought among minorities, this is an area in need of more serious study.

CONCLUSION

Practicing hospital chaplains, like the general public, are in favor of organ donation. Theological dogma or religious precepts do not seem to be the greatest concerns for this professional group when considering organ donation. Rather, chaplains can be seen as being in touch with the emotional aspects of the donation process: grief, suffering, coercion, etc. Further, hospital chaplains identify with the family of brain-dead patients as advocates in a process filled with grief and sudden loss.

This study indicates that chaplains are already very involved in organ procurement. Although some chaplains see their role as one of support and working principally with the grief of the donor family, some see themselves as more pro-active; for them, donation is a positive step in the grief process and consistent with religious faith. This study also shows that chaplains are willing to participate in the process of organ donation and their main concern is for the emotional well-being of the family, even above and beyond religious or theological concerns.

Attending to the emotional needs of a family as they consider the issue of donating organs of loved ones can be a very important part of a comprehensive approach to organ donation. Obtaining transplantable organs need not prevent us from providing the kind of care and concern we wish to give families in the midst of grief and sudden loss. In addition, providing care and support to a family while they are considering the possibility of organ donation may increase organ procurement. Studies considering the relationship of family care to procurement rates are needed.

Several recommendations are in order. Hospitals that use a team approach to fulfill required request laws indicate a higher level of grief and crisis counseling (DeLong, 1989). Chaplains seem willing to perform in this kind of team concept. The donation process could benefit by using chaplains as a liaison and advocate within the medical team, providing care and compassion, grief and counseling, religious and ethical guidance, emotional support, and more.

Chaplains involved in organ donation need to consider the strong feelings of families concerning the resurrection of the body. Religious and theological issues need to be worked out in a manner that is easily communicated to families asking such questions. Further, chaplains should be aware of those religious groups that object to organ donation.

Finally, chaplains are a valuable resources to address the religious, mythical, and superstitious issues surrounding the reduced level of organ donation among nonwhites. Chaplains, trained in the use of religious and spiritual imagery, may be more able to understand and communicate fears that minority groups have toward the medical community and organ donation.

Institutions that are concerned about the quality of their organ donation program should consider utilizing the chaplain as a resource person for training nurses, social workers, medical residents, and others about the supportive role of the chaplain and the religious questions asked of them by families of brain-dead patients.

REFERENCES

Batten, H., & Prottas, J. (1987). Kind strangers: the families of organ donors. *Heath Affairs, 6,* 35.

Callendar, C., Bayton, J., & Clark, J. (1982). Attitudes among blacks toward donating kidneys for transplantation: a pilot project. *Journal of the National Medical Association, 74,* 807.

DeLong W. (1989). Required request: who is asking? *Nursing Management, 20,* 112R.

Perez, L., Schulman, B., Davis, F., Olson, L., Tellis, V., & Matas A. (1989). Organ donation in three major American cities with large Latino and black populations. *Transplantation, 46,* 553.

Prottas,J., & Batten H. (1988). Health professionals and hospital administrators in organ procurement: attitudes, reservations,and their resolutions. *American Journal of Public Health, 78,* 642.

Prottas, J. (1989). The organization of organ procurement. *Journal of Health Politics, Policy, and Law, 14,* 41.

Youngner, S., Allen, M., Partlett *et al.* (1985). Psychological and ethical implications of organ retrieval. *New England Journal of Medicine, 313,* 321.

Youngner, S., Landefeld, S., Coulton, C., Juknialis, B., & Leary, M. (1989). Brain death and organ retrieval: a cross sectional survey of knowledge and concepts among health professionals. *JAMA, 261,* 2205.

EDITOR'S COMMENTS

This study is a good start as concerns a very important medical/pastoral subject. It begs for a follow-up study which asks whether families donate available organs more frequently when chaplains are involved. Such results will likely command continuing attention.

1 0

Health Locus of Control and Helpfulness of Prayer

Theresa L. Saudia
Marguerite R. Kinney
Kathleen C. Brown
Leslie Young-Ward

ABSTRACT

The purpose of this study was to examine the relationship between health locus of control and helpfulness of prayer as a direct-action coping mechanism in patients before having cardiac surgery. The Multidimensional Health Locus of Control Scales and the investigator-developed Helpfulness of Prayer Scale were issued to 100 subjects one day before cardiac surgery. Ninety-six subjects indicated that prayer was used as a coping mechanism in dealing with the stress of cardiac surgery, and 70 of these subjects gave it the highest possible rating on the Helpfulness of Prayer Scale. No relationship was found between health locus of control and helpfulness of prayer. Individuals of each locus orientation perceived prayer to be helpful. Findings suggest that prayer is perceived as a helpful, direct-action coping mechanism and warrants support by health personnel. It is recommended that further research explore the effect of prayer on patients' ability to cope with stressful situations.

Reproduced with permission of Mosby-Year Book, Inc. from *Heart and Lung*, (1991), 20(1), 60-6

A n estimated 200,000 people annually undergo coronary artery bypass grafting (CABG), which remains the major treatment for coronary occlusive disease, the leading cause of death in western societies (Cooley, 1987). CABG surgery is generally accepted as a stressful event requiring activation of individual coping processes (Dubin, Field, & Gastfriend, 1979; Janis, 1958). The view of the heart as a center of emotion produces vast emotional overtones and can magnify the stress perceived by the individual facing CABG surgery (Cohen, 1982).

Individuals scheduled for CABG may appraise the stress in terms of harm or loss, threat, or challenge (Lazarus & Folkman, 1984). Anticipated harm or loss may be threatening to the patient awaiting CABG surgery. In other instances, surgery may be viewed as more of a challenge because of the potential gain for increased oxygen supply to the heart muscle. A situation that is appraised as more threatening than challenging can come to be appraised as more challenging than threatening because of cognitive coping efforts that enable the person to view the episode in a more positive light (Lazarus & Folkman, 1984).

One factor that has been identified as influencing the manner in which a person appraises and reacts to a stressful situation is locus of control (Johnson, Christman, & Stitt, 1985). Locus of control is a psychologic concept that addresses individual control beliefs (Rotter, 1966). The locus of control construct has been further expanded to specifically addressed health-related behaviors (Levenson, 1973; Wallston, Wallston, Kaplan, & Maides, 1976; Wallston, Wallston, & DeVillis, 1978). Individual control beliefs affect perception of stressful events and, therefore, influence choices of coping strategies (Johnson, *et al.*, 1985). Little is known about the use of prayer as a direct action coping strategy and how psychologic concepts such as locus of control are related to perceptions of the helpfulness of prayer in patients before cardiac surgery.

PURPOSE

The purpose of this study, therefore, was to examine the relationship between health locus of control and helpfulness of prayer in patients before cardiac surgery. The researchers had observed in practice that prayer was helpful to patients, but no studies were found supporting the use of prayer by patients having cardiac surgery. Although nursing claims a holistic approach to assessment of the individual, the spiritual dimension of care is rarely addressed. Prayer is a tool of expression of the spiritual dimension of the individual. Relating helpfulness of prayer to an individual's health locus of control may be one way to identify types of individuals who find prayer helpful in dealing with the stress of cardiac surgery.

Question for Study

One major question was posed for study. Is there a relationship between health locus of control and helpfulness of prayer as a direct-action coping mechanism in patients before cardiac surgery? Specifically, the research addressed the question: Is there a relationship between internal health locus of control, between chance health locus of control, and between powerful others health locus of control and helpfulness of prayer as a direct-action coping mechanism in patients before cardiac surgery?

Conceptual Framework

The conceptual framework used for this study includes Chrisman and Fowler's Systems-in-Change Model (1980), Rotter's Social Learning Theory (1966) and Lazarus' Stress Appraisal and Coping Theory (1966). Chrisman and Fowler's framework depicts the individual as including biologic, social, and personal systems interacting with each other and with the environment on a developmental continuum. Disruptions inside or outside the system have an impact on the balance of the whole and produce stress. Each system must be evaluated to determine individual components that enable the person to return to a state of equilibrium. Cardiac surgery is a change in the environment that produces stress and disrupts equilibrium, the remaining systems must be assessed for resources available to the individual. Relating prayer to locus of control addresses the resources within the personal system of the individual, because the spiritual dimension is a subset of the personal system. Prayer could also be associated with the religion component of the social system (Chrisman & Fowler, 1980).

According to Rotter's Social Learning Theory (1966), the individual is constantly interacting with both internal and external aspects of the environment, giving reinforcement for behavior. The individual's expectations influence whether a certain behavior is practiced. One construct developed from social learning theory in relation to personality is locus of control orientation as either internal or external reinforcement. A belief in external control occurs when an individual perceives that the event is contingent on his or her own behavior (Wallston et al., 1978). Wallston et al. (1978) have developed this construct further to tap beliefs that reinforcement for health-related behaviors is primarily internal, a matter of chance, or under the control of powerful others.

In Lazarus' (1966) theory on stress appraisal and coping, cognitive appraisal involves a series of processes by which the individual evaluates the event, its significance, and the internal and external resources available for dealing with the event. Individual control beliefs contribute to the individual's initial evaluation of the event, or primary appraisal. The individual then determines what coping mechanisms are acceptable, or secondary appraisal. "Secondary appraisal is a complex evaluative process that takes into account which coping options are available, the likelihood that a given coping option will accomplish what it is supposed to, and the likelihood that one can apply a particular strategy or set of strategies effectively" (1984). Prayer is one coping strategy selected after secondary appraisal.

Locus of control has been studied in a number of settings including those reported by Rock *et al.* (1987), Folkman (1984), King (1984), and Stoll (1985). Rock *et al.* reported that, in their study of health behaviors of 400 healthy subjects, Multidimensional Health Locus of Control (MHLC) Scales were accurate predictors of individuals' willingness to participate in health-specific activities. They also established reliability and validity coefficients of clusters within the MHLC Scales and suggested that knowledge of a patient's cluster membership could be used to predict patient interest in and ability to perform self-care behaviors.

Folkman (1984) reported that for individuals to achieve more positive outcomes in stressful situations, it must be known whether the person's belief in control is general or specific to the situation. This belief influences whether the individual appraises the event as threatening or challenging and influences selection of coping strategies.

King (1984) used Lazarus'(1966) theory as the framework for an exploratory correlational study on coping with cardiac surgery. Coping strategies were examined in 50 subjects before and after surgery. Patients having cardiac surgery were found to appraise surgery more as a challenge than as a threat. King identified prayer as one of several mechanisms in the category of direct-action strategies used to cope with surgery. Direct-action techniques were found to be more useful after than before surgery. Baines (1984) also identified several mechanisms used by family caregivers to manage stress and found prayer to be the primary method of coping.

Stoll (1985) studied 108 hospitalized adults and found that 50% of the respondents believed that religious influence on their lives was significant, and that prayer and positive relationships with self and others were most helpful in coping with the experience and difficulties of illness.

Study Design and Method

A descriptive correlational design was used. Variables studied were health locus of control and helpfulness of prayer in patients before cardiac surgery. Protection of human subjects was evaluated by the Institutional Review Board of the University of Alabama at Birmingham and approval to conduct the study was given. Permission to conduct the study was also obtained from the nursing department of the hospital. In addition, permission to use the MHLC Scales was obtained from the authors. A pilot study was conducted to determine whether procedures were satisfactory; no changes were required, and the study was completed as planned. Potential subjects who were identified from the surgical schedule one day before surgery were approached by the researcher to determine their willingness to participate. The instruments were given to each subject after informed consent, and were collected by an investigator when completed.

Data Collection Instruments

Two instruments were used for data collection. The MHLC Scales were used to determine the individual's orientation of control (Wallston, 1978). The MHLC Scales have three subscale scores that represent a belief in internal, chance, and powerful other components. Each subscale contains six items scored on a six-point Likert-type scale with one indicating *strongly disagree* and six indicating *strongly agree*. Low scores indicate low internality. Eight different patterns that may describe a person's belief pattern have been determined by combining the scores from each component. For example, type I, or "pure internal," indicates a score above the mean from the internal subscale and below the mean from both the powerful others and chance subscales (Wallston & Wallston, 1982). External validity, construct validity, and a high degree of reliability were found in six different patterns of the original eight proposed in a study with healthy adults (Rock *et al.*, 1987). Construct validity was addressed through significant correlations with Levenson's (1973) multidimensional scale ($r = 0.508$ to 0.733). Levenson was the first to measure three distinct dimensions of locus of control, splitting externality into two components.

The Helpfulness of Prayer Scale that we developed (Figure 1) was used by subjects to rate helpfulness of prayer in coping with the stress of cardiac surgery. Individuals were asked to indicate whether they used prayer to deal with the stress of their upcoming surgery. Those who responded positively were asked to rate the helpfulness of prayer on a numbered rating scale, ranging from 0 to 15, with 0 indicating *not helpful* and 15 indicating *extremely helpful*.

A panel of three experts with graduate degrees in theology established content validity of the instrument. Test-retest reliability was established through administration of the instrument within a one-week interval to five subjects who had undergone CABG within the previous 6 months. One hundred percent agreement was found.

FIGURE 1

Helpfulness of Prayer Scale

Instructions

Several methods have helped people relax while getting ready for cardiac surgery. Prayer as communication with a Higher Being is one method found to help people cope with the stress of surgery. Please indicate whether this method is helpful to you. Rate how helpful on the scale provided.

1.Have you used prayer to help you prepare for cardiac surgery?

_____Yes

_____No

If yes, how helpful is it?

0 1 2 3 4 5 6 7 8 9 10 11 12 13 14 15

Not at all   Extremely

helpful   helpful

Sample

Nonprobability sampling resulted in a total of 129 subjects being approached for inclusion in the study. Twenty-eight patients who were not told the nature of the study refused to participate. Most of the refusals were from individuals who verbalized a feeling of exhaustion as a result of preparation for surgery. One additional subject failed to complete the MHLC Scales and was eliminated from the study. Thus, the sample included 100 subjects. The majority of the subjects were male (72%), married (84%), and Protestant (87%). Ninety-six subjects indicated that they used prayer as a coping mechanism to deal with the stress of cardiac surgery. Two subjects indicated that they did not use prayer themselves but that others prayed for them, and two did not use prayer at all.

Analysis of Data

A two-tailed Spearman's rho was used to test each of the three hypotheses. None of the correlations was significant at the 0.05 level; thus, no relationship was found between internal, chance, or powerful others health locus of control and helpfulness of prayer as a coping mechanism in patients before cardiac surgery.

TABLE 1
Subscale Scores of MHLC Scales

Subscale	N	Mean	Range	SD
Internal health locus of control	100	24.74	6-36	6.35
Chance health locus of control	100	15.87	6-36	6.47
Powerful others health locus of control	100	23.07	6-36	6.62

Descriptive statistics were tabulated for the three subscale scores. The data in Table 1 reveal that the sample perceived an internal control over their health with a mean of 24.74, followed closely by the belief that powerful others are in control of their health with a mean of 23.07. Perception that the control of health is a result of luck, fate, or chance received the lowest mean of 15.87. No significant differences between men and women in any MHLC scores were found in the study.

Descriptive statistics for the Helpfulness of Prayer Scale are presented in Table 2. Of the 96 subjects who used prayer, 70 rated prayer as extremely helpful. One subject who used prayer did not believe prayer could be rated, and the rating given by the remaining 25 subjects was from 6 to 14 (mean prayer rating 13.29).

TABLE 2
Rating of Helpfulness of Prayer
by Subjects Using Prayer (N=95)

Prayer rating	n	%
15	70	70
14	4	4
13	1	1
12	5	5
11	5	5
10	8	8
9	1	1
6	1	1
0	0	0

Typologies within the MHLC Scales as proposed by Wallston and Wallston (1982) were analyzed with the Kruskal-Wallis one-way analysis of variance and are shown in Table 3. The typologies are based on patterns of scores taken from the MHLC Scales.

TABLE 3
Kruskal-Wallis One-Way Analysis of Variance for Prayer
Rating for Typologies Within MHLC Scales

Typology*	n	Mean rank
1	25	44.68
2	7	49.43
3	6	65.50
4	14	57.39
5	11	55.95
6	4	19.38
7	22	48.14
8	11	58.05

Uncorrected for ties: chi-square, 9.2929; significance, 0.2323. Corrected for ties: chi-square, 14.1636; significance, 0.0483.

*Each type is categorized as follows: type 1, "pure" internal=high internal health locus of control (IHLC), low powerful others locus of control (PHLC) and change health locus of control (CHLC); type 2, "pure" powerful others external=high PHLC, low IHLC and CHLC; type 3 "pure" chance external=

high CHLC, low IHLC and PHLC; type 4, double external= higher PHLC and CHLC, low IHLC, type 5, believer in control=high IHLC and PHLC, low CHLC; type 6 (not named because expected to occur rarely)=high IHLC and CHLC, low PHLC; type 7, "yea-sayer"=high IHLC, CHLC, and PHLC; type 8 "nay-sayer"=low IHLC, CHLC, and PHLC.

The Mann-Whitney U test was used to examine differences in paired samples. Type 6, which is above the mean on the internal health locus of control and chance health locus of control scales and below the mean on the powerful others health locus of control scale, was the only group found to have a statistically significant different mean when compared with other groups. Four subjects fall into this pattern. Table 4 demonstrates a statistically significant difference between type 6 and types 3, 4, 5, 7, 8, and prayer rating when corrected for ties. This group was not found in healthy subjects in studies by Rock *et al.* (1987). The typologies within the MHLC Scales have not been investigated extensively; thus the finding of the type 6 pattern within hospitalized adults is a notable occurrence.

TABLE 4

Results of Mann-Whitney U Test of Paired Samples
With Type 6 Pattern Within MHLC Scales

Type	n	Corrected for ties Z	Two-tailed p
1	25		
6	4	-1.4687	0.1419
2	7		
6	4	-1.5896	0.1119
3	6		
6	4	-2.8935	0.0038*
4	14		
6	4	-2.7849	0.0054*
5	11		
6	4	-2.4442	0.0145*
7	22		
6	4	-1.9765	0.0481*
8	11		
6	4	-2.8113	0.0049*

*Significant difference in means.

DISCUSSION

No relationship was found between health locus of control and helpfulness of prayer as a coping mechanism in patients before cardiac surgery. Lack of variability in subjects could account for failure to obtain a relationship because 70% of the subjects rated prayer as extremely helpful and 96% stated that they used prayer as a coping strategy. This study revealed that prayer was perceived as helpful, regardless of orientation of control.

The current study supports both Chrisman and Fowler's model (1980) and Lazarus' (1966) stress appraisal and coping theory in that prayer was perceived as a helpful mechanism to cope with the stress of cardiac surgery. Prayer was perceived to be helpful in dealing with the stress of cardiac surgery in 96 of 100 subjects in the current study.

Findings of the current study concur with studies by Sodestrom and Martinson (1987) in patients with cancer, and by Fordyce (1982) and Stoll (1985) in hospitalized adults. Benson (1984) indicated that prayer provides physiologic responses, such as a decreased heart rate, decreased blood pressure, and decreased episodes of angina in cardiology patients. Both Hurley (1980) and Zaichkowsky and Kanen (1978) found that meditation and relaxation training provided subjects with a physiologic benefit but did not affect locus of control scores. Although the tendency to view prayer as helpful indicates a strong belief that powerful others control one's fate, the current study found prayer to be perceived as a helpful coping mechanism in individuals with both an internal and external locus of control orientation.

The time frame chosen for data collection could have increased the likelihood that individuals would rate prayer as helpful. Data were collected as subjects prepared for surgery, which may have contributed to a sense of urgency. The stability of locus of control orientation may be questionable during periods of extreme stress, which also could contribute to a lack of variability in rating helpfulness of prayer. Cowles (1988) discussed the influences of sensitive issues that evoke emotional responses on the collection of data. Objectivity and avoidance of situational influence are especially difficult. Responding to a questionnaire during the stress of preparing for cardiac surgery when the outcome is unknown could cause individuals to believe that they could not deny that prayer is helpful to them. The statement introducing the prayer instrument could have influenced subjects to agree that they too found prayer helpful. Other limitations of the study include:

1.   Subjects were limited to patients in a specific hospital in a Southern region who may be more inclined to use prayer than the general population. Thus, it is not possible to generalize the findings to all patients scheduled for CABG surgery.

2.   Subjects may differ in the regular use of prayer, which may alter their perceptions of helpfulness of prayer.

3.   Subjects who do not use prayer may not have been willing to participate in the study.

4.   The topic is a sensitive subject and may have an impact on individual emotions, which could affect the manner in which the MHLC Scales were completed (1988).

5.   Insufficient reliability and validity data for the Helpfulness of Prayer Scale limit the generalizability of the findings.

Results from the subscale scores of the MHLC Scales are similar to those acquired by Wallston and Wallston (1982) with patients having a chronic illness. The eight typologies initially proposed by Wallston and Wallston occurred with subjects in this sample.

Summary

Selection of prayer as a means to cope with the stress of cardiac surgery was not found to be related to the individual's locus of control. Individuals of each locus of control orientation perceived prayer as helpful. The study finding that 96% of all respondents used prayer in dealing with the stress of cardiac surgery is consistent with the assumption that prayer is a direct-action coping mechanism (King, 1984; Ziemer, 1982). Four recommendations for further research suggested by this study are:

1.   Examination of the relationship between use of prayer and coping to determine whether prayer enhances the individual's ability to cope with stressful situations.

2.   Replication of this study in a postoperative setting where the individual is not facing an unknown and threatening situation to determine whether the findings are similar.

3.   Replication of this study with subjects earlier in the preparation for the surgical event to determine whether timing of data collection influences the results.

4.   Replication of this study with subjects preparing for other types of surgery to determine whether the nature of the surgery influences the findings.

In this study we examined the relationship between the individual's beliefs of control and helpfulness of prayer as a coping mechanism before cardiac surgery. The results indicate that there is no relationship between health locus of control and helpfulness of prayer because individuals of each locus of control orientation perceived prayer to be helpful. This study validates the assumption that prayer is a beneficial strategy to patients in dealing with stressors associated with cardiac surgery.

REFERENCES

Baines, E. (1984). Caregiver stress in the older adult. *Journal of Community Health Nursing, 1*, 257-63.

Benson, H. (1984). The Faith Factor. *American Health, 5*, 50-3.

Chrisman, M., & Fowler, M. (1980). The systems-in-change model for nursing practice. In J. Riehl & C. Roy (Eds.) *Conceptual models for nursing practice.* (2nd ed. pp.74-82), Norwalk, Connecticut: Appleton-Century-Crofts.

Cohen, C. (1982). On the quality of life: some philosophical reflections. *Circulation, 66*, 29-33.

Cooley, D. (1987). Revascularization of the ischemic myocardium: c u r r e n t results and expectations for the future. *Cardiology, 74*, 275-85.

Cowles, K. (1988). Issues in qualitative research on sensitive topics. *Western Journal of Nursing Research, 10*, 163-79.

Dubin, W., Field, H., & Gastfriend, D. (1979). Post-cardiotomy delirium: a critical review. *Journal of Thoracic and Cardiovascular Surgery, 77*, 586-94.

Folkman, S. (1984). Personal control and stress and coping processes: a theoretical analysis. *Journal of Personality and Social Psychology, 46*, 839-52.

Fordyce, E. (1982). An investigation of television's potential for meeting the spiritual needs of hospitalized adult patients. (Unpublished dissertation, Catholic University of American, Washington, D.C., 1981), *Dissertation Abstracts International.*

Hurley, J. (1980). Differential effects of hypnosis, biofeedback training and trophotropic responses on anxiety, ego strength, and locus of control. *Journal of Clinical Psychology, 36*, 503-7.

Janis, I. (1958). *Psychological stress.* New York: John Wiley & Sons.

Johnson, J., Christman, N., & Stitt, C. (1985). Personal control interventions: short and long-term effects on surgical patients. *Research in Nursing & Health, 8*, 131-45.

King, K. (1984). Coping with cardiac surgery. (Unpublished dissertation, University of Rochester, Rochester, N.Y.) *Dissertation Abstracts International, 1*, 161.

Lazarus, R. (1966). *Psychological stress and the coping process.* New York: McGraw-Hill.

Lazarus, R., Folkman, S. (1984). *Stress, appraisal and coping.* New York: Springer Publishing.

Levenson, H. (1973). Multidimensional locus of control in psychiatric patients. *Journal of Consulting and Clinical Psychology, 41*, 397-404.

Rock, D., Myerowitz, B., Maisto, S., & Wallston, K. (1987). The derivation and validation of six multidimensional health locus of control scale clusters. *Research in Nursing and Health, 10*, 185-95.

Rotter, J. (1966). Generalized expectancies for internal versus external control of reinforcement. *Psychological Monograph, 80*, 1-28.

Sodestrom, K., & Martinson, I. (1987). Patients' spiritual coping strategies: a study of nurse and patient perspectives. *Oncology Nursing Forum, 14*, 41-6.

Stoll, R. (1985). Spirituality: a new perspective on health. In R. Fehring, J. Hungelmann, & R. Stollenwerk, (Eds.) Paper presented at the conference on the spiritual dimension of health at Marquette University College of Nursing, Milwaukee, Wisconsin, 7:1-7, 32.

Wallston, B., Wallston, K., Kaplan, G., & Maides, S. (1976). Development and validation of the health locus of control (HLC) scales. *Journal of Consulting and Clinical Psychology, 44*, 580-5.

Wallston, K., Wallston, B., & DeVillis R. (1978). Development of the multidimensional health locus of control (MHLC) scales. *Health Education Monograph, 6*, 161-70.

Wallston, K., & Wallston, B. (1982). Who is responsible for health? The construct of health locus of control. In G. Sanders, J. Suls, (Eds.) *Social psychology of health and illness*. Hillsdale, New Jersey: Lawrence Erlbaum & Associates, 65-95.

Zaichkowsky, L., & Kanen, R. (1978). Biofeedback and meditation: effects on muscle tension and locus of control. *Perceptual and Motor Skills, 46*, 955-8.

Ziemer, M. (1982). Coping behavior: a response to stress. *Topic in Clinical Nursing, 82* (6),4-12.

EDITOR'S COMMENTS

Prayer is an extremely important activity for many hospital patients as well as family members and pastoral researchers must be interested in its study. There are, however, few quantitative reports on the subject. This study makes a contribution, but must be interpreted carefully. I will take this occasion to comment on the limitation of retrospective studies and on the difficulties created by "social desirability."

Broadly speaking, research studies demonstrate two styles: prospective and retrospective. Prospective studies look forward, gathering data as time passes; retrospective studies ask participants to indicate how they thought or felt in the past. The assumption is that the respondent's memory is accurate and trustworthy. This style is widely used in the behavioral sciences, but there is increasing evidence that the results must be interpreted with caution. Let me summarize some of the existing evidence.

In the last three or four decades scattered reports have appeared which compare data from long-term research records with the subject's memory. Usually these reports emerge from longitudinal studies of children who are followed in a research study into adulthood. As a sideline in such a project, a researcher constructs a questionnaire or an interview with these persons who are now adults, asking them to report what they remember from childhood. In this way, the accuracy of memory can be checked against the existing records which were gathered over the years. The results are generally not very good. In one of the latest studies (Henry, Moffitt, Caspi, Langley, & Silva, 1994), the authors draw two conclusions: 1) Psychosocial variables revealed the lowest level of agreement between prospective and retrospective measures, and 2) Even when retrospective reports correlated significantly with prospective data, the absolute level of agreement between the two sources was quite poor. This is not the place to explore this subject in depth, but it is important to know that a retrospective research design (*i.e.*, asking respondents to report on the basis of their memory), contains significant difficulties. This may be particularly true as regards retrospective studies of religion and spirituality because these subjects are emotionally loaded for many people. This brings us to the concerns about social desirability.

Social desirability has been a research concern for a long time. Essentially, social desirability is the name given to the practice of research subjects providing what they perceive to be the socially desirable answer regardless of whether it is true. Some subjects respond in terms of what they believe the research wants them to say. This involves "second guessing" and, since reading minds is inappropriate, such responses contaminate data. At least one other form of social desirability exists. It consist of affirming that which represents cultural values, whether or not it is particularly true for the respondent. Some respondents are known to routinely respond in a socially desireable manner and they do not make appropriate research subjects. Most of us, however, are more likely to respond in this manner when we are in a compromised position, when we are vulnerable, hurting, and unsure of the future. Responding in this perceived desirable manner functions as a kind of insurance policy so as not to offend anyone because we might need them in the future. This concern is relevant for the researcher gathering data from hospital patients and family members, particularly if they are facing a critical time. Thus, it is always important for researchers to explore whether situational conditions will increase the possibility that respondents will give socially desireable answers, thus confounding the data.

Sometimes it seems that faulty memory involved in the retrospective methodology combines with social desirability to create the difficulty and this can be illustrated by summarizing a recent study concerning church attendance (Hadaway, Marler, & Chaves, 1993). For decade, retrospective research has reported that approximately 50% of Americans attend church or synagogue regularly. The data are usually gathered in a telephone call by simply asking, "Did you, yourself, happen to attend church or synagogue in the last seven days?" The result have been widely believed for years. The researchers cited above, however, went to the trouble of conducting a more objective prospective-styled study. They selected a specific county, identified all the churches/synagogues, and, using an elaborate and extended effort, obtained the actual or estimated attendance counts. By self-report in response to the telephone poll, the attendance for the county was 35.8%; by actual or estimated count the attendance was 19.6%. This discrepancy is likely due to a combination of factors, two of which are faulty memory and the lingering social standard that church/synagogue should be attended.

Now we come to this study which explores the helpfulness of prayer preceding cardiac surgery. In light of the discussion above, it is not surprising that the data reflects an extensive use of prayer and its helpfulness. The patients are asked to remember something under very difficult circumstances and what they are asked to remember is likely a desireable thing to do when in this vulnerable position of facing surgery. Thus, these data must be interpreted with caution; the researchers themselves acknowledge this.

But now comes the most important point of all. When studying the frequency and helpfulness of prayer in such a situation, what research design changes could be made which would likely diminish these difficulties?

REFERENCES

Hadaway, C., Marler, P., Chaves, M. (1993). What the polls don't show: A closer look at U.S. church attendance. *American Sociological Review, 58,* 741-752.

Henry, B., Moffitt, T., Caspi, A., Langley, J., Silva, P. (1994). On the "Remembrance of things past": A longitudinal evaluation of the retrospective method. *Psychological Assessment, 6*(2), 92-101.

11

Religious Perspectives of Doctors, Nurses, Patients, and Families

Harold G. Koenig
Lucille B. Bearon
Margot Hover
James L. Travis, III

ABSTRACT

Reports the results of a survey examining religious denomination, belief in a higher power, church attendance, and religious coping among physicians (N=130), nurses (N=39), patients (N=77), and families (N=60). Differences are noted and discussed. Notes that while a large proportion of patients and families found religion to be the most important factor enabling them to cope, only a small percentage of physicians felt that way. Observes that the results of this and other studies may indicate a gap in religious orientation between health care providers and patients and that such a gap could hinder the recognition of and proper care for spiritual needs in the hospital setting.

Over the past fifty years, Gallup polls have repeatedly demonstrated a relatively high prevalence of religious beliefs and behaviors among adults in the United States (Princeton Religion Research Center, 1985). During times of physical and emotional illness, particularly hospitalization, religion may be used as a means of coping with the

Reproduced with permission of the Journal of Pastoral Care Publishers, Inc. from the *Journal of Pastoral Care*, (1991), 45(3), 254-267.

stress that accompanies these conditions (Obrien, 1982; Koenig, Smiley, & Gonzales, 1988). Surveys conducted in general, nonsectarian hospitals have found that about 50% of patients say they have spiritual needs (Martin, Burrows, & Pomilio, 1983). About half of these patients, in turn, say that their spiritual needs were not completely met during the hospital stay. Chaplain programs in hospitals are major providers of spiritual resources to medical and psychiatric inpatients through emotional support and listening, prayer, administration of sacraments, chapel services, provision of religious literature, and communication with local clergy (Gulko, 1983; Miller, 1984; Moyer, 1989; Eimer, 1989).

Health care professionals, however, often control access to pastoral services and can be a major source of patient referrals. Unfortunately, studies (Gartner, Lyons, Larson, Serkland, & Peyrot, 1990) have shown that only a small percentage of hospitalized patients (12% to 33%) are referred to chaplain services by hospital staff (doctors, nurses, and social workers), the vast majority of contacts being initiated by chaplains themselves. Records from the Pastoral Services Department at Duke Hospital indicate that, among health professionals, 88% of unsolicited referrals are from nurses, 8% are from physicians, and 4% are from social workers (Hover, unpublished data). Consequently, research which focuses on identifying barriers to patient referral by hospital staff, especially among physicians, is needed. One explanation for nonreferral may be personal views and attitudes of health care professionals toward religion which hinder their ability to recognize spiritual needs and take the necessary actions to ensure their fulfillment. Such views might also affect clinical care in general, particularly in the mental health field. Some investigators (Szasz, 1970) have found that the more a patient's values deviate from those of his or her therapist, the more likely that patient is to receive a severe diagnosis or poor prognosis.

There is evidence that religious backgrounds and beliefs, as well as the importance attributed to religion, may differ between health professionals (particularly academicians) and adults in the general community. The best data available come from surveys of mental health professionals. Examining religious beliefs in a random sample of 555 psychologists from the American Psychological Association (APA), Ragan and colleagues (1980) found that 43% believed in God, 27% attended church twice a month or more often and only 9% held leadership positions in their congregations. With regard to psychiatrists, a similar proportion (40-70%) profess a belief in God (American Psychiatric Association, 1975). Data on church attendance or involvement in church leadership, however, are not available. There is a stark contrast between these figures and those reported for Americans in general, among whom 95% believe in God and 40% attend church at least once per week or more often, figures that have remained relatively constant over the past twenty years (Princeton Religious Research Center, 1985). The religious backgrounds of psychologists in Ragan's study also differed from adults in the general population, with 51% being Protestant (vs. 69% for the general population), 15% Catholic (vs. 25%), and 19% Jewish (vs. 3%). Similar results were reported in an earlier study of American Psychological Association members by McClintock and colleagues (1965). They found that 64% either did not consider religion a major force in life or were not religious, compared with only 13% of Americans who find religion "not very important" (Princeton Religious Research Center, 1985).

In another report, Marx and Spray (1969) compared adherence to religious faith (Christianity or Judaism) among psychiatrists, psychologists, and psychiatric social workers using biographical directories of the American Psychiatric Association, the American Psychological Association, and Professional Social Workers in Chicago, Los Angeles and New York. They found that 39% of psychiatrists, 40% of psychologists, and 29% of psychiatric social workers did not adhere to religious backgrounds and currently considered themselves atheists or agnostics, or else had no position regarding religion.

The proportion of religiously oriented health care professionals reported in these studies does not differ significantly from that found in the early 1930s. In 1931, Lehman and Witty examined the percentage of eminent scientists who stated their church membership in their biographies in Who's Who in America. Interestingly, those from the basic sciences of physics, chemistry, and mathematics reported the highest proportion of church membership (30-37%), while those in the health professions (medicine, surgery, and psychology) were among the lowest (17-18%). In a 1934 article in *Harper's Monthly*, James Leuba examined the proportion of scientists from various professions who believed in God or in immortality. A random sample of men were selected from James Cattell's *American Men of Science* and sent a questionnaire inquiring about religious views. Leuba found again that the highest proportion of believers in God (38%) and in immortality (41%) were found among physicists, and the lowest percentages (10% and 9%, respectively) among psychologists (the only health profession surveyed).

This brief review suggests that the religious beliefs and activities of health professionals may, at least in some specialties, diverge sharply from those of the patients they serve. However, no study has yet examined in any detail the religious beliefs or activities of doctors and nurses who provide direct medical and psychological care to patients hospitalized in the acute care setting. In particular, no study has looked concurrently at the religious beliefs and orientations of these health care professionals and of the patients and families under their care. The present study is such an attempt. Based on the differences in religious orientation found here, we speculate on the impact of these differences on patterns of patient referral to chaplain services.

METHODS AND SAMPLE

A sample of 130 physicians, 38 nurses, 77 inpatients, and 60 inpatient families from Duke University Medical Center (DUMC) were surveyed concerning their attitudes toward and involvement with the hospital's chaplain service, their personal religious beliefs, activities, and backgrounds, and their use of religion as a coping behavior. Questionnaires were mailed to doctors, nurses, while volunteers distributed questionnaires to inpatients in their rooms and to family members in the waiting areas. (A description of the survey and questionnaire has been reported elsewhere (Hover, Travis, Bearson & Koenig, 1990), but pertinent details and sample characteristics are presented here.)

DUMC Pastoral Services designed a twenty-eight-item questionnaire to examine patients' and families' attitudes towards chaplains, their interactions with them and personal religious characteristics (the questionnaire was slightly modified for administration to physician and nurses). Of interest here are the questions exploring personal religious characteristics and patient referrals. The following questions were asked:

◆   Many people believe in a Higher Power, whether they attend church regularly or not. Do you believe in a Higher Power?

◆   When you are not in the hospital, how often do you usually attend church services?

◆   To what extent do your religious beliefs or activities help you to cope with or handle your situation? (This was rated on a visual analogue scale from 0 to 100, with 0 indicating "not much or not at all" and 100 indicating "the most important thing that keeps me going.")

◆   What is your religious denomination?

A final question about referral of patients to chaplain services was asked of nurses and physicians:

◆   How many patients or family members have you referred to Pastoral Services in the past six months?

The questionnaire was sent to a random sample of attending physicians (n=200) and all interns, residents, and fellows (n=875) at DUMC during the second week of March, 1990. Only a single mailing was possible because of the anonymous nature of the survey, and the response rate was predictably low (130/1075 or 12%). No information was known about nonrespondents. Demographic characteristics of physicians and other sample groups are presented in Table 1. This group was predominantly male (75%) and 66% were middle-aged (ages 30-59). Twenty-nine percent were attending physicians. Fifty-one percent were from family medicine, pediatrics or internal medicine, 33% from surgery, and 16% from psychiatry. These proportions approximate the breakdown of specialties at Duke Hospital. Head nurses and assistant head nurses from the medical and surgical wards were surveyed (n=90) following the same method as physicians. The response rate (38/90 or 42%) was also generally poor, although better than with doctors. Nurses were predominantly female (93%) and middle-aged (89%).

TABLE 1
Demographic Characteristics of Sample

Characteristic	Patients (n=77) %	Families (n=60) %	Nurses (n=39) %	Physicians (n=130) %
Sex				
Male	49.4	26.7	7.3	74.6
Female	50.6	73.3	92.7	25.4
Age				
< 30 years	14.3	NA*	10.8	29.2
30-59 years	49.3		89.2	66.0
60 years or over	36.4		0.0	3.2

*NA=not available

On March 14, 1990, the hospital computer identified all inpatients at Duke Hospital (except those on pediatric and psychiatric wards), resulting in a list of 413 names. After the patients' primary physicians had been notified and solicited for their permission, volunteers from the Pastoral Services department (without identifying their affiliation) distributed questionnaires to patients in their rooms over a six-hour period on that day. Of the 413 possible patients, 201 were ineligible for a variety of reasons, including early discharge (9%), severity of illness (5%), severe cognitive impairment (6%), sleeping (15%), visual problems (2%), nurse or doctor refusal (3%), absence from room (48%), or visitation by doctor, nurse, friends or relatives (6%). Thirteen other patients from the list could not be located. Of the remaining 199 patients who were eligible and received questionnaires, seventy-seven (38%) completed them. Among the 122 eligible patients who did not respond, 63% were refusals, 34%

had other reasons for not participating, and 6% did not complete enough of their questionnaires to provide useful data.

The nonrespondent patient group was distinguished by a greater proportion of severe mental impairment (30% vs. 6%) and severe physical illness (36% vs. 4%) among its members, which may have influenced the decision not to participate. The demographic characteristics of patient respondents are presented in Table 1. The group was equally divided by gender (49% male, 51% female). Patient age ranged from 13 to 85, with 36% over the age of 60. Fifty-two percent were from medical services and 48% from surgical services; no psychiatric patients were included in the sample. Thirty percent of the respondent group required some help with questionnaire completion from family or nursing staff.

On the same day as the patient survey, questionnaires were distributed to families sitting in the waiting areas of the hospital. A total of 65 forms were distributed, but five of these were not sufficiently completed to provide useful data. Sixty out of 65 family members (92%) completed questionnaires. Relationships of family members to patients were as follows: 45% father or mother, 25% son or daughter, 17% husband or wife, 8% sister or brother, and 5% grandparent. Nearly three-quarters of family respondents were female.

RESULTS

Table 2 compares the religious characteristics of patients, families, nurses, and physicians. Belief in a higher power was ubiquitous, although physicians lagged a bit behind the other groups in this regard (93.5% vs. 100%). Church attendance was at least weekly among 62% of patients, 59% of families, 51% of nurses, and 35% of physicians. Religious coping was noted as the most important factor enabling individuals to cope (i.e., a score of 100 on visual analogue scale) among 44% of patients, 56% of families, 26% of nurses, and 9% of physicians. The religious denominations of physicians and nurses varied substantially from those of patients. Patients and family members tended to be affiliated with such conservative Protestant denominations as Baptists, Assembly of God, Pentecostals (43% of patients and 49% of family members), which is typical of residents of central North Carolina. Among physicians, only 2.4% were from conservative Protestant denominations; most were from Catholic, Presbyterian, Episcopalian, Methodist, or Jewish backgrounds. Only 1.3% of patients and 1.7% of families were Catholic; none were from Jewish traditions. There were no agnostics, atheists, or persons without a religious denomination among patients or families, while 9% of physicians were in this group.

TABLE 2

*A Comparison of Religious Characteristics Between
Patients, Families, and Health Care Provider*

Characteristic	Patients (n=77) %	Families (n=60) %	Nurses (n=39) %	Physicians (n=130) %
Belief in Higher Power (Yes)	100.0	100.0	100.0	93.5
Church Attendance				
Several Times/Wk.	23.5	24.1	5.1	6.9
Once/wk.	38.2	35.2	46.2	27.7
Several Times/mo.	5.9	1.9	5.1	8.5
Several Times/yr.	7.4	13.0	25.6	17.7
Seldom or Never	25.0	26.0	17.9	39.2
Extent Religious Beliefs Help with Coping				
Most Important Factor (100)	43.8	56.1	25.6	8.7
Large Extent or More (75-99)	37.5	35.1	36.1	33.0
Moderate Extent (50-74)	11.0	5.2	30.6	34.6
Low Extent/Not at all (0-50)	7.8	3.6	7.7	23.7
Religious Denominations				
Fundamentalist/ Evangelical	5.2	8.4	0.0	0.8
Baptist	37.7	40.1	34.2	1.6
Methodist	11.7	35.1	11.4	13.1
Presbyterian	7.8	5.0	18.4	10.6
Lutheran	0.0	0.0	7.9	4.1
Episcopal	0.0	1.7	2.6	9.8
Protestant (unspecified)	6.5	1.7	0.0	2.4
Nondenominational	10.4	0.0	2.6	4.9
Catholic	1.3	1.7	21.0	26.0
Miscellaneous Christian	5.2	5.0	0.0	8.0
Unknown	14.3	0.0	0.0	0.0
Jewish	0.0	0.0	0.0	9.8
Agnostic, Atheist, none None	0.0	0.0	0.0	8.9

Religious characteristics of physicians were next examined by medical or surgical subspecialty and sex (Table 3). Although the Ns are small, belief in a higher power was generally high among all specialties, except for a slight drop among obstetricians, pediatricians, and psychiatrists. Church attendance was highest among family physicians and surgeons and lowest among psychiatrists and neurologists. Religious coping was also highest among family physicians and surgeons and lowest among psychiatrists and neurologists. Male physicians scored slightly higher than females on all religious characteristics measured, a reversal of the trend typically seen in the community (Princeton Religious Research Center, 1985).

TABLE 3
Religious Characteristics by Physician Specialty and Sex

	Higher Power (Yes) %	Church Attendance (>once/wk.) %	Religious Coping (>75 rating) %
Specialty			
Family Medicine (n=10)*	100.0	50.0	60.0
Pediatrics (n=11)	81.1	36.4	44.4
Internal Medicine (n=24)	100.0	39.1	37.5
IM Subspecialties (n=13)	100.0	35.7	46.2
Neurology (n=4)	100.0	25.0	25.0
OB/GYN (n=7)	85.7	0.0	28.6
Surgery (n=22)	90.5	45.5	50.0
Misc. Subspecialties (n=11)	100.0	36.4	45.5
Psychiatry (n=20)	90.0	25.0	36.8
Sex			
Male (n=97)	94.3	35.8	41.8
Female (n=33)	93.5	31.3	21.2

*Ns may vary by as much as 13%

Referral rates for chaplain services differed greatly between nurses and physicians. In the previous six months, 48.9% of physicians and 14.0% of nurse had made no referrals to chaplain services, 45.8% of physicians and 39.5% of nurses made one to 10 referrals, and 5.3% of physicians and 46.5% of nurses had made more than 10 referrals. Attending physicians made more referrals than fellows, residents or interns; 59% of attendings (vs. 49% of fellows, residents or interns) had made one or more referral in the prior six months. Among specialists, psychiatrists made the fewest referrals (23.8% made one referral or more), while internal medicine and surgery made the most (80.0% and 72.7%, respectively). Differences in patterns of referral were partly influenced by the amount of inpatient vs. outpatient responsibility for each specialty. Jewish physicians tended to refer more patients than did non-Jewish physicians (75.0% vs. 48.7% referred at least one patient in previous six months). Physicians noting no religious denomination were less likely to refer patients than those claiming a religious denomination (28.6% vs. 52.4%, respectively).

DISCUSSION

The religious backgrounds, beliefs, activities, and coping behaviors of patients and families were notably different from those of health care providers, particularly physicians. This finding is consistent with previous surveys that have separately examined the religious characteristics of health professionals (primarily psychologists) and community-dwelling adults. The present study, however, is the first to address this issue among health care providers, patients, and families in the same setting at the same time. The differences found here raise the possibility of a bias in religious perspective among health care providers that might interfere with their ability to recognize and respond to the spiritual needs of patients. Our data indicated that this bias may be particularly strong among physicians, a group who can control patients' access to spiritual resources.

Recognizing Spiritual Needs

The recognition of a spiritual need is prerequisite to that need being adequately met. The differences between physicians' religious backgrounds and those of patients and families could make it difficult for doctors to detect spiritual issues when they arise during hospitalization. Even religious denomination seems to make a difference in the type of spiritual need that is most important to sick patients. A study of spiritual needs of 90 adult general hospital patients in New York asked Protestants and Catholics to rank the importance of seven spiritual needs (Martin, Burrows, & Pomilio, 1983). For Protestants, knowledge of God's presence, expression of caring and support from another person, and prayer were primary. In Catholics, relief from fear of death, visit from a clergyman, and receiving the sacraments (communion, etc.) were most salient. In our sample, the greatest proportion of patients came from conservative (Roof & McKinney, 1987) Protestant denominations (43%), while physicians were primarily from Catholic (26%), Jewish (10%), or liberal Protestant (20%) affiliations, or were agnostic or atheist (9%).

Education about patients' differential spiritual needs is not part of the curriculum of most medical schools. Thus physicians are often forced to depend on their own religious experiences in dealing with such issues. When personal religious experience is markedly different from that of patients, conflict may result (Redlener & Scott, 1979). Interestingly, Jewish physicians in our sample made more chaplain referrals than non-Jewish physicians. (Perhaps these doctors more readily recognized spiritual needs among their Christian patients and, being unable to address them, chose to obtain help from pastoral services.)

Physicians in general referred many fewer patients to chaplain services than did nurses, a fact that may also reflect a greater divergence in religious perspective between physicians and patients than between nurses and patients. The gap in religious orientation between physician and patient appears to be particularly acute in the area of mental health. This is unfortunate, given that the spiritual needs of the mentally ill may be greater than those of any other group (Eimer, 1989). In some inpatient psychiatry units, including that of Duke Hospital, a doctor's order may be required for a chaplain or even the patient's own pastor to visit, thus giving total control over access to spiritual resources to the psychiatrist (Weikert, 1984). In the present study we found that belief in a higher power, church attendance, and religious coping were all lowest among psychiatrists, who also referred the fewest patients for pastoral services of any physician specialty.

Referral rates to pastoral services may, however, be affected by factors other than personal bias. The greater number of referrals by nurses may be due to a greater amount of time spent at the patient's bedside. Traditionally, caring for spiritual needs of patients may be seen as more of a nursing responsibility than a medical one. This may not always be the case, however. One study (Koenig, Bearon, & Dayringer, 1988) of doctors' attitudes toward religious issues in older patients found that 36% of physicians felt that nurses should never or rarely address religious issues, 41% felt nurses could "sometimes" address such issues, and only 23% noted that they should often or always do so. Thus, while it is true that nurses often have greater contact than physicians with both patients and chaplains, there is little reason for physicians to abdicate to the nursing staff total responsibility for ensuring that patients' spiritual needs are being met. Such abdication may, in fact, be unwise, given the impact that religious factors may have on both physical (Koenig, Moberg, & Kvale, 1988) and mental health (Koenig, Kvale, & Ferrel, 1988), healthcare utilization (Schiller & Levin, 1988), and decision making in chronic and terminal illness (Wennberg, 1989).

Religion and Medical Training

One might ask why the religious orientation of physicians is so different from the rest of the population. Throughout most of human history, medicine and religion have been closely linked, the former actually evolving out of the latter (Kuhn, 1988). Most medical care was originally delivered by monks or priests, and the first hospitals were operated by religious orders. Even after practitioners of medicine no longer belonged to religious orders, they were still closely controlled by the church. In fact, until the fourteenth century the church issued all medical licensure, and no doctor could see a patient until the patient had confessed their sins to a priest. Not until the late 1700s, after the French revolution, did medicine and the church sharply separate. Today, medicine is a profession based upon scientific principles and built upon an objective and verifiable base of data—not on mystery or faith (though some would debate this).

Becoming a practicing physician requires an eleven- to fifteen-year training period which begins in the midteens and during which survival is dependent upon the rigorous application of logic and the scientific method for long hours each day. During this prolonged training period, life for the student takes on a structure and a value system which is continually reinforced by colleagues and teachers. Religion is not typically part of that structure or value system (Stark, 1963). Religion is often the butt of jokes or an object of ridicule in professional circles, either at work or during social gatherings. It may be viewed as the province of the weak-minded, the uneducated, and the socially outcast. Seldom is there time to cultivate and nurture both one's spirituality and one's specific prowess in medicine. Consequently, the former may fall into disuse and its importance in life may fade. Religion may be seen by one's medical colleagues as destructive, damaging, or inimical to established medical prescriptions or procedures. Rather than complement and affirm each other, medicine and religion may often compete in an adversarial fashion (Weikert, 1984). This competition may result in one side devaluing the other and its potential contribution.

The professional and social factors which act to diminish the value of religion and the spiritual aspects of life for the physician may gather particular strength in the academic environment. In the 1930s, Leuba (1934) and others (Lehman & Witty, 1931) examined belief in God among lesser and more prominent scientists. Belief was much less common among the "greater" and older, more eminent scientists. Examining a representative sample of 2,842 American graduate students in 1963, Rodney Stark found that religious involvement decreased as the quality of undergraduate education increased and as the exposure to scientific scholarship increased.

Lehman (1972) notes that there is something fundamentally different between the religious stance and the scholarly stance and that they are alternative approaches to making sense out of the world. He found that among faculty of both sectarian and nonsectarian institutions commitment to the scholarly perspective, characterized by pursuing personal curiosities and interests, experiencing greater satisfaction from research projects than from working with students and placing greater importance on national reputation than on local peer relationships was inversely related to religious belief, ritual, and experience. In another investigation, Lehman and colleagues (1968) found that faculty of academic disciplines in which human behavior and thought processes were studied (sociology and psychology) were less religious than in the physical sciences (such as physics) and engineering.

Medical training is more closely linked with the social and behavioral sciences than with the physical sciences or engineering. It is not difficult, then, to see how the traditional or conservative religious beliefs of those in such training might be challenged both subtly and not so subtly. If the physician remains in the academic environment, the value system and worldview of the scholarly perspective is often reinforced by both peers and superiors. Academic advancement and salary may be linked to adherence to the scholarly stance. Given these considerations, the differences in religious perspective found between patients, families, and physicians are not unexpected. The concern, however, is the effectiveness of a health care system led by individuals holding a "scholarly" perspective on behavior in meeting the spiritual needs of patients living life according to a religious perspective.

Response Bias

We recognize that the low response rates in this study, particularly by physicians, may limit the validity and generalizability of our conclusions. However, any response biases which may have affected physicians in their decisions to participate probably also contributed to the low response rates by nurses and patients. What might be the nature and direction of these response biases? We suspect that health care providers who did respond were more likely to have some strong feeling toward chaplain services or religion that prompted them to take the time to fill our the questionnaires. We also speculate that these feelings were of a generally positive nature with regard to religion and pastoral services. Conventional wisdom would suggest that physicians or nurses for whom religion has little personal relevance, or who see pastoral services as offering little to patients in the hospital setting, might simply discard such a questionnaire. Consequently, our physician and nurse sample may have included a disproportionate number of health professionals more likely to be religious themselves, and our results may overestimate the religious characteristics of this group.

While the patient sample, like the physician and nurse samples, may have been biased toward more religiously oriented respondents and those having favorable contact with pastoral services, we have no reason to suspect that this bias was any stronger in patient participants than in their health care providers. There is some evidence to suggest, in fact, that an additional response bias acted on patient participation in the opposite direction. Among respondents, further data analyses indicated that the more physically ill patients were more likely than the healthier patients to attend church and hospital chapel services and to use religion to cope. Comparison of the health characteristics of respondents and nonrespondents indicated that physical illness was more severe among patient nonresponders than responders. Thus, our patient sample may have been biased towards a healthier population and perhaps patients with lower church attendance and less religious coping.

Generalizability

While the results of this study may with some safety be generalize to other large university-affiliated teaching hospitals in the southeastern United States, they should be applied only cautiously to smaller private, community, or veterans hospitals and to hospitals in other parts of the region or country. Duke Hospital is located in the Bible Belt, a factor which may partly explain the high prevalence of religiously oriented patients and families in our sample. Physicians who care for patients at this medical center come from many different areas in the United States (and from all over the world) to obtain training and do research; they may not be typical of doctors who practice in the community, or even in the Southeast.

We believe, however, that the differences in religious perspective found here between health care providers, patients and families are real and represent a more general phenomenon. This belief is based on the studies reviewed in this report and on the preliminary results from similar investigations currently addressing this issue in other areas of the country. These differences may hinder effective recognition and fulfillment of spiritual needs and may interfere with the smooth and effective functioning of pastoral care departments in hospitals.

Future Research and Education

Further research is needed in other areas of the United States to document the extent to which such differences exist elsewhere. Surveys of this type may help educate physicians about the vital role that religion plays in enabling their patients to cope with the stresses of physical and emotional illness, demonstrate the value of chaplain services in serving the real needs of inpatients, and facilitate collaboration between health care providers and chaplains in the hospital setting.

It may be necessary to begin the process of sensitizing physicians and other health care providers to the spiritual needs of physically and mentally ill patients early in their training—in medical and nursing schools. A first step would be the inclusion of chaplains, along with house staff, medical students, nurses, and social workers, as part of the health care team in patient rounds and patient conferences. Incorporating lectures by pastoral care educators into the medical curriculum and providing the opportunity to attend a chaplain on rounds at patients' bedsides would increase the exposure of physicians to chaplains and perhaps increase their comfort level in working with them. In the present study, we asked physicians and nurses what ways chaplains either were or might be unhelpful to patients. Among those with no experience working with pastoral services, many of the fears expressed were based on simple lack of knowledge of what chaplains do (Hover, Travis, Bearon & Koenig, 1990). Correction of such misconceptions through proper education is a vital step in closing the gap in religious perspective between health care providers and the people they serve.

REFERENCES

American Psychiatric Association. (1975). *Task Force Report 10: Psychiatrists' Viewpoints on Religion and Their Services to Religious Institutions and the Ministry.* Washington, DC: APA.

Eimer, K. (1989). The Assessment and Treatment of the Religiously Concerned Psychiatric Patient. *The Journal of Pastoral Care, 43*(3), 231-41.

Gartner, J., Lyons, J., Larson, D., Serkland, J., & Peyrot, M. (1990). Supplier-Induced Demand for Pastoral Care Services in the General Hospital: A Natural Experiment. *The Journal of Pastoral Care, 44*(3), 266-270.

Gulko, J. (1983). Chaplain's Medical Approach to Psychiatric Patients. *The Journal of Religion and Health, 22*, p. 280;

Hover, M. Unpublished data.

Hover, M., Travis, J., Bearon, L., & Koenig, H. (1990). Research: A Tool for Supervision of Clinical Pastoral Education Students. *The Journal of Pastoral Care,*(in submission).

Koenig, H., Bearon, L., & Dayringer, R. (1988). Physician Perspectives on the Role of Religion in the Physician-Older Patient Relationship. *Journal of Family Practice, 28,* 441-48.

Koenig, H., Kvale, J., & Ferrel, C. (1988). Religion and Well-Being in Later Life. *Gerontologist, 28,* 18-28.

Koenig, H., Moberg, D., & Kvale, J. (1988). Religious Activities and Attitudes of Older Adults in a Geriatric Assessment Clinic. *Journal of the American Geriatrics Society, 36,* 362-74.

Koenig, H., Smiley, M., & Gonzales, J. (1988). *Religion, Health, and Aging.* Westport, CT: Greenwood Press, 15-37.

Kuhn, C. (1988). A Spiritual Inventory of the Medically Ill Patient. *Psychiatric Medicine, 6,* 87-100.

Lehman, E. (1972). The Scholarly Perspective and Religious Commitments. *Sociological Analysis, 33,* 199-216.

Lehman, E., & Shriver, D. (1968). Academic Discipline as Predictive of Faculty Religiosity. *Social Forces, 47,* 171-82.

Lehman, H., & Witty, P. (1931). Certain Attitudes of Present-Day Physicists and Psychologists. *American Journal of Psychology, 43,* 664-78.

Leuba, J. (1934). Religious Beliefs of American Scientists. *Harper's, 169* (August), 291-300.

Martin, C., Burrows, C., & Pomilio, J. (1983). Spiritual Needs of Patients Study. In S. Fish and J. Shelly (Eds.). *Spiritual Care: The Nurse's Role.* Downer's Grove, IL: Inter-Varsity Press, 160-76.

Marx, J., & Spray, S. (1969), Religious Biographies and Professional Characteristics of Psychotherapists. *Journal of Health and Social Behavior, 10*, 275-88.

McClintock, C., Spaulding, C., & Turner, H. (1965). Political Orientations of Academically Affiliated Psychologists. *American Psychologist, 20*, 211-21.

Miller, W. (1984). Hospital Chaplaincy: 1984. *The Journal of Pastoral Care, 43*(2), 171-98.

Obrien, M. (1982). Religious Faith and Adjustment to Long-Term Hemodialysis. *Journal of Religion and Health, 21*, 68-80.

Princeton Religion Research Center. (1985). *Religion in America, 50 Years: 1935 - 1985.* Princeton, NJ: The Gallup Poll.

Ragan, C., Malony,N., & Beit-Hallahmi, B. (1980). Psychologists and Religion: Professional Factors and Personal Belief. *Review of Religious Research, 21*, (Spring), 208-17.

Roof, W., & McKinney, W. (1987). *American Mainline Religion.* New Brunswick, NJ: Rutgers University Press.

Redlener, I., & Scott, C. 1979). Incompatibilities of Professional and Religious Ideology: Problems of Medical Management and Outcome in a Case of Pediatric Meningitis. *Social Science and Medicine, 13*, 89-93.

Schiller, P., & Levin, J. (1988). Is There a Religious Factor in Health Care Utilization? A Review. *Social Science and Medicine, 27*, 1369-79.

Stark, R. (1963). On the Incompatibility of Religion and Science: A Survey of American Graduate Students. *Journal for the Scientific Study of Religion, 3*, 3-21.

Szasz, T. (1970). *The Manufacturer of Madness: A Comparative Study of the Inquisition and the Mental Health Movement.* New York, NY: Harper & Row.

Weikert, R. (1984). When the Doctor and the Minister Disagree. *Hastings Center Report, 14*, 30-31.

Wennberg, R. (1989). *Terminal Choices: Euthanasia, Suicide, and the Right to Die.* Grand Rapids, MI: Eerdmans.

Editor's Comments

There is much which recommends this study; its simplicity is eloquent and its results revealing. It is the kind of study which begs to be repeated by more chaplains. They too would gain from the results. It would acquaint more physicians, nurses, and social workers with pastoral services, reveal the religious stereotypes held by these professionals about chaplains, and indicate the different levels of importance given to religious/spiritual concerns among these professionals and their patients. Chaplains who wish to conduct their own study should consult an additional published report (Hover, Travis, Koenig, & Bearson, 1992) about the project. In any additional studies of this nature, the only addition I would recommend is to find a way to gather data from the hospital administrative team. Certainly their attitudes and belief influence the pastoral care department.

Reference

Hover, M., Travis, J., Koenig, H., Bearson, L. (1992). Pastoral research in a hospital setting: A case study. *The Journal of Pastoral Care, 46*(3), 283-290.

12

Identifying the Spiritually Needy Patient: the Role of Demographics

Larry VandeCreek

ABSTRACT

This empirical study of hospital patients and community persons uses Reker's Life Attitude Profile-Revised (LAP-R) to determine the extent to which the basic demographic data of patients is associated with spiritual neediness. The LAP-R is a 36-item scale with six dimensions. ANOVA results suggest that male hospital patients possess more spiritual need than females ($F=4.51$; $p=0.04$), and that those with less education are more needy ($F=4.46$; $p=0.01$). Those who never or infrequently attend worship services are also more needy than those who attend twice per week ($F=3.39$; $p=0.01$). When all the demographic variables in the ANOVA model are considered together, they explain 27 percent of the variance in the LAP-R scores. The various dimension scores and their relationship to demographic variables is further elucidated. Analysis of data from persons in the community revealed both fewer and less powerful associations. The results suggest that chaplains can use demographic data to estimate the spiritual neediness of patients and to rank the list of patients whom they need to visit.

Suppose that the chaplain of a general hospital has 25 patients to visit (a frequent situation for some chaplains). Suppose too that there simply is not enough time to visit them all (a common

Reprinted with permission of the College of Chaplains, Inc. from *The Caregiver Journal,* (1991), 8(3), 38-47.

problem). How can the chaplain rank the list of patients, giving priority to those with the most spiritual needs? Who needs the visit most? Who should be placed higher or lower on the priority list?

The answer to that question depends on the patients' spiritual needs. Such needs are unique and individualized. They are likely products of personal history, levels of family support, intensity of discomfort, diagnosis, history of spirituality, and many other factors. And their unpredictable influence on the patient makes it difficult to rank the list of patients.

The chaplain usually has some information about the patient, although the amount varies according to the data provided at admission or as a result of the initial visit. Such information, however, is often taken for granted— sometimes even regarded as unimportant.

Now suppose–again–that all the personal, idiosyncratic needs of these 25 patients are set aside. Can certain demographic or identifying information itself help the chaplain rank the list of patients? Are the traditional demographic factors linked to trends in spiritual need? Or to ask the question another way, can demographic factors themselves provide the chaplain with at least some guidance as to who ought to be placed higher on that priority list? For example, if the chaplain has 10 men and 10 women patients to visit–and no additional information, which of the two groups is likely to possess the most spiritual needs?

A corollary of this concern is equally important. Each chaplain already possesses an opinion, perhaps even a stereotype, as to how the demographics of a patient reveal something about the type and intensity of spiritual need. For example, a researcher could demonstrate this by taking an opinion poll at the national meeting of chaplains, asking "In general, are greater spiritual needs experienced by younger or older open heart surgery patients?" Respondents would use their opinions concerning the relationship of age (a demographic variable) to open heart surgery, ranking one age group above the other. The question with which I began, therefore, can be framed differently by asking whether statistical analysis can enlighten and inform assumptions which chaplains already hold about the relationship between demographic characteristics and spiritual needs of patients.

A related question is whether the relationship between demographic characteristics and spiritual need changes when a person becomes seriously ill and enters the hospital. Are the relationships identical to those possessed by persons in the community? This concern can be answered by measuring the spiritual needs and demographic characteristics of a community sample to whom the hospital patients could be compared.

One difficulty–at least--has to be resolved. An instrument which measures spiritual needs in a numerical manner must be found. The results can then be analyzed in a way which reveals the influence of the demographic factors on the scores. Having found no literature which describes the relationship between spiritual needs and demographic features, I describe the results of a study which generates a response to these concerns.

METHOD

Materials

This study used a questionnaire which hopefully will generate considerable future interest from pastoral researchers. It is reasonably short, contains categories of interest to chaplains as well as parish clergy, and appears to be psychometrically sound (VandeCreek, 1992). The Life Attitude Profile-Revised (LAP-R) is a 36-item measure of selected attitudes toward life and death on a 7-point Likert scale, responses ranging from *strongly disagree* (1) to *strongly agree* (7) (Reker & Peacock, 1981). It consists of 6 dimensions, each with a score range from six to 42. In this project, these scores are interpreted as referring to spiritual well-being. Lower scores are described as representing the extent of spiritual neediness.

The *Purpose* dimension tests for the presence of life goals, a mission in life, a sense of direction and personal worthwhileness. A sample items reads, "I have discovered a satisfying life purpose." The *Coherence* dimension refers to a sense of order in one's life and a reason for existence. One of its items reads, "I have a framework that allows me to understand or make sense of my life." The *Existential Vacuum* dimension is a negative one which describes the lack of meaning in life, a lack of goals or direction and a free-floating anxiety. A sample item is, "I feel that some element which I can't quite define is missing from my life." The *Life Control* dimension reflects the freedom to make life choices and to exercise personal responsibility. It includes a sense of the internal control of life events, as for example, in the item, "I determine what happens in my life." The *Death Acceptance* dimension describes the absence of anxiety about death and the acceptance of it as "a natural, unavoidable aspect of life." The *Goal Seeking* dimension is also negative and refers to the need to reach out beyond the routine of life, to search for new experiences and challenges, as exemplified in the item, "A new challenge in my life would appeal to me now." Each of these dimensions generates its own score.

Reker proposed that these dimensions also generated two summary scores. First, a *Personal Meaning Index* (PMI) is created by summing the Purpose and

Coherence scores (range 12 to 84). This Index score reports the level at which the respondent possesses life goals as well as an integrated, consistent understanding of the self and the world.

The *Life Attitude Balance Index* (LABI) is a total score, obtained by summing the scores of all the dimensions except for Existential Vacuum and Goal Seeking which are subtracted from the total. The range of possible scores for the LABI dimension is -60 to 156.

SUBJECTS

I arranged to gather data from hospital patients (n=170) who were in a large university-related tertiary-care hospital. A research assistant solicited their participation after she determined that they possessed the mental clarity and necessary stamina to complete a questionnaire which would measure their spiritual needs. This questionnaire contained a face sheet which gathered the demographic information and these data are reported in Table 1. I gathered four additional types of information about the patients as well so that I could specify more carefully the characteristics of those who had contributed the data. The first concerned their physician's specialty. Surgeons managed 42 percent (n=72) of these patients and internal medicine physicians were involved with 30 percent (n=51). Eighteen percent (n=30) were OB/GYN patients and the physician of 10 percent of the patients (n=17) could not be identified.

TABLE 1
Demographics of the Community and Patient Groups

	Community	Patients
Gender		
Males	47(33%)	73(45%
Females	97(67%)	90(55)
Age (mean years)	59.6	45.6
Race		
Black	3(2%)	21(13%)
White	143(97%)	144(86%)
"Other"	1(1%)	1(1%)
Marital Status		
Never Married	20(14%)	29(17%)
Married	87(60%)	99(60%)
Divorced/Widow(er)	39(26%)	38(23%)

(Table 1, continued)

Education

High school graduate	19(13%)	94(57%)
Some college	58(39%)	39(23%)
College Graduate	72(48%)	33(20%)

Religious Background

Protestant	127(86%)	92(55%)
Catholic	13(9%)	25(15%)
"Other"	8(5%)	49(30%)

The columns may not add to the total respondents because of missing data. The percentage data are category and group specific.

An item asked patients to report their perception concerning the seriousness of their illness. This was important information because some patients were too ill to participate. Responses (n=162) indicated that 40 percent (n=65) believed they were not seriously ill, 38 percent (n=62) reported they were moderately ill and 22 percent (n=35) indicated they were seriously ill.

I included an item which asked patients to report the length of time they had known their diagnosis. In response to this item (n=160), 35 percent (n=56) reported an awareness of their diagnosis for less than one month, 35 percent (n=56) knew of it from one month to one year, and 30 percent (n=48) had been informed of their diagnosis more than one year earlier.

I also asked patients to indicate the distance from their home to the hospital. Residency within the county was reported by 26 percent (n=45) and outside of the county but within 100 miles by 46 percent (n=79). Twenty-four percent of the patients (n=41) lived more than 100 miles away from the hospital.

In addition to the demographic details in Table 1, therefore, the participants were surgical, medical, and OB/GYN patients who generally live within 100 miles of the hospital, who have known their diagnosis for one year or less, and who regard themselves as moderately or "not seriously" ill. Approximately 25 percent of the subsample report that they either live further away, have known their diagnosis longer or regard themselves as seriously ill.

As noted above, this study would be stronger if the responses could be compared to a sample of persons from the community. In that way it would be possible to determine what pastoral needs emerged when persons became patients in the hospital. This group (n=150) was composed of members in a Woman's Club, an Eastern Star lodge, a Kiwanis Club, or a corps of hospital volunteers.

In addition to the general demographic information reported in Table 1, they were asked whether they themselves had been a hospital patient for three days or more during the last year and whether they were worried on a daily basis about their own health or that of a family member/friend. I asked about these experiences because persons who answer "Yes" to them might display results more like the patients. Only 11 percent (n=17) had been hospital patients although 39 percent (n=59) were worried on a daily basis about health issues.

The data from the two groups were entered into a personal computer and analyzed with a statistical program (SPSSPC, Version 3). The respondent's age was entered in one of six categories (16 through 29 years; 30 through 39 years; 40 through 49 years; 50 through 59 years, 60 through 69 years, and 70 plus years). The statistical test of choice is the ANOVA, the analysis of variance. This test displays a statistical F score which indicates the level of association between the LAP-R scores and the demographic or other variables of interest from the face sheet (hereafter referred to as "independent variables"). The advantage of the ANOVA is that it creates its results from a model in which the selected independent variables are all entered and the analysis performed in a single computer run. Thus, all the selected independent variables are considered at once. This creates an F score for each independent variable which describes its level of influence on the LAP-R dimension score, adjusting for the other independent variables. This F score, in turn, is interpreted into a p value which describes the number of chances per 100 of obtaining the F score within the range of statistical significance when in reality there is no association between the variables. The alpha level for this study was set at the traditional $p<0.05$, that is, I am willing to believe that an association is present between a LAP-R score and an independent variable when there are five chances out of 100 that no association exists. (For those interested in the technical details, continuous data from Likert scales were entered as covariates, ie. "How seriously ill are you?").

The additional advantage of an ANOVA procedure is that its results also indicate what percentage of the variance in the test scores is explained by the independent variables in the model. This is particularly valuable because a statistically significant difference below $p=0.05$ may still be unimportant from a practical point of view because it explains very little of the actual difference between individuals or groups. But if I can demonstrate, for example, that demographic variables themselves account for 20 percent of the differences in dimension scores, then these data should be regarded as important in a practical way. It is true that this leaves 80 percent of the variance to be explained by idiosyncratic patient characteristics, but 20 percent is at least a hint which will help the chaplain anticipate the presence of spiritual need.

The ANOVA model for each of the dimension scores included respondents' gender, age, marital status, educational level completed, religious heritage, pattern of attendance at worship, distance between the patient's home and the hospital, length of time the patient has known the diagnosis, and a self-report of how seriously ill they believed they were. Some of these variables go beyond those usually considered as "demographic". They were included here because data concerning them can be gathered in an initial visit and used to shape the pastoral care plan. Data concerning respondents' race could not be used in the analysis because too few non-white persons were present in the sample.

RESULTS

The Patient Data

Three independent variables were associated with the LAP-R totals (LABI scores) at $p<0.05$: gender of the patient (F=4.51; p=0.04), educational level achieved by the patient (F=4.46; p=0.01), and the patient's frequency of attendance at worship (F=3.39; p=0.01). Concerning gender, the ANOVA reported a significant difference in spiritual need between the sexes because the mean score for men was lower (70.25) than for women (74.10). This means that, as a group of patients in this hospital and as measured by this questionnaire, the men reported more spiritual needs than the women. Concerning the association between the score and the educational level completed by the patient, the ANOVA reported a significant difference because those patients who possessed a high school education or less created a lower mean score (68.93) than those who had finished college (79.67). The third group as designated in Table 1 (those with some college experience) created a mean which fell between these extremes. (In the remainder of this report I will describe only the groups which generate the high and low means and the reader should assume that those which are not mentioned created means between the two extremes.) Concerning the patient's frequency of attendance at worship, the mean score of those who attended twice-per week was significantly higher (86.45) than those who almost never attended (64.17). These three variables were the most active in relation to the LABI scores. When the influence of all the independent variables in the model are considered, they explain 27 percent of the variance in the LABI scores. These findings imply that when all the LAP-R scores are taken together as a registry of spiritual needs, the most needy hospital patients are males, patients with little education, and patients who seldom attend worship.

If the 25 patients I referred to at the beginning were ranked on the basis of spiritual need, these should be placed near the top. All these data are likely not available to the chaplain before the first visit is made, but these results suggest that they are important agenda for that introductory pastoral visit.

I can be more specific than the summary LABI scores allow because each dimension or subject area produced a score. The Personal Meaning Index combined the purpose and coherence dimensions and the ANOVA model which used that score accounted for 25 percent of the variance, producing three significant associations: educational level achieved by the patient (F=4.91; p=0.009), the frequency of attendance at worship (F=2.50; p=0.05), and how seriously ill the patients reported themselves to be (F=5.76; p=0.02). Thus, the score which reported a sense of purpose and coherence in life was lower when the patient possessed a high school education or less (61.11) than when they had completed college (66.96). The significant association between the score of the two dimensions and the frequency of attendance at worship continued the pattern reported above: those who attended twice per week created higher mean scores (68.60) than those who almost never attended (59.86). The seriousness of illness data were continuous (Likert scale) and were entered as a covariate. This procedure does not produce a mean score. Instead, ANOVA produces a positive or negative beta score which indicates both the direction and strength of the relationship. For this relationship the beta was 0.88. It is positive–which means that purpose and coherence scores rise with the seriousness of the illness score. These findings mean that if we define spiritual need only in terms of the level of purpose and sense of coherence in life, then the patients who need a chaplain most are those with little education, those who attend worship infrequently, and those who are less severely ill.

These findings required an examination of the purpose and coherence dimensions scores separately. The ANOVA model involving the purpose scores explained 20 percent of their variance, two variables being active below the p=0.05 level. Educational level completed by the patient was significant (F=5.92; p=0.004) because those who had completed high school or less created lower mean scores (29.69) than those who had completed college (33.78). The seriousness of the patient's illness was associated with purpose scores (F=3.73; p<0.05), creating a beta of 0.45, a positive relationship between the two variables.

The ANOVA model for the coherence dimension explained 23 percent of the variance and the scores were related to the frequency of attendance at worship (F=2.87; p=0.03) because those who were not members created lower means (29.23) than those who attended twice per week (35.10). The relationship between seriousness of illness and coherence is again a positive one (beta=0.43) with an F score of 4.83 and p=0.03.

The remaining four LAP-R dimensions comprise two cognitatively related sets: life control/death acceptance and existential vacuum/goal seeking. In the first dyad, 20 percent of the variance in the life control dimension was explained by the model and a substantial part of this was due to the influence of marital status (F=3.23; p=0.04). Those who were never married created lower life control scores (30.00) than those who were divorced or widowed (33.10). The model which analyzed the death acceptance scores accounted for 15 percent of the variance, but no demographic variable was significantly associated with it. This lack may be related to the relative absence of severely ill and dying patients in the sample and merits further investigation.

The models which analyzed the negative dimensions which comprise the second dyad, existential vacuum and goal seeking, explained 27 and 26 percent of the variance respectively. Five significant associations were present. In interpreting these scores, remember that higher scores now reflect increased spiritual need. The most existential vacuum was reported by the divorced/ widowed patients (F=4.11; p=0.02) who produced higher mean scores (24.07) than those who were married (20.03). Existential vacuum was also associated with the frequency of worship attendance (F=5.16; p=0.001) because those who attended worship twice per week reported less vacuum (15.55) than those who seldom attended (24.07). The goal seeking dimension scores were associated with gender (F=15.14;p=.000), because men generated higher scores (28.41) than women (26.03). It was also related to marital status (F=3.21; p=0.04) because patients who were never married demonstrated more need (29.52) than those who were married (26.09). Finally, goal seeking scores were related to the length of time the patients had known their diagnosis (F=2.79; p=0.04) because those who had known their diagnosis for a year or more reported that they were more involved in seeking goals (28.54) than those who knew of their diagnosis for a month or less (25.00). These findings suggest that a number of demographic features and patient characteristics are significantly associated with spiritual need.

Data From Persons in the Community

In light of these findings, it is instructive to describe the significant levels of association between the scores and the demographic characteristics of a group of persons from the community. After all, the associations reported above may also characterize those persons who are not in the hospital.

The ANOVA model for this group included gender, age, marital status, educational level completed, religious heritage, frequency of attendance at worship, whether they had been a patient in the hospital in the last three years, and whether they were daily worried about their health or that of a family member/friend.

The analysis of the LABI summary scores for the community participants explained eight percent of the variance and did not produce any significant associations with demographic variables. Analysis of the Personal Meaning Index scores explained 10 percent of the variance and produced no p values below 0.05. Analysis of the individual dimensions revealed that 11 percent of the variance in the purpose scores was explained and a significant amount of this was accounted for by the respondent's marital status ($F=4.09$; $p=0.02$). Those who were married produced higher mean scores (32.66) than those who were divorced/widowed (30.16). The models for the coherence, life control, and death acceptance dimensions explained six, four, and 11 percent of the variances respectively and only one statistically significant relationship. The death acceptance scores were significantly different ($F=3.57$; $p=0.03$) for Protestants who produced a mean score of 30.25 and the Catholics with their score of 24.07. The analysis of the negative dimension scores revealed even less results. Analyses of the existential vacuum and goal seeking scores explained two percent and five percent of the variances respectively and no statistically significant relationship to demographic variables.

DISCUSSION

Chaplains can use these results to prioritize the list of hospital patients on whom they intend to call. Selected demographic characteristics are associated with various types of need as represented by the dimensions of the LAP-R. Age is the only patient characteristic which is not significantly associated with any of the scores. The other demographic variables when taken together explain between 15 and 27 percent of the variance in the dimension scores.

The most consistent finding is that the frequency of the patient's attendance at worship is significantly related to the LAP-R scores. Those who seldom attend create scores which reflect more spiritual need. This is important to the chaplain because their lack of involvement in a congregation likely implies that a parish pastor is not visiting them and that the hospital chaplain is their resource. This is one perspective from which to understand the need for hospital chaplains. The finding also implies that if hospital chaplains tend to visit active church members they are probably neglecting the most needy patients.

The surprising result was the positive relationship between the seriousness of the illness and the purpose/coherence scores. Do these results imply that patients have worked out a deeper sense of purpose and coherence as they become more ill? Perhaps so. Are the results an artifact of the specific items in the LAP-R? A review of these items suggests that this is not likely. This finding requires further investigation and replication.

The analysis of data from the two groups suggests that specific demographic features are more frequently associated with variations in spiritual need among hospital patients than persons in the community. This suggests that demographic characteristics may not help the parish pastor rank the pastoral care needs of parishioners in the community.

The study contains a number of limitations which should be recognized. First, the data are gathered by questionnaire, a methodology which limits patient participation. From an ill patient's point of view, considerable mental energy is required to complete the material and some found it impossible. The methodology excludes many whose data would be very instructive. A brief standardized interview or conversation may be necessary if data are to be gathered from them.

Another limitation is the restriction imposed by the content of the questionnaire, any questionnaire. The results in this study assume that the complex phenomenon of spirituality is measured by the LAP-R and that it is reasonably comprehensive. The questionnaire is as broad and as narrow as the content of its 36 items. Perhaps other aspects of pastoral concern lie outside its focus and require measurement.

The inclusion of a community sample is helpful, but the results are limited by the cross-sectional nature of the research design. That is, the data would be stronger if the community sample contained the hospital patients before they became ill. From a practical point of view this is not feasible, but it would remove the current assumption that the community sample is similar to the patients before their illness.

The other limitation of the comparison between samples is their difference in the various categories of Table 1. Each sample was selected in a non-random process and the differences in education level and religious heritage are notable. These differences may affect the findings reported above.

The ANOVA models contained independent variables of interest, but other characteristics of the respondents probably exist which would at least somewhat modify these findings. For example, I gathered no data on the socioeconomic level of respondents. This or other variables may, so to speak, lie behind those included here and influence the results.

In the end, I return to the theme with which I began. The spiritual needs of hospital patients certainly grow out of their personal history, sense of family support, seriousness of the diagnosis and many other factors. This study has demonstrated, however, that the traditional demographic data also reflect spiritual needs and can at least be used to initially rank the list of patients whom the chaplain needs to visit. Hopefully such visits will lead into fruitful ministry. The field of pastoral care awaits studies which report the outcome of various strategies in meeting these spiritual needs.

REFERENCES

Reker, G., & Peacock E. (1981). The Life Attitude Profile (LAP): A multidimensional instrument for assessing attitudes toward life. *Canadian Journal of Behavioral Science, 13*(3), 264-273.

VandeCreek, L. (1992). Pastoral assessment of selected attitudes among hospital patients and family members. *Sciences Pastorales, 11*, 67-80.

Coping with Breast Cancer: The Roles of Clergy and Faith

Sarah C. Johnson
Bernard Spilka

ABSTRACT

This paper describes the experiences of 103 breast cancer patients with home pastors and hospital chaplains. Attention was directed at the activities of clergy, the degree to which religious and nonreligious interactions were satisfying to the women, and how these related to their personal faith orientation. Because of the issues of sexual identity and attractiveness entailed by breast cancer, the role of female clergy was also explored. It is evident that religion is an extremely important resource for the majority of these breast cancer patients, and an intrinsic religious orientation helps one cope with breast cancer.

"When misery is the greatest, God is the closest" (Gross, 1982). Perhaps nowhere is misery greater than when an individual contracts cancer. Potential terminality immediately becomes a salient issue, along with expectations of pain, anguish, and suffering. Physical problems are compounded with a host of psychological difficulties, not the least of which are feelings of isolation, separation, dependency, and helplessness. In such circumstances, religion and prayer have a high likelihood of becoming

Reproduced with permission of the Plenum Publishing Company, from the *Journal of Religion and Health*, (1991), 30(1), 21-33.

prime supports for the individual (Acklin, Brown, & Mauger, 1983; Peteet, 1985; Spilka, Spangler, Nelson, 1983; Weidman-Gibbs, & Achterberg-Lawlis, 1978).

Different forms of malignancy create their own unique adjustment problems, and breast cancer poses special difficulties for women. Most commonly, treatment means surgery, and the result can be perceived as mutilation. Early research revealed that mastectomy patients felt that their bodies were deformed and distorted (Bard, 1952). More recent work discloses coping problems in a variety of areas –work, marriage, and sexual function. As might be expected, unmarried mastectomy patients do not function as well as their married counterparts (Bloom, Pendergrass & Burnell, 1984). As Bard (1952) put it, one must appreciate the ramifications of breast cancer, since an "organ of great psychic significance" is removed.

Uniformly, workers in this area point to the need the breast cancer patient has for social support. Jenkins and Pargament (1988) note that support from clergy is often not provided cancer patients even though research shows that 64 to 90 percent of cancer patients consider religion to be personally important. In addition, Yates, Chalmer, St. James, Follansbee, and McKegney (1981) report that among advanced cancer patients feeling close to God, believing prayer is helpful, and attending religious services relate positively to life satisfaction, positive emotional states, and less perceived pain. Unhappily, even in major research programs on breast cancer, religion as a potentially significant variable has often been ignored (Taylor, 1983; Taylor & Levine, 1976).

Theory suggests that the beneficial effects of religion may be a function of its roles in providing meaning, maintaining or enhancing one's sense of control, and supporting self-esteem (Spilka, Shaver & Kirkpatrick, 1985). When cancer strikes, meaning, control, and esteem suffer. The patient must resolve such questions as "why me?" and "why cancer?" Control over one's life is placed in the hands of others; powerlessness ensues, and self-esteem is adversely affected. In these situations, religion can be a constructive alternative, and may be mediated by 1) the personal spiritual orientation of the patient, and 2) religious representatives — the clergy.

In the 1960s, Gordon Allport (1967) and his students formulated the concepts of intrinsic and extrinsic religion. Where an intrinsic personal orientation is regarded as a search for truth, a "meaning-endowing framework" (Donahue, 1985), an extrinsic orientation is utilitarian and instrumental. One turns to religion in times of need, while intrinsic religion is an ever-present frame of reference. Research shows that intrinsic religion also relates to constructive thinking and behavior, and aids the person in coping with life (Spilka, Hood & Gorsuch, 1985).

Spiritual support when cancer strikes is normally provided by clergy (Peteet, 1985). Increasingly, these representatives of institutional religion are being trained in clinical pastoral skills and crisis management, yet what they actually do with the patient and the latter's responses to the clergy are still largely unexamined. Breast cancer, because of its sexual significance, implications about attractiveness, and female identity, could impose unique constraints on the pastor-patient interaction. Both male clergy and female patients may be less willing to confront these pertinent issues than might be true if the cleric is female. The purpose of the present research was to gain such information and relate it to the form of the patient's faith.

Given the foregoing, certain hypotheses are suggested.

1.   Because of both their pastoral role and familiarity with the patient, home pastors will use religious activities more than will hospital chaplains. In like manner, home pastors will be perceived as discussing the patient's family more and as being more understanding than will hospital chaplains. In contrast, the latter, owing to their training, will be viewed as engaging more in counseling.

2.   Satisfaction with home pastors and hospital chaplains will be positively related to using religious activities during the visits. Perceived reluctance to discuss the breast cancer and its importance for sexual identity and attractiveness will be viewed negatively by the women.

3.   Because of the implications of breast cancer for female identity and attractiveness, patients who encounter female pastors and hospital chaplains will be particularly pleased with such clerics. In general, a preference will be expressed for female clergy.

4.   To the extent the women are intrinsically oriented, they will be favorably disposed toward clergy visits to the home and hospital, religious activities on the part of the clergy, and will be satisfied with clerical efforts. In contrast, extrinsic tendencies will relate to nonreligious clerical actions and oppose religious ones.

METHOD

Sample

The participants were 103 women volunteers who were recruited through the American Cancer Society (ACS). All were mastectomy patients currently associated with the ACS Reach-to-Recovery support group for women with breast cancer. Their average age was 53.4 years (S.D. = 11.05). Most of the women (81.3%) had some college education; 14 percent were high school graduates, while four percent attended vocational school after high school.

Of the 103 respondents, 71.8 percent indicated a specific church affiliation; and of these, 70 percent were Protestant, 14 percent were Catholic, six percent were Jewish, and eight percent indicated "other." Nineteen religious bodies were represented, with the largest groups being Methodist (51%), Lutheran (11%), and Baptist (10%). Half of the women (49%) indicated that they attended church weekly prior to their illness. Only 9.7 percent reported no church attendance. Eighty-eight percent stated that religion was important to very important to them, while 12 percent considered religion unimportant. No significant change was evident from pre-illness time to the present in religious attitudes and involvement.

Measures

A two-part questionnaire was employed. One part used the Allport-Ross (1967) version of the intrinsic-extrinsic scale with a six-point Likert format in which responses ranged from strongly disagree to strongly agree. The reliabilities for these instruments were: intrinsic faith, $r_{tt} = .85$; extrinsic faith, $r_{tt} = .60$.

Part two of the questionnaire contained 99 items that asked about religious perspectives and activities, clergy-patient interactions, self-perceptions of emotions, coping with the cancer, and a variety of demographic characteristics (age, education, and so on). Concern here is with the interaction of the patients with both home pastors and hospital chaplains. Questions were asked about patient requests for clerical contact, the number of such interactions both in the home and the hospital, and what activities took place during the meetings. On the basis of previous work, attention was directed at prayer, Bible, or other religious reading, counseling, talking about the church, family, the future, irrelevancies, and the feeling that the pastor or chaplain understood the patient (Spilka & Spangler, 1979). Open-ended items permitted consideration of other possible activities, as well as what was satisfying or displeasing to the patient. Similar information was also sought on involvement with female clergy.

RESULTS AND DISCUSSION

Contacts with the clergy

Table 1 provides the basic information on contacts between clergy and the breast cancer patients. Twenty-eight (27.2%) of the women were visited in their home by their own minister, and 58 (56.3%) saw their pastor when hospitalized. Thirty-eight (36.9%) of the women saw a hospital chaplain, but only 31 chaplains were perceived as spending much time with the women. This may have been due to rejection by the women, or a failure on the part of some chaplains to follow up an initial introductory visit.

TABLE 1

Data on Patient-Clergy Contacts, Actions, and Evaluations

Visits by Clergy (Percentages of Total Sample)

Home Pastor

In home:	22.3% (23)[1]	Requested visits: 5.0% (5)
In hospital:	52.4% (58)	Requested visits: 6.8% (7)
Mean number of visits: 2.6		

Hospital Chaplain

In home:	9.5% (8)	Requested visits: 9.5% (8)
In hospital:	39.3% (38)	Requested visits: 2.4% (2)
Mean number of visits: 1.9		

Satisfaction with home and hospital visits by clergy (percentages of patients visited)[2]

Home pastor:	home	hospital	Chaplain: home	hospital
Pleased	92.7	96.2	98.0	97.1
Displeased	7.2	3.8	2.0	2.9

Actions of clergy during visits (percentages)

	Home pastor (N=58)	Hospital chaplain (N=31)	t-test
Offer to pray for you	58.6	71.0	1.159
Offer to pray with you	50.0	35.5	1.317
Actually pray with you	53.4	29.0	2.216*
Did religious readings (Bible, etc.)	13.8	13.2	1.589
Counseled with you	15.5	12.9	.332
Talked irrelevancies	15.5	38.7	2.468*
Understood feelings, concerns	53.4	45.2	.741
Talked about church affairs	17.2	0.0	2.468*
Talked about your family	43.1	29.0	1.376

(Table 1, Continued)

Talked about your future	17.2	19.4	.259
Seemed in a hurry to leave	3.6	9.1	1.090

Had difficulty identifying hospital chaplain: 8.3
Visited by female clergy: 16.8 (N=17)
If not, would have preferred female cleric: 20.0
Degree of satisfaction with female cleric: Pleased: 76.5
Displeased: 23.5

[1]Sample sizes (N's) given in ().
[2]Since the sample sizes are given above, only percentages of the samples who saw clergy are given in the remainder of the table.
*Indicates significance at .05 level.

The women were generally well pleased with the visits of both home pastors and the hospital chaplains. In only one instance was dissatisfaction expressed with a minister's home visit, and only twice with similar visits to the hospital. Displeasure was expressed for only three of the visits by hospital chaplains.

Clergy activities

Hypothesis one gains some support in relation to religious activities. As expected, home pastors actually pray with the patient more than do hospital chaplains. The former, for obvious reasons, also tend to discuss church affairs. Hospital chaplains are seen as speaking about irrelevant matters significantly more than home clergy. This may relate to the chaplain's being a stranger who needs time to determine what is relevant to each patient. In general, however, from the patient's viewpoint, home pastors and hospital chaplains are quite similar in their pastoral actions.

Satisfaction with clergy

As noted, the women were very favorably disposed toward both their home pastors and hospital chaplains. The reasons for this positive attitude only partially support hypothesis two. Understandably, if the patients were satisfied with their visits of their own minister to the home, they were also pleased with the hospital visits. The same holds true for the few times hospital chaplains visited the home. This implies a general feeling of being positive or negative toward the home pastor, a view also bolstered by the high correlations between satisfaction and the feeling of being understood by the clergy. Being understood, however, is independent of all of the other activities by which the home minister relates to the patient. Apparently, there is a quality in the relationship that counts, and this may or may not involve any of the expected pastoral actions of the home clergy. The same appears to be true for the hospital chaplain; however, there is one exception. In patient-chaplain interactions, a rather strong association is found between the feeling of being understood and considering the patient's future ($r = .54$, $P < .01$). Still, satisfaction with the chaplain is independent of such discussions even if they imply understanding.

TABLE 2
Correlations Between forms of Personal Faith and Clergy Variables

Religious orientation	Home pastor Satisfaction		Hospital chaplain Satisfaction
	Home	Hospital	Hospital[2]
Clergy variables:			
Number of visits to home	.00	.26[*1]	—
Number of visits to hospital	-.02	-.05	-.19
Total visits	.51***	.12	-.17
Home visits requested	.11	.04	—
Hospital visits requested	.25	.11	.30*
Satisfaction with home visits	—	.70***	.81**
Offer to pray for patient	.05	-.17	.37**
Offer to pray with patient	.02	-.09	.39**
Actually pray with patient	.19	.13	.22
Read Bible etc.	.05	-.28**	-.07
Counsels patient	.09	-.15	.33*
Talks irrelevancies	.13	-.16	-.18
Understands patient	.50***	.30**	.41**
Talks about church affairs	.36**	.19	—
Talks about patient's family	.05	.07	.34*
Talks about patient's future	.13	-.08	-.14
Perceived in hurry to leave	—	-.08	-.14
Discuss sexual/attractive issues	.12	-.06	.23
Reluctance to discuss br. cancer	-.28	-.45***	-.22
Reluctance to discuss woman's role	-.30	.00	.00
Reluctance to discuss male relations	.11	-.16	.00

(Table 2, Continued)
[1]The coefficients are based on different size samples due to variations in patient response.
[2]In seven instances, hospital chaplains visited homes; however, because of this small sample, home variables are not considered.
*Indicates significance at .10 level; **at .05 level; ***at .01 level.

Hypothesis two relates differentially to the home pastor and hospital chaplain (see Table 2). Where these expectations gain no support for home clergy, the opposite is sometimes true for the chaplains. Not only is satisfaction independent of religious activities for the home pastor, but in the instance of reading from the Bible or other religious material, such behavior is viewed negatively. Could such actions be perceived as preparing the woman for death? Whatever the reason, this is not what these women desire. In contrast, offers by the hospital chaplain to pray for and/or with the patient are greeted positively. The feeling that the chaplain is counseling is also favorably received, as are discussions about the patient and her family. Apparently women with breast cancer respond favorably to a much greater range of activities than just those with religious connotations.

The role of the female pastor

Hypothesis three is not supported (see Table 2). Seventeen of the women related to female pastors and chaplains, but only 20 percent of the entire sample would have preferred a female. The age of the patient is clearly a factor here, as age correlated -.42 (p < .01) with preference for a female cleric. It appears the older women feel more comfortable with the traditional male churchman. This may explain why approximately three-quarters (76.5%) of those who saw a female cleric were pleased with this contact when, as Table 1 indicates, general satisfaction with clergy ranged from 92 to 98 percent.

Sexual identity was of some concern to approximately half the sample (52.4%), and of great import to 20.6 percent of the women; 76.5 percent were also anxious about the effect of the cancer on personal attractiveness. In other words, three-quarters of the women were indeed anxious about these issues. Still, only three of the women discussed these matters with either male or female clergy. A contributing factor might have been the sensitivity of such concerns, as 12 of the women saw their home pastor as reluctant to deal with the breast cancer; seven of the women felt similar reticence on the part of the hospital chaplains. These small numbers do not, however, explain the discrepancy between the expressed concern and lack of communication about female identity and attractiveness. Whether the cleric was male or female, the issue rarely came up.

The role of personal faith

Table 3 reveals that hypothesis four is partially supported. For the home pastor, frequency of visits to the home, hospital, and, therefore, obviously the total number of visits correlate positively and significantly with intrinsic faith. In addition, actually praying with the patient also associates meaningfully with an intrinsic orientation. Persons with this outlook are disinclined to see their pastors as in a hurry to leave, and since such individuals are often quite constructive in viewpoint, working with them may be rewarding to the ministers.

TABLE 3

Correlations Between Forms of Personal Faith and Clergy Variables

Religious orientation	Home pastor		Hospital chaplain	
	Intrinsic	Extrinsic	Intrinsic	Extrinsic
Clergy Variables:				
Number of visits to home	.22*	.05[1]	—	—
Number of visits to hospital	.22**	-.04	-.13	.32***
Total visits	.32**	-.21	.40**	-.18
Home visits requested	.07	.11	—	—
Hospital visits requested	.06	.08	.03	.07
Satisfaction with home visits	.27	-.40**	.51	.38
Satisfaction with hospital visits	.19	-.29*	.16	.24
Offer to pray for patient	.04	.00	-.28	.32
Offer to pray with patient	.10	.16	-.13	.39*
Actually pray with patient	.49***	-.19	-.01	.31
Read Bible etc.	.21	-.16	-.27	-.25
Counsels patient	.06	-.19	-.19	-.27
Talks irrelevancies	-.16	.30**	-.01	-.04
Understands patient	.21	.04	.07	-.12
Talks about church affairs	.02	-.19	—	—
Talks about patient's family	.12	.10	-.28	.15
Talks about patient's future	.19	-.22	-.12	-.20
Perceived in hurry to leave	-.32**	.15	.03	.18

(Table 3, Continued)
[1]The coefficients are based on different size samples due to variations in patient response.
*Indicates significance at .10 level; **at .05 level; ***at.01 level.

Relative to the hospital chaplain, the total number of visits also affiliates with an intrinsic perspective, while not expected is a positive tie between extrinsic religion and the number of visits chaplains make in the hospital. One might infer that this is expressing a utilitarian need for religious support. Extrinsity further associates with an offer to pray with the patient. These findings with religious orientation are sparse, but, in the main, meaningful.

There is much evidence that faith can be a great comfort when one is threatened with cancer. In the present sample, 85.4 percent of the women reported that religion helped them cope with their illness. We also saw that well over 90 percent of our sample were pleased with the ministrations of their home pastors and the hospital chaplains. Despite these crucial observations, the hypotheses advanced here were only partially supported. A number of factors may account for and qualify these findings.

The need for supportive phenomenological analysis

Clearly, crisis situations are complex, and the full import of breast cancer on a woman's psychological state may not be capable of exacting evaluation by single, simple, objective items. Low or non-statistically significant results could result from the unreliability of individual items, even though they may be excellent markers. Scales would have been desirable; hence, many more questions would have had to be constructed, and this is an avenue that might be fruitful in future research.

A strong case can be made for phenomenological analysis, and our request for open-ended written responses resulted in many indications of the deep significance that faith had in this extremely stressful situation. In addition, the volunteered remarks help clarify the objective findings.

The meaning of clergy visits

The general satisfaction with clergy was manifested primarily in the pleasure conferred by the presence of either the home pastor or hospital chaplain. Remarks such as, "Just came to visit, a show of caring", "concerned about me," and "Simply, he was there-cared" were most common. These were encapsulated in the summary statement of one woman, "Just to feel that someone cares," and indeed this was a fundamental need of these women that was often met by a visit from her minister or the chaplain. In one instance, a minister and his wife drove over 100 miles to see the patient; the beneficial psychological effect of such an occurrence cannot be calculated. The words "care" and "caring" were repeatedly employed, and were evidently a core concept for many of the women. Clergy visits as a sign "that someone cares" acquired additional significance, for a number of the women expressed a touch of pleased guilt that their busy home pastor took the time to visit and help.

An interesting problem was how long a visit should be. Some women complained of a visit's brevity; others, that it was too long. Clergy obviously need to be sensitive to cues provided by patients regarding visit length.

The roles of prayer and ritual

Caring was repeatedly associated with prayer. Not only personal praying with a cleric, but the prayers of others were much appreciated. One woman was very pleased that her church 1600 miles away held prayer sessions for her; another appreciated "praying for me during a mass."

The "power of prayer" is not to be taken lightly. It represents a form of control that identifies the individual with ultimate power sources (Swatos, 1987). Prayer has also been treated as an active cognitive coping strategy that relates positively both to problem-focused and successful emotion-focused coping (Folkman et al., 1986; Holahan & Moos, 1987).

Of secondary significance to most of the women were formal religious activities. One appreciated a "mini-service," and "receiving communion." The opposite was also true. A patient objected to "pushing generalized formal religion," or being "pushy about attending mass more." The consolation of ritual should not, however, be underplayed; neither ought it be considered a necessity without regard for the patient's feelings. Ceremony may be functional in that participation in ritual can imply ingratiation and identification with church and God (Pruyser, 1968). Some of the women also distinguished sharply between institutionalized religion and individual faith. A sensitive pastor will attempt to test the situation in order to determine what "works."

The importance of God relationships

It is quite understandable that, in these stressful circumstances, God relationships might become crucial. One woman stated that she knew "no matter what happens, God is with me. I am never alone. He will give me the strength I need." Another averred that "we knew God was not punishing us with cancer because we had been bad. . . . I believed that it was in the Lord's hands and that the outcome would be the right one for me and my family." For this woman, there was little if any ambiguity; meaning was present. Though it is not objectively clear what this meaning might be, another woman gained similar courage through meaning. She claimed, "I had no idea God could answer so many of my questions." Control was in the hands of a benevolent God. Both of these patients were thus able to maintain their self-esteem in the face of the cancer threat. These points were frequently stated: God was indeed a source of strength; God offered answers; and, in one form or another, it was repeatedly asserted that "My God does NOT cause cancer." One woman attributed the cancer to the devil.

In a parallel manner, others became the tools or agents of God. A patient spoke "of the wonders of God's works and the talents he gave doctors, ministers and lay people to help someone when they really hurt."

Sources of dissatisfaction

This was not a time to be judgmental and callous, yet some clerics were certainly unfeeling. One woman wanted her minister to pray for a miracle, but he refused. Another told the patient that she was dying, and he would pray for her soul to go to heaven. In a similar vein, a pastor told the patient that she was a sinner and unsaved.

A more passive but equally distressing situation was reported by two women. Though active in their churches, no minister visited them. As one put it, "I felt abandoned by my church–but not necessarily by God.... I cannot bring myself to return." In this day of pastoral sophistication, it is hard to believe that such insensibility still exists. Obviously, the actual experience of patients can be very instructive and should become a more significant part of clinical pastoral education.

Similar signs of unhappiness were frequently noted, but these occurrences were obviously not strong enough to counter the positive feelings most of the women experienced toward the clergy.

The issues of identity and attractiveness

The largely negative objective results with respect to female clergy could be a function of the relative importance of the various patient concerns. As noted under direct questioning, sexual identity and attractiveness were sources of apprehension to one-half to three-quarters of the women, yet only one woman spontaneously referred to "society's emphasis on 'breast' size as a sign of femininity." Female identity and attractiveness took a back seat to what was often termed "life and death." This theme was repeated with words like "dying," "life expectancy," "reoccurrence," "spreading." The simple statement, "I didn't want to die" encapsulated the core concern of these women.

A secondary theme, but also one that was continually reiterated, dealt with the abandonment of children, husband, and other relations. A number of times, faith entered the picture. One woman's main concern was "to become closer to God"; another associated her family's protection with her relationship to God. A third patient feared that she would die before she "completed my spiritual growth during this life time."

Still, there were indications that female sexual identity and attractiveness were important issues. One woman who did not discuss this with a cleric did talk to a male nurse who was comforting. Another dealt with attractiveness with her female friends; in a similar manner, a receptive male friend was a good sounding board regarding attractiveness.

Perceived reluctance on the part of clergy to consider these matters was a source of distress to more than a few of the women. Though one stated that "sexuality needs to be discussed," most commonly noted was an aversion on the part of the clergy to address breast cancer while talking about cancer per se. Somewhat caustically, one patient, in referring to her interaction with a pastor, remarked that "He even mentioned breast cancer in conversation." Without question, the women were sensitive to the topic. About half felt comfortable with the matter, while others offered explanations as to why it was not treated. In one instance, the patient considered herself the problem. She noted, "I wanted to appear strong and in control. I didn't want to talk about it (guess I thought it would go away)." The issue was indeed delicate, and lack of discussion was attributed to the shyness of a pastor, not knowing a cleric well enough, the "awkwardness" of the problem, and the belief that clergy "are not certain a woman wants to discuss it with them." Despite expectations that a female pastor might be in a better position to bring up these concerns, we had no indication that the female pastor had any advantage over her male counterpart. It was, however, abundantly evident that the patients themselves were quite unlikely to broach the topic.

Religion's help in dealing with breast cancer

No question elicited more of a response from the women than, "Was your religion any help in dealing with your breast cancer?" In only two instances was religion viewed as irrelevant. Many of the women wrote at length about

God in their lives, the importance of prayer, and having a faith that endowed one with courage. A theme that was repeatedly echoed was that God was an ever-present supportive healer and companion in whom the patient could confide. If a lesson can be learned from these remarks, it is that religion is an extremely important resource for almost all breast cancer patients, particularity, as in the present study, with upper middle class, rather well-educated women. There is also little doubt from the findings on the role of personal faith that an intrinsic spiritual orientation is particularly meaningful in perceiving religion as an aid in dealing with the cancer. The latter correlates .70 (p < .01) with an intrinsic faith, while an extrinsic orientation is independent of help from religion (r = -.05).

SUMMARY

This research examined the experiences of breast cancer patients with home pastors and hospital chaplains. Attention was directed at the pastoral activities of the clergy, and their effectiveness with these women. Because of the psychological import of breast cancer, the role of female clerics and the issues of female sexual identity and attractiveness were also studied. Sources of satisfaction and dissatisfaction with clergy were identified. Since the nature of the personal faith of the women might be a significant mediating variable, the place of intrinsic and extrinsic spiritual orientations was explored and found to be an important factor in the relationship of religion and coping behavior.

It is evident that religion is an extremely important resource for the great majority of the women in the present sample. This confirms other research on cancer patients. Visits by home pastors and hospital chaplains were greatly appreciated. Satisfaction with clergy centered about the idea of being understood. Since this did not relate to any of the activities assessed here, more research needs to be undertaken to know what this really means. Though sexual identity and attractiveness are a source of concern to most of the women, such issues are rarely discussed with clergy. Perceived reluctance to deal with these matters is a source of patient dissatisfaction with pastors. Female clerics did not demonstrate any advantages over their male peers in dealing with breast cancer patients, and were actually preferred less than male pastors. Finally, there are indications that an intrinsic religious orientation does help one cope with breast cancer.

Inconsistency in the objective findings suggests that research of this nature be buttressed by the gathering of subjective data that can be phenomenologically examined. Such information is likely to be of much utility in clinical pastoral education. These programs need to consider in greater depth the actions of clergy who deal with breast cancer patients. In conclusion, it is felt that the recipients of pastoral care are really a largely unexplored teaching resource, not only for this condition, but for illness in general.

REFERENCES

Acklin, M., Brown, E., & Mauger, P. (1983). The Role of Religious Values in Coping with Cancer. *Journal of Religion and Health, 22*, 322-333.

Allport, G., & Ross, J. (1967). Personal Religious Orientation and Prejudice. *Journal of Personality and Social Psychology, 5*, 432-443.

Bard, M. (1952). The Sequence of Emotional Reactions in Radical Mastectomy Patients. *Public Health Reports, 67*, 1144-1148.

Bloom, J., Pendergrass, S., & Burall, G. (1984). Social Functioning of Women with Breast Cancer: Validation of a Clinical Scale. *Journal of Psychosocial Oncology, 21*, 93-101.

Donahue, M. (1985). Intrinsic and Extrinsic Religiousness: Review and Meta-analysis. *Journal of Personality and Social Psychology, 48*, 400-419.

Folkman, S., Lazarus, R., Dunkel-Schetter, C., DeLongis, A., & Gruen, R. (1986). Dynamics of a Stressful Encounter: Cognitive Appraisal, Coping, and Encounter Outcomes. *Journal of Personality and Social Psychology, 50*, 992-1003.

Gross, L. (1982). *The Last Jews in Berlin*. New York: Simon and Schuster, 242.

Holahan, C., & Moos, K. H. (1987). Personal and Contextual Determinants of Coping Strategies. *Journal of Personality and Social Psychology, 52*, 946-955.

Hunt, R., & King, M. (1971). The Intrinsic/Extrinsic Concept: A Review and Evaluation. *Journal for the Scientific Study of Religion, 10*, 339-356.

Jenkins, R., & Pargament, K. (1988). The Relationship Between Cognitive Appraisals and Psychological Adjustment in Cancer Patients. *Social Science and Medicine, 26*, 625-633;

Peteet, J. (1985). Religious Issues Presented by Cancer Patients Seen in Psychiatric Consultation. *Journal of Psychosocial Oncology, 3*, 53-56.

Pruyser, P. *A Dynamic Psychology of Religion*. New York: Harper & Row, 1968.

Spilka, B., Spangler. J., & Nelson, C. (1983). Spiritual Support in Life-Threatening Illness." *Journal of Religion and Health, 22*, 98-104.

Spilka, B., Shaver, P., & Kirkpatrick, L. A. (1985). A General Attribution Theory for the Psychology of Religion. *Journal for the Scientific Study of Religion, 22*, 1-20.

Spilka, B., Hood, R., & Gorsuch, R. (1985). *The Psychology of Religion: An Empirical Approach.* Englewood Cliffs, N.J., Prentice-Hall.

Spilka, B., & Spangler, J. (1979). *Spiritual Support in Cancer: Patient Encounters with Clergy.* Paper presented at the Convention of the Society for the Scientific Study of Religion, San Antonio, Texas.

Swatos, W. (1987). The Power of Prayer: Observations and Possibilities. In W. Swatos (Ed.), *Religious Sociology: Interfaces and Boundaries*, pp 103-113. New York, Greenwood.

Taylor, S. (1983). Adjustment to Threatening Events: A Theory of Cognitive Adaptation. *American Psychologist, 38*, 1161-1173.

Taylor, S., & Levine, S. (1976). *The Psychological Impact of Breast Cancer: Theory and Practice.* San Francisco, West Coast Cancer Foundation.

Weidman-Gibbs, H., & Achterberg-Lawlis, J. (1978). Spiritual Values and Death Anxiety: Implications for Counseling Terminal Cancer Patients. *Journal of Counseling Psychology, 25*, 563-569.

Yates, J., Chalmer, B., St. James, P., Follansbee, M., & McKegney, F. (1981). Religion in Patients with Advanced Cancer. *Medical and Pediatric Oncology, 9*, 121-128.

14

Contributions of Religious Experience to Psychological and Physical Well-Being: Research Evidence and an Explanatory Model

Jared D. Kass

ABSTRACT

Religious experiences may be a resource in primary preventive care. Using Tillich's model, in which ontological anxiety contributes to psychological and physical illness, this paper proposes that religious experience can contribute to well-being. Data supporting these relationships, drawn from studies of psychotherapeutic workshop participants, medical outpatients and divinity school students, are reviewed. Further evidence is reviewed which suggests that the development of an internally-focussed perceptual orientation may facilitate the occurrence of religious experience.

In *The Courage To Be*, Paul Tillich (1952) showed great insight when he described our century as "the age of anxiety." Tillich accurately predicted that anxiety would emerge as a major contributor to the psychological and physical illnesses of our times. In the psychological domain, there has been a well-documented proliferation of anxiety-related disorders,

Reproduced with permission of the College of Chaplains, Inc. from *The Caregiver Journal,* (1991), 8(4), 4-11.

which Beck and Emery (1985) define as the excessive functioning or malfunctioning of normal survival mechanisms. Similarly, in the medical domain, it is now recognized that anxiety contributes to many physical illnesses caused or exacerbated by stress (Gatchel & Baum, 1983). Through the fight or flight response, in which the hypothalamus activates the sympathetic nervous system and the endocrine system to produce hyperarousal and lowered immunologic functioning (Table 1), anxiety can contribute to illnesses ranging from the common cold to hypertension.

TABLE 1

Physiological Correlates of Anxiety/Stress

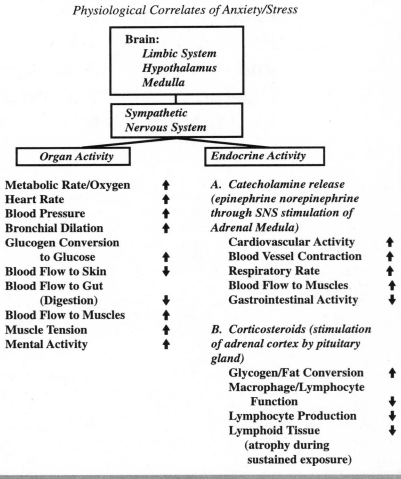

Organ Activity		Endocrine Activity	
Metabolic Rate/Oxygen	↑	**A. Catecholamine release**	
Heart Rate	↑	**(epinephrine norepinephrine**	
Blood Pressure	↑	**through SNS stimulation of**	
Bronchial Dilation	↑	**Adrenal Medula)**	
Glucogen Conversion		Cardiovascular Activity	↑
to Glucose	↑	Blood Vessel Contraction	↑
Blood Flow to Skin	↓	Respiratory Rate	↑
Blood Flow to Gut		Blood Flow to Muscles	↑
(Digestion)	↓	Gastrointestinal Activity	↓
Blood Flow to Muscles	↑		
Muscle Tension	↑	**B. Corticosteroids (stimulation**	
Mental Activity	↑	**of adrenal cortex by pituitary**	
		gland)	
		Glycogen/Fat Conversion	↑
		Macrophage/Lymphocyte	
		Function	↓
		Lymphocyte Production	↓
		Lymphoid Tissue	↓
		(atrophy during	
		sustained exposure)	

But Tillich may have shown even greater insight when he analyzed the causes of anxiety. Unlike many psychologists who viewed anxiety merely as an outgrowth of stressful life circumstances, Tillich views anxiety as an outgrowth of the underlying world view through which stressful life circumstances are interpreted. Specifically, Tillich proposed that "ontological insecurity" was a primary cause of anxiety. Ontological insecurity is the perception that life lacks fundamental meaning and that no God (or Ground of Being) exists. Guided by such a world view, humans respond to stressful life circumstances with high levels of anxiety and distress. The solution, Tillich suggested, was to re-establish our relationship with the Ground of Being. The resulting "ontological harmony," as this author describes the converse of ontological insecurity (Kass, 1991), provides a perspective that reduces anxiety, even in the face of stressful life circumstances (Table 2).

TABLE 2

Tillich's Model: Underlying Causes of Anxiety

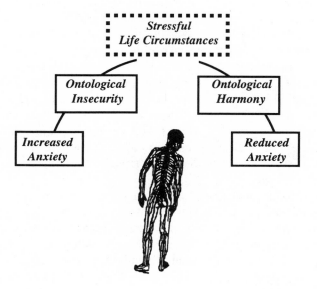

Thus, from Tillich's point of view, a relationship with the Ground of Being is an essential characteristic of the healthy personality. Whether this relationship is with the impersonal or the personal form of the Ground of Being, Tillich suggested that the development of this relationship required, not simply belief, but personally meaningful experience. Tillich's emphasis on the importance of personally-experienced spirituality was similar to Allport's (1967) focus on the value of intrinsically-oriented religiosity (which included "experiences of the divine") as well as Buber's (1970) concept of the "I-Thou" relationship.

Evidence from research

The premise that personally-experienced spirituality is possible, as well as health-promoting, is an unusual approach to theology and scientific investigation within a culture that emphasizes rational non-metaphysical thought. Further, the theologian and the scientist are trapped within the paradox that, precisely because the culture has moved so far away from the assumption that there is a human capacity to experience the Ground of Being, it is difficult to find scientifically acceptable populations with which to investigate this hypothesis. Nevertheless, the investigation of spiritual experience has progressed. Without being comprehensive, let me name several examples of this research. Large random sample surveys by Greeley (1974) in conjunction with the National Opinion Research Center in the United States and by Hay and Morisey (1978) in Great Britain have suggested that somewhere between 30% and 40% of Americans and Britons have had experiences which have convinced them of the existence of the Ground of Being. Although Greeley's estimations have been reduced by analyses conducted by Thomas and Cooper (1978), there is still convincing evidence that such experiences happen to a large number of people.

Hay and Morisey's study also suggested that such experiences contribute to psychological well-being. Further, Hood's (1975, 1979) research suggests that mystical experiences are part of a human being's normal perceptual capacities and contribute to psychological health. Additional corroboration that such experiences are part of a human being's normal perceptual capacities come from psychophysiological "states of consciousness" research using the EEG suggesting that mystical experiences are a function of a deepened ability to achieve internally-focussed states of consciousness (Davidson, 1976; Murphy & Donovan, 1988; Kass, 1991), and that these states of consciousness produce a highly beneficial relaxation response that counters the fight or flight response (Benson, 1975). Let me focus now on several studies in which I have been involved, and which further corroborate this hypothesis:

From 1975-1979, I worked with the psychologist Carl Rogers (1961) on the staff of the Person-Centered Approach Project, an extension of Rogers' earlier research in client-centered psychotherapy. By helping to create very specific conditions within the interpersonal environment of these person-centered workshops (that included a high degree of empathy, congruence, and unconditional positive regard), we found that participants could begin to experience their inner selves as trustworthy sources of guidance (Bowen, Justyn, Kass, Miller, Rogers, Rogers, & Wood, 1978; Rogers, 1980). In addition, I learned that as participants began to experience their inner selves as trustworthy sources of guidance, a significant proportion began to experience their inner selves as "greater than themselves" and, subsequently, "rooted in the Ground of Being" (Table 3). Because the Ground of Being was experienced as within

TABLE 3

PROCESS CONCEPTION for **Experiences of the Spiritual Core within an Interpersonal Environment Providing Empathy, Congruence, and Unconditional Positive Regard:**

The individual experiences:
↓

self as untrustworthy source of personal guidance
↓

self as trustworthy source of personal guidance
↓

self as "greater than oneself"
↓

self as rooted in the Ground of Being

the person, it seemed accurate to describe these phenomena as "experiences of the spiritual core" (Kass, 1983; Kass, 1991).

These observations seemed significant from two points of view: First, these experiences of the spiritual core were taking place in a non-theologically driven framework. While it is clear that interpretations and explanations of reality are, in large part, socially constructed (Berger & Luckmann, 1966), something more than social construction seemed to be reflected in the participants' experiences. Their perceptions seemed to be part of a natural spectrum of human experience, rather than simply a function of social or theological belief. Second, these experiences seemed to contribute significantly to the perception that life is meaningful and coherent, even during negative life circumstances. But would it be possible to verify these effects using quantitative procedures? Working with Drs. Herbert Benson, Richard Friedman and other colleagues at the Section on Behavioral Medicine at Boston's Deaconess Hospital, I developed an Index of Core Spiritual Experiences (INSPIRIT) (Kass, Friedman, Leserman, Zuttermeister, & Benson, 1991). This index contains seven questions which help to identify experiences of the spiritual core. Using outpatients in a 10-week behavioral medicine program, we found that patients who entered these programs having previously had core spiritual experiences showed higher increases in life purpose and satisfaction (Table 4), as well as greater decreases in the frequency of stress- related medical symptoms (Table 5), than those who had not had such experiences. These results suggested a measurable relationship between core spiritual experiences and a) psychological strength during crises, and b) the ability to gain control over stress-related medical symptoms.

Most recently, I have worked with Dr. Larry Burton, Chairperson of the Department of Religion and Health at Chicago's Rush Presbyterian/St. Luke's Medical Center; Lucy Ferranti, Roman Catholic Chaplain at Harvard Divinity School, and Dr. Frank Davis at Lesley College Graduate School, to explore the relationship between core spiritual experience and psychological well-being in divinity school students at Harvard University. We chose this population because these students are a reasonably mainstream group of people who are seriously committed to their religious lives. But we suspected that not all of them would have had core spiritual experiences. If there were any special relationship between core spiritual experiences and life purpose and satisfaction, we proposed that such a relationship should show up in this population. These data seem to support our hypothesis (Kass, Burton, Ferranti & Davis, 1991). Among these divinity school students, there is a significant degree of correlation between core spiritual experiences and life purpose and satisfaction. In addition, we

TABLE 4

Medical Outpatients:
Relationship Between
Change in Life Purpose and
Satisfaction and Core Spiritual Experiences*

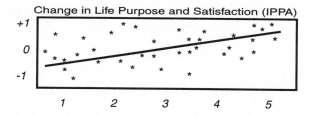

Change in Life Purpose and Satisfaction (IPPA)

Core Spiritual Experiences
(INSPIRIT)

*Forward step-wise multiple regression analysis controlling for demographic data.
N=72
B=.15, p=.02

TABLE 5

Medical Outpatients:

Relationship Between
Change in Frequency of
Stress-Related Medical Symptoms
and Core Spiritual Experiences*

Change in Average Frequency of Symptoms (MSCL)

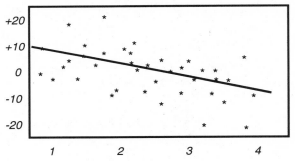

Core Spiritual Experiences (INSPIRIT)

*Forward step-wise multiple regression analysis controlling for demographic data.
N=53
B=.31, p=.005

have tested to see if the occurrence of core spiritual experiences are correlated with psychotic or obsessive-compulsive symptoms, as psychoanalytic theory has suggested, or with intolerance of ambiguity, as some sociological theory would suggest. No such correlations were found in this population.

In summary, within samples of divinity school students and medical outpatients, we are finding that core spiritual experiences do occur. These experiences are not associated with psychological disturbance. On the contrary, these experiences are associated with the presence of life purpose and satisfaction. In addition, it seems that these experiences can contribute to the stress-related aspects of physical health.

Can we facilitate core spiritual experiences?

These studies would be less noteworthy from the viewpoint of primary preventive care if we were not also learning to identify processes that facilitate these experiences. These processes are not "quick-fix" methods. They require time and disciplined, supervised practice. But it is increasingly clear that spiritual practices which help the individual to develop an internally-focussed perceptual orientation increase the likelihood that core spiritual experiences will take place (Kass, 1991). This can be seen in EEG data which suggest that as internally-focussed states of consciousness lower the frequency of electrical impulses within the brain, qualitative changes in personal experience take place. These frequency patterns are not direct correlates or guarantees of specific psychological states; however, a pattern can be discerned in which an internally-focussed perceptual orientation reduces arousal, increases feelings of peacefulness, increases internal imagery and intuitive modes of learning, and increases the likelihood of experiences of the spiritual core (Table 6).These findings were corroborated in the outpatient study described above where we found a positive relationship between length of time meditating and core spiritual experiences (Kass *et al.*, 1991). They were also corroborated by a study I conducted using graduate students in psychology. This study used the students' baseline scores for a 2-week period on the Hood Mysticism Scale as a self-control. The students were then assigned to practice meditation within a spiritual tradition of their choice on a daily basis, after two weeks, paired independent T-tests showed that mysticism scores had increased significantly (Kass & Price, 1991).

TABLE 6

Effect of Internally-Focused Perceptual Orientation (IFPO)
on Electrical Activity of the Brain and
Phenomenology of Consciousness
(During Meditation)

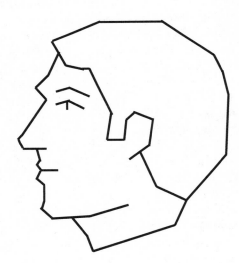

Externally-focused
perceptual orientation:
arousal and anxiety

Initial IFPO: reduced
arousal and increased
peacefulness

Intermediate IFPO:
intuitive processes and
hypnagogic imagery

Deep IFPO: transpersonal
experiences (experiences of
spiritual core)

Beta   13-26 cps
Alpha 8-12 cps
Theta 4-7 cps
Delta 0-3 cps

In conclusion, these studies suggest that core spiritual experiences may be a natural capacity of the human organism. Further, these experiences seem to contribute.to psychological and physical health. From the methodological viewpoint, a note of caution should be added. More rigorous testing of this hypothesis is required before we can claim solid conclusions. But in an era when the prevention of stress has become an important goal, these studies offer strong exploratory evidence that the utilization of this potential resource should be studied more fully. Stated more strongly, these studies suggest that our culture's failure to recognize the value of an internally-focussed perceptual orientation may be denying many individuals an important health-promoting resource: the experience of our spiritual core.

REFERENCES

Allport, G., & Ross, J. (1967). Personal religious orientation and prejudice. *Journal of Personality and Social Psychology.* 5(4), 432-443.

Beck, A., & Emery, G. (1985). *Anxiety disorders and Phobias: a cognitive perspective.* New York: Basic Books.

Benson, H. (1975). *The relaxation response.* New York: Morrow.

Berger, P., & Luckmann, T. (1966). *The social construction of reality.* Garden City, New York: Doubleday.

Bowen, M., Justyn, J., Kass, J., Miller, M., Rogers, C., Rogers, N., & Wood, J. (1978). Evolving aspects of person-centered workshops. *Self and Society* (Great Britain) 6(2), 43-49.

Buber, M. (1970). *I and thou.* New York: Scribners.

Davidson, J. (1976). The physiology of meditation and mystical states of consciousness. *Perspectives in Biology and Medicine, Spring 19,* 345-379.

Gatchel, R., Baum, A. (1983). *An introduction to health psychology.* Reading, Ma.: Addison-Wesley.

Greeley, A. (1974). *Ecstasy: a way of knowing.* Englewood Cliffs, New Jersey: Prentice-Hall.

Hay, D., & Morisey, A. (1978). Reports of ecstatic, paranormal, or religious experiences in Great Britain and the United States--A comparison of trends. *Journal for the Scientific Study of Religion.* 17(3), 255-268.

Hood, R., Jr. (1975). The construction and preliminary validation of a measure of reported mystical experience. *Journal for the Scientific Study of Religion, 14*(1), 29-41.

Hood, R. Jr., Hall, J., Watson, P.J., & Biderman, M. (1979). Personality correlates of the report of mystical experience. *Psychological Reports, 44*(3), 804-806.

Kass, J. (1983). *Effects of meditative practices and spiritual experiences on psychological development: observations and preliminary hypotheses from field research.* Seminar presentation, Tenth Annual Colloquium, Institute for the Arts and Human Development, Lesley College Graduate School.

Kass, J. (1991). *Integrating spirituality into personality theory and counseling practice.* Paper presented to the American Association for Counseling and Development, Reno, Nevada, April 22, 1991.

Kass, J., Friedman, R., Leserman, J., Zuttermeister, P., & Benson, H. (1991). Health outcomes and a new measure of spiritual experience. *Journal for the Scientific Study of Religion, 30*(2), 203-211.

Kass, J., Burton, L., Ferranti, L., & Davis, F. (1991). Relationships between core spiritual experience and life purpose among divinity students: further validation of the index of core spiritual experience. Manuscript in preparation.

Kass, J., & Price, C. (1991). Relationship of mystical experience to an internally focussed perceptual orientation. Manuscript in preparation.

Murphy, M., Donovan, S. (1988). *The Physical and physiological effects of meditation.* San Rafael, Ca: Esalen Institute.

Rogers, C.R. (1961) *On becoming a person.* Boston: Houghton-Mifflin.

Rogers, C.R. (1980). *A way of being.* Boston: Houghton Mifflin.

Thomas, L., & Cooper, P. (1978). Measurement and incidence of mystical experiences: an exploratory study. *Journal for the Scientific Study of Religion, 17*(4), 433-437.

Tillich, P. (1952). *The courage to be.* New Haven: Yale University Press.

EDITOR'S COMMENTS

This article is a shortened, less statistical version of material published in *The Journal for the Scientific Study of Religion* (See Kass, 1991 in the references). From that more detailed account, it becomes clear that this is a strong study, in part, because it uses a pretest-intervention-posttest design.

In this way, the researcher knows baseline scores and these can be compared to scores created after the intervention, in this case learning the relaxation response. This is one of very few, if any, studies which uses this strong, time-consuming design. I have addressed design concerns in previous Comments, but this is opportunity to note that the classic text concerning research designs is Campbell and Stanley (1963). Readers who are interested in such concerns should consult it or other publications authored by them. It spells out the strengths and weaknesses of 16 designs and, while it may be too advanced for beginning students, provides both an overview and details of various approaches. A relevant text for the pastoral researcher is *Research in Pastoral Care and Counseling: quantitative and qualitative approaches* (1994).

This study is important for two other reasons. First, it demonstrates in its own way, as do other studies in this volume, that those persons who possess religious/spiritual resources (here described as "core spiritual experiences") create more positive outcomes. In this instance, patients who "entered these programs having (such resources) showed higher increases in life purpose and satisfaction... as well as greater decreases in the frequency of stress related medical symptoms."

The additional reason this study is important lies in its introduction of the INSPIRIT instrument. Its statistical characteristics are further described in the *Journal for the Scientific Study of Religion* report. The advantage of this scale is its attention to spiritual "experience" whereas many other instrument gather data concerning religious behaviors (*i.e.* church attendance, prayer), beliefs (*i.e.* orthodoxy scales), or attitudes. The respondent's description of their experiences may be better indicators of spiritual resources than behaviors, beliefs, or attitudes because it may be less "socially desirable" to report such experiences.

REFERENCES

Campbell D., Stanley, J. (1963). *Experimental and Quasi-experimental Designs for Research.* Chicago: Rand McNally College Publishing Co.

VandeCreek, L., Bender, H., Jordan, M. (1994). *Research in Pastoral Care and Counseling: Quantitative and Qualitative Approaches.* Decatur: Journal of Pastoral Care Publishers, Inc.

15

Spiritual Well-Being, Religiousness and Hope Among Women With Breast Cancer

Jacqueline R. Mickley
Karen Soeken
Anne Belcher

ABSTRACT

The purpose of this study was to clarify spiritual health by examining the role of spiritual well-being (SWB), religiousness and hope in spiritual health. This was accomplished by obtaining questionnaire information from a convenience sample of 175 women diagnosed with breast cancer. Patients classified as intrinsically religious were found to have significantly higher scores on SWB than did those classified as extrinsically religious. There was no difference in hope scores between intrinsically religious and extrinsically religious patients, although hope was positively correlated with SWB. Existential well-being, a component of SWB, was the primary contributor of hope. The two major prognostic variables, stage of disease at diagnosis and number of positive lymph nodes, did not predict any of the scores.

Although nurses have considered spiritual health as an important component of the total health of an individual, what it means to be spiritually healthy has not been conceptually clarified. For example, how is spiritual health related to religion? What is the relationship

Reproduced with permission of the International Honor Society of Nursing from *IMAGE: Journal Of Nursing Scholarship*, (1992), 24(4), 267-272.

between spiritual health and psychological health? What role does spiritual health play in the coping responses of patients to devastating physical illness? Answers to these questions are necessary for nurses to promote spiritual health in clients.

REVIEW OF LITERATURE

There is little available research that examines spiritual health. What is available focuses primarily on spiritual well-being and religiousness. Both of these concepts have been implicated in health. The literature suggests that spiritual well-being and religiousness are conceptually linked. But are they the same? A review of current literature examines the similarities and differences between spiritual well-being and religiousness and the rationale for selecting hope as the psychological variable in the present study.

Spiritual Well-Being

Spiritual well-being (SWB) has been the most clearly described indicator of spiritual health. SWB can be described as the behavioral expression or helpful approximation of the state of spiritual health (Ellison, 1983; Stoll, 1989). Vaughan (1986) describes SWB as characterized by "a sense of inner peace, compassion for others, reverence for life, gratitude and appreciation of both unity and diversity" (pp. 20-21). Indicators of SWB may include a satisfying philosophy of life, supportive relationships with other people, realistic orientations toward loss and deprivation, wholesome self-concepts and ethical conduct (Moberg, 1974). It is important to note that the behavioral expressions of spiritual well-being are through emotional and physical means (Stoll, 1989).

SWB is most frequently described as being multidimensional. The two most frequently cited dimensions include the existential and the religious. The existential focuses on purpose and meaning in life. The religious concerns, clearly overlapping with religiousness, focus on a relationship with God. As used here, SWB is defined as the affirmation and satisfaction with life and a relationship with God, as well as the perception that one's life has meaning.

Paloutzian and Ellison (1982) designed the spiritual well-being scale to address the spiritual dimensions of subjective well-being. It includes a measure of religious well-being (RWB) that focuses on one's relationship to God, and a measure of existential well-being (EWB) that focuses on life purpose and satisfaction. Examples of items that target existential well-being are: "I believe there is some real purpose for my life" and "I feel that life is a positive experience."

SWB and its subscales, RWB and EWB, are positively correlated with several indicators of well-being including self-esteem, assertiveness and finding meaning and purpose in life. In addition, SWB was shown to be negatively correlated with loneliness and depression (Bufford, Paloutzian & Ellison, 1991; Ellison, 1983; Fehring, Brennan & Keller, 1987). However, there are little empirical data concerning SWB in samples of ill persons. Miller (1985) found an inverse relationship between SWB and loneliness in 64 chronically ill adults with rheumatoid arthritis and 64 randomly selected healthy adults. There was no significant difference between the ill and healthy group on EWB scores but the ill group had significantly higher RWB scores.

Religiousness

Until the 1960s, religiousness was narrowly defined by association or attendance in institutional terms. Today, religiousness is usually viewed as much broader in scope providing both general and multidimensional measures. In this paper, religiousness is defined as the personal meaning that individuals attach to a particular system of beliefs, values, rules of conduct and rituals.

One useful conceptualization of religiousness has been provided by Allport (1967) who described two different types of orientation to religion, intrinsic and extrinsic. People with an intrinsic religious orientation endeavor to internalize a religious creed and follow it fully; religion becomes a master motive in their lives. Those with an extrinsic religious orientation tend to regard religion in a utilitarian manner, *i.e.* to provide security or sociability. While individuals have both intrinsic and extrinsic dispositions, they usually lean in one direction or another. According to Allport, psychological health and religiousness are related in profound ways. He predicts that people of any faith who are intrinsic in the interpretation and living of their faith should be more psychologically healthy than those who use faith in a utilitarian fashion.

When intrinsic religiousness is compared to extrinsic religiousness, a pattern emerges that is basically consistent with Allport's theory. Several studies have shown that intrinsic religiousness is negatively correlated and/or extrinsic religiousness is positively correlated with anxiety and fear of death (Donahue, 1985). Although a majority of studies conclude that intrinsically oriented persons are psychologically more healthy than those extrinsically oriented, these generalizations do not always hold true. For example, Nelson (1989) reported a positive correlation between depression and intrinsic orientation in a sample of black and while elderly. Although black group members were more intrinsically oriented than whites, they also scored higher on the Geriatric Depression Scale. Thus, a more complex association between religious orientation and psychological health is suggested.

Religiousness may be an important aspect of a person's social, psychological and physical health. Several nursing studies have examined religious variables in cancer patients. Religious belief was often found to be a prominent factor in coping with the disease (Brandt, 1987; Herth, 1989; Northouse, 1989). These studies did not differentiate between subjects who were religiously intrinsic or extrinsic. However, based on Allport's theory, it seems logical to ask: (1) is the use of religion as a positive coping response a reflection of intrinsic religiousness; and (2) is this another expression of SWB? One can see similarity between intrinsic items from the Feagin Religiousness Scale ("Religion is especially important to me because it answers many questions about the meaning of life" and "It is important to me to spend periods of time in private religious thought and meditation") and items from the SWB scale ("I have a personally meaningful relationship with God" and "I feel most fulfilled when I'm in close communion with God.")

Hope

In addition to the conceptual overlap between spiritual well-being and religiousness which interferes with a concise description of spiritual health, another important issue confounding the description of spiritual health is how it relates to psychological health. The differences between the spiritual dimension and the psychological dimension of humans have been described theoretically (Hiatt, 1986; Piepgras, 1968; Vastyan, 1986). However, the behavioral expressions of the spiritual and psychological dimensions can be very similar. For example, an individual who is experiencing spiritual joy may express it through laughter, smiles and a general feeling of well-being. It would be extremely difficult to tease out whether the antecedent of these behaviors was spiritual or psychological health. Consequently, there is little empirical evidence to support the theoretical differences between spiritual and psychological health.

The psychological variable hope was chosen to study for several reasons. For the purpose of this research, hope is defined to mean a multidimensional dynamic attribute of an individual which includes the dimensions of possibility and confidence in a future outcome, active involvement which comes from within, relations with others and spiritual beliefs. This definition illustrates both the secular as well as the religious aspects of hope which conceptually links hope to both SWB and religiousness. Ellison (1983) views hope as an integral part of SWB that would help enable a person to find purpose and meaning beyond the immediate situation and to relate positively to God. Thus, hope can address secular concerns such as future plans and relationships with others, as well as religious concerns of an afterlife and a relationship with God or a higher power.

Second, hope has vast implications for how one copes with illness. Several authors, looking at hope in cancer patients, have identified hope as both a spiritual and psychological concern for these patients. Many of these studies have used cancer patients as their target population (Brandt, 1987; Dufault, 1981; Herth, 1989; Owen, 1989). Developing a preservation of hope can maximize psychological adjustment and can fortify both psychological and physiological defenses (McGee, 1984; Owen, 1989). Conversely, the loss of hope may prevent a person from accepting the diagnosis, complying with treatment or planning for the future (Owen, 1989).

The relationship between SWB and hope has been examined in two samples: baccalaureate nursing students (Carson, Soeken & Grimm, 1988) and HIV+ males (Carson, Soeken, Shanty & Terry, 1990). In both groups hope was correlated significantly with SWB. Also, in both groups the relationship between hope and EWB was significantly stronger than the relationship between hope and RWB. No studies were located that investigated the relationship between hope and religiousness. The present study is unique because it examines the relationship between the three variables, SWB, hope, and religiousness, in a group of ill adults.

METHODS

Subjects

Women with breast cancer were chosen as the target population for this study to adequately address all three variables of SWB, religiousness and hope. To date, SWB has not been described in cancer patients. The number of men with breast cancer is so small as to preclude adequate sample size.

The study was conducted at two outpatient oncology treatment centers in Texas using convenience sampling. Sample selection criteria included: age 21 or older, English literate, physically and mentally able to participate by answering the questionnaire and a confirmed diagnosis of breast cancer. At the time of recruitment subjects ranged from Stage 1 through Stage 4 disease. In general, Stage I disease involves a primary tumor with no regional lymph node metastasis and no distant metastasis. Stage II and III involve varying lymph node metastasis while Stage IV disease involves both regional lymph node and distant metastasis (Beahrs, Hensen, Hutter & Myers, 1988).

Instruments

In addition to demographic and medical data, the questionnaire included three scales: the Spiritual Well-Being Scale (Ellison, 1983), Feagin's Intrinsic/Extrinsic Religiousness Scale (Feagin, 1964) and the Nowotny Hope Scale (Nowotny, 1989).

The Spiritual Well-Being Scale consists of 20 items presented in a Likert-type format with six response options ranging from strongly agree to strongly disagree. The scale yields three scores; a total scale score (SWB), a score for religious well-being (RWB) and a score for existential well-being (EWB). The religious and existential subscales each contain 10 items.

Test-retest reliability using a student sample was .86 and above; internal consistency as measured by coefficient alpha was .78 and above (Ellison, 1983; Paloutzian & Ellison, 1982). Coefficient alpha for the total SWB score and for the RWB and EWB subscales for the present sample was .91, .92, and .84 respectively.

Assessments of criterion validity have included a negative correlation with the UCLA Loneliness Scale and positive correlation with the Purpose in Life Test and a measure of self esteem (Ellison, 1983). Norms have also been published for the scale (Bufford *et al.*, 1991).

The Feagin Intrinsic/Extrinsic Religiousness Scale was used to measure religiousness. This scale, derived from the Religious Orientation Scale developed by Allport and Ross (1967), consists of 12 items divided into two subscales confirmed through factor analysis that measure intrinsic and extrinsic religious orientation using a Likert five-point response format. Item-to-scale correlations have been .54 to .71 for intrinsic religiousness and .48 and .68 for extrinsic religiousness (Feagin, 1964). The alpha coefficients for intrinsic religiousness and extrinsic religiousness for the data in the current study were .80 and .79 respectively.

The Nowotny Hope Scale contains 29 items on six subscales resulting from factor analysis: confidence in the outcome, relates to others, possibility of a future, spiritual beliefs, active involvement and comes from within. The scale uses a four-point Likert format with a high score indicating a high level of hope. Content validity was established in that items were based on a literature review and on other nurses' and the author's clinical experience. In addition, a panel of six experts on hope reviewed the items and subscales. Concurrent validity was established through correlation with the Beck Hopelessness Scale ($r=-.47, p<.001$). Reliability using Cronbach's alpha was .90 in a sample of 306 subjects that included both well adults ($n=156$) and adults with cancer ($n=150$) (Nowotny, 1989). Coefficient alpha for the current study was .90.

Procedure

Written approval for the project was obtained from each clinic and the university review committees. Results of a pilot study with 27 subjects were used to establish initial reliability estimates for the intended sample, assess any changes necessary in procedure and test for any differences related to the order of the presentation of scales.

A list of patients who met the selection criteria was obtained from the clinic staff. Each patient was given a cover letter that explained the purpose and procedures of the study. Those subjects who expressed interest in participating signed and received a copy of a consent form before completing the questionnaire. Questionnaires were distributed in the clinics by the first author and occasionally by the charge nurses. A written script was used to field commonly asked questions. The respondent could complete the questionnaire either in the clinic or at home, returning it by mail.

Medical information collected included the following: date of diagnosis, stage of disease at diagnosis, present stage, type of surgery, number of positive lymph nodes at surgery, adjuvant therapy, whether the subject was pre- or post-menopausal at diagnosis and other health problems. The investigator collected all medical data from medical records except menopausal status which was supplied by the subjects.

RESULTS

Demographic Variables

The total sample consisted of 175 women ranging in age from 29 to 89 years (M=58.70; SD=12.6) with a majority of the women aged 50 through 69 years (57.2 percent). Over two-thirds (108) had schooling beyond high school. Most of the women were Anglo-Americans (n=141, 80.6 percent) and married (n=108; 61.7 percent). Of the participants, 99 (56.6 percent) were Protestant, and 56 (32 percent) were Roman Catholic with only 9 (5.1 percent) stating no religious preference.

One woman (0.6 percent) had Stage 0 disease, 44 (25.1 percent) had Stage I disease, 85 (48.6 percent) had Stage II disease, 21 (12 percent) had Stage III disease and 16 (9.1 percent) had Stage IV disease at time of diagnosis. The stage was not recorded for 8 (4.6 percent) of the women. Approximately 33 percent of the sample were within one year of diagnosis at the time of the study. Most of the subjects (n=141; 80.6 percent) had undergone a modified radical mastectomy, 10 (5.7 percent) did not have surgery and the rest (n=24; 13.7 percent) had other types of breast surgery.

At surgery, most subjects (74 percent) had between 0 and 4 positive lymph nodes. All patients who received adjuvant therapy had chemotherapy, radiation therapy or hormonal therapy either alone or in combination. Only five of the women did not receive any adjuvant treatment. A majority of the women (n=120; 68.6 percent) reported no other major health problems. The rest reported currently receiving treatment for conditions such as diabetes, arthritis, or cardiac problems.

Spiritual Well-Being, Religiousness and Hope

Means, medians and standard deviations for the scales are presented in Table 1. The means for SWB, RWB, and EWB are all above scale midpoint suggesting an overall positive level of SWB for the sample. A mean of 95.4 on the hope scale indicates an overall hopeful level of the sample according to M. L. Nototny (Personal communication, April 26, 1989).

TABLE 1
Mean, Standard Deviation and Median
for Spiritual Well-Being, Intrinsic Religiousness,
Extrinsic Religiousness and Hope

Scale	Mean	Standard Deviation	Median
Spiritual Well-Being	99.8	15.19	103
Religious Well-Being	50.8	10.19	54
Existential Well-Being	49.1	7.57	50
Intrinsic Religiousness	23.5	5.17	24
Extrinsic Religiousness	20.6	5.07	21
Hope	95.4	9.72	95

Using the theoretical midpoints of the two religiousness scales, subjects were categorized as intrinsic (high on intrinsic, low on extrinsic), extrinsic (high on extrinsic, low on intrinsic), indiscriminate (high on both scales), or nonreligious (low on both scales) (Donahue, 1985). A second categorization used the median split procedure. Because consistent results were found using both methods, results are presented here based on the median split. Women categorized as intrinsically religious (n=41) tended to have higher SWB (t=4.73, p<.001) as well as RWB (t=3.83,p<.001) and EWB (t=3.56,p<.001) scores than women categorized as extrinsically religious (n=27).

Using a paired t-test, it was determined that women categorized as intrinsically religious had higher RWB scores than EWB scores (t=4.49, df=40, p<.001). Thus, women in this sample who were intrinsically religious not only had higher spiritual well-being, but the religious component, i.e., one's relationship with God, was more important to their spiritual well-being. In contrast, women who were intrinsically religious did not have higher hope scores than women who were extrinsically religious (t=1.94,p>.05).

Hope, however, was positively correlated with intrinsic religiousness (r=.363, p<.001) but not correlated with extrinsic religiousness using the entire sample. Hope was also positively related to SWB (r=661,p<.001) as well as its components RWB (r=.443,p<.001) and EWB (r=.732,p<.001). Thus women who reported higher levels of hope also tended to have higher levels of SWB, both religious and existential.

To further explore the relationship between SWB and hope, multiple regression analyses were conducted with hope as the criterion variable. First, the components of SWB (RWB and EWB) were used as predictor variables. Then for each of the remaining analyses, a set of variables (religiousness, demographic characteristics, prognostic indicators, and treatment variables) was entered along with SWB (Table 2). Using only RWB and EWB as predictors, 54.9 percent of the variability in hope was explained (F=97.84; df=2, 172;p<.001). However, EWB uniquely accounted for 53.6 percent of the variance in hope.

TABLE 2

Multiple Regression Results for Hope Scores with Sets of Variables as Predictor Variables

Predictor Set	Total # of Variables	R^2	F
EWB & RWB	2	.549	97.84*
EWB, RWB & Religious Variables	4	.556	49.73*
EWB, RWB & Demographic Variables	7	.563	24.32*
EWB, RWB & Prognostic Variables	7	.615	29.66*
EWB, RWB & Treatment variables	6	.575	30.60*

Note: *p<.001

When other sets of variables were entered in addition to EWB and RWB, the set of prognostic variables produced the largest increase in explained variance, from 54.9 percent to 61.5 percent. The treatment variables set was the only other set to significantly increase the explained variance from 54.90 percent for EWB and RWB alone to 57.5 percent (F for change= 5.72, df=7, 167, p<.01). When the individual variables in each set were examined, EWB was found to be a consistently significant predictor of hope. In addition, age and date of diagnosis in the prognostic indicator set were significant.

Last, all variables were entered into the multiple regression analysis in blocks using a hierarchial entry with time ordering determining the order of entry (Table 3).

TABLE 3
Multiple Regression Results for Hope Scores
Using Hierarchial Entry with
Demographic Variables, Medical Variables, Religious Variables
and Spiritual Well-Being as Predictors

Block	R^2	F	Variables	Final Beta
1	.079	1.484	Age	-.252
			Race	.344
			Income	.096
			Marital Status	-.142
2	.123	0.848	Surgery Type	.061
			Data Of Diagnosis	.087
			No. of +Lymph Nodes	-.072
			Health Problems	.076
			Stage At Diagnosis	-.011
			Adjuvant Therapy	-.036
			Menopausal Status	.081
3	.283	2.028	Intrinsic Religious	.105
			Extrinsic Religious	.105
4	.567	5.778*	RWB	.037
			EWB	.609*

Note: *$p<.001$

When the demographic, medical (prognostic and treatment variables) and religious variables were controlled, an additional 28.38 percent of the variability in hope was accounted for by RWB and EWB, a significant increase ($F=51.4$; $df=2$, 157;;$p<.001$). However, EWB was the only significant variable ($p<.001$). Thus, there does not appear to be a direct relationship between age and hope, religiousness and hope, or date of diagnosis and hope.

Additional Analysis

Several additional analyses were performed to determine the relationships between the demographic and medical variables on the scores. Older women in this sample had significantly lower hope and SWB scores (r=-.253,p<.001 and r=-.131,p<.05, respectively). As age increased scores tended to be lower on RWB and EWB and, as noted earlier, lower on intrinsic religiousness but higher on extrinsic religiousness.

Both education and income were negatively correlated with extrinsic religiousness (r=-.348, p<.001 and r=-.439,p<.001, respectively). Also income was positively correlated with EWB (r=.173, p<.05) and negatively correlated with intrinsic religiousness (r=-.154,p<.05). The correlation between education and income was r=.505 (p<.001). These results were consistent with another report that older adults, the less well educated (high school or less), and those with lower income are more likely than others to state that religion is very important to them (Religious Education Association, 1987).

DISCUSSION

The original questions posed in this study were: (1) How is spiritual health related to religion?, (2) What is the relationship between spiritual health and psychological health?, and (3) What role does spiritual health play in the coping responses of patients to devastating physical illness?

The fact that intrinsically religious women scored higher on SWB than extrinsically religious women is consistent with the work of Allport (1950, 1967) who has described religiousness as one reflection of a healthy personality. Religiousness may help people create meaning and coherence in the world. It follows that those whose orientation is intrinsic should score higher than those extrinsically oriented on religious well-being since a relationship with God is described as being important by its own right and helps provide purpose and meaning in life. If religiousness is important to the patient, the nurse can plan interventions to allow religious expression. For a majority of women, religiousness was important in some aspects of their lives. However, for some of the women religiousness was not salient. Asking the patient about the role of religion and God in her life can be an important initial nursing assessment question.

In this study there was a positive relationship between SWB and hope, primarily due to EWB. Any effects of age, medical variables or religious variables on hope appear to be through SWB. In addition, medical variables were not significantly related to SWB, religiousness or hope. Women who had a poorer prognosis were not necessarily less spiritually or psychologically well. In other words, physical health was independent of SWB and hope in this sample. The idea that physical health and spiritual health are not necessarily correlated has been supported theoretically (Frankl, 1963; Glueck, 1988) and warrants further empirical verification.

The identified relationship between hope and SWB, especially EWB, has several implications for nursing. First, nurses may help patients explore the meaning of illness and what can be learned from the experience. Helping patients and families find meaning in pain and suffering is sometimes described as one of the primary goals of nursing practice (Travelbee, 1971). Several patients wrote that their relationship with others were "seen in a new light" or that they "learned to take one day at a time" as a result of having cancer.

Finally, what role does spiritual health play in the coping responses of patients to devastating physical illness? Since hope and SWB are positively related, SWB may be important to coping responses. Carson et al. (1988) emphasize that nursing interventions that foster hope should also foster SWB and vice versa. Maintaining social support networks and religious beliefs are two strategies that may foster hope (Farran and McCann, 1989). Structuring the environment to allow such things as church member visitation or group prayer may facilitate both social support and religiousness. Although some nurses are uncomfortable addressing religious issues, most nurses are able to listen, accept and explore patient questions about existential concerns and can address the secular aspects of promoting hope in their patients. It must be emphasized that it is not usually considered helpful for the nurse to give patients answers but rather to allow patients to discover their own meanings and their own reasons for believing what they do (Burnard, 1987).

There was no difference between the hope scores of intrinsically religious women and extrinsically religious women in this sample. This finding would seem to contradict Allport's assertion that extrinsic religiousness may hinder healthy psychological responses. Religiousness is important in both intrinsic and extrinsic orientations. However, extrinsically oriented women accept religiousness as part of their lives, not the focus of their lives. Thus, these women may have viewed religiousness in a functional sense. That is, religiousness may have met some personal needs of sociability, status, and protection.

A recent nursing study helps illustrate this interpretation. Northouse (1989) examined factors that helped both women and their husbands cope with mastectomy. The importance of religious beliefs was the second most frequent factor listed while the women were in the hospital. However, one month later, emotional support, attitude, information, distraction and tangible aid were all listed more frequently than religious beliefs as coping factors. The women may have been using religiousness in a functional manner, *i.e.*, something to help them cope. Similarly, the women categorized as extrinsic in the present study may have viewed religiousness in a functional sense resulting in high levels of hope.

There are several implications for further research on spiritual health. Because this study was cross sectional, age-related, and developmental issues that may affect SWB, religiousness, and hope over time could not be assessed. Similarly, crisis and illness may also affect these variables over time. Finally gender differences were not explored in this study. The possibility that men and women experience spiritual health differently and may require different nursing interventions for spiritual distress requires empirical testing. By helping to clarify aspects of spiritual health, nurses may begin testing strategies that could help foster or increase spiritual health in clients.

REFERENCES

Allport, G.W. (1950). *The individual and his religion.* New York: Macmillan.

Allport, G. W. (1967). Behavioral science, religion and mental health. In D. Belgum (Ed.), *Religion and medicine: essays on meaning, values, and health,* 83-95. Ames, IA: Iowa State University Press.

Allport, G. W., Ross, J. M. (1967). Personal religious orientation and prejudice. *Journal of Personality and Social Psychology, 5,* 432-443.

Beahrs, O. H., Hensen, D. E., Hutter, R., Myers, H. H. (Eds). (1988).*Manual for staging of breast cancer* (3rd ed.). Philadelphia: J. B. Lippincott.

Brandt, B. T. (1987). The relationship between hopelessness and selected variables in women receiving chemotherapy for breast cancer. *Oncology Nursing Forum, 14*(2), 35-39.

Bufford, R. K., Paloutzian, R. F., Ellison, C. W. (1991). Norms for the spiritual well-being scale. *Journal of Psychology and Theology, 19,* 56-70.

Burnard, P. (1987). Spiritual distress and the nursing response: theoretical considerations and counseling skills. *Journal of Advanced Nursing, 12,* 377-382.

Carson, V., Soeken, K. L., Grimm, P. M. (1988). Hope and its relationship to spiritual well-being. *Journal of Psychology and Theology, 16,* 159-167.

Carson, V., Soeken, K.L., Shanty, J., Terry, L. (1990). Hope and spiritual well-being: essentials for living with AIDS. *Perspectives in Psychiatric Care, 26*(2), 28-34.

Donahue, M. J. (1985). Intrinsic and extrinsic religiousness: review and meta-analysis. *Journal of Personality and Social Psychology, 48,* 400-419.

Dufault, K. J. (1981). Hope of elderly persons with cancer. (Doctoral Dissertation, Case Western Reserve University). *Dissertation Abstracts International, 42,* 1820-B.

Ellison, C. W. (1983). Spiritual well-being: conceptualization and measurement. *Journal of Psychology and Theology, 11,* 330-340.

Farran, C. J., McCann, J. (1989). Longitudinal analysis of hope in community-base older adults. *Archives of Psychiatric Nursing, 3,* 293-300.

Feagin, J. R. (1964). Prejudice and religious types: A focused study of Southern fundamentalists. *Journal for the Scientific Study of Religion, 4,* 3-13.

Fehring, R. J., Brennan, P.R., Keller, M. (1987). Psychological and spiritual well-being in college students. *Research in Nursing and Health, 10,* 391-398.

Frankl, V. (1963). *Man's search for meaning.* Boston: Beacon Press.

Glueck, N. (1988). Religion and health: a theological reflection. *Journal of Religion and Health, 27,* 109-118.

Herth, K. A. (1989). The relationship between level of hope and level of coping response and other variables in patients with cancer. *Oncology Nursing Forum, 16*(1), 67-72.

Hiatt, J. F. (1986). Spirituality, medicine and healing. *Southern Medical Journal, 79,* 736-743.

McGee, R. F. (1984). Hope: a factor influencing crisis resolution. *Advances in Nursing Science, 6*(4), 34-44.

Miller, J. F. (1985). Assessment of loneliness and spiritual well-being in chronically ill and healthy adults. *Journal of Professional Nursing, 1,* 79-85.

Moberg, D. O. (1974). Spiritual well-being in late life. In J. F. Gubrium (Ed.), *Late Life: Communities and Environmental Policy,* 256-279, Springfield, Ill: Charles C. Thomas.

Nelson, P. B. (1989). Ethnic differences in intrinsic/extrinsic religious orientation and depression in the elderly. *Archives of Psychiatric Nursing, 3,* 199-204.

Northouse, L. L. (1989). The impact of breast cancer on patients and husbands. *Cancer Nursing, 12,* 276-284.

Nowotny, M. L. (1989). Assessment of hope in patients with cancer: development of an instrument. *Oncology Nursing Forum, 16*(1), 57-61.

Owen, D. C. (1989). Nurses' perspectives on the meaning of hope in patients with cancer: a qualitative study. *Oncology Nursing Forum, 16*(1), 75-79.

Paloutzian, R. F., Ellison, C. W. (1982). Loneliness, spiritual well-being and the quality of life. In L. A. Peplau And D. Perlman (Ed.), *Loneliness: A sourcebook of current theory, research and therapy,* 224-236, New York: John Wiley & Sons.

Piepgras, R. (1968). The other dimension: Spiritual help. *American Journal of Nursing, 68,* 2610-2613.

Religious Education Association of the United States and Canada. (1987). *Faith development in the adult life cycle: The report of a research project.* Mineapolis, MN: Author.

Stoll, R. I. (1989). The essence of spirituality. In V. B. Carson, *Spiritual dimensions of nursing practice,* 4-23, Philadelphia: W. B. Saunders.

Travelbee, J. (1971). *Interpersonal aspects of nursing*(2nd ed.). Philadelphia: F. A. Davis.

Vastyan, E. A. (1986). Spiritual aspects of the care of cancer patients. *CA-A Cancer Journal for Clinicians, 36,* 110-114.

Vaughan, F. (1986). *The inward arc: Healing and wholeness in psychotherapy and spirituality.* Boston: New Science Library.

16

Spiritual Well-Being: A Predictor of Hardiness in Patients with Acquired Immunodeficiency Syndrome

Verna Benner Carson
Harry Green

ABSTRACT

This study examined the relationship between spiritual well-being and hardiness in a group of 100 subjects who either tested positive for the human immunodeficiency virus (HIV+) or who had diagnoses of acquired immunodeficiency syndrome (AIDS)-related complex (ARC) or AIDS. Each subject completed the Spiritual Well-Being Scale, the Personal Views Survey (to measure hardiness), and a Demographic Data Survey. Analysis of data included Pearson Product Moment Correlation Coefficients and multiple regression techniques. The results demonstrated that there was a significant relationship between spiritual well-being and hardiness (multiple $R = .4165$; $p<.001$) as well as between the existential component of spiritual well-being and hardiness (multiple $R = .5047$; $p<.001$). The conclusions of the study are that in this sample those individuals who were spiritually well and who were able to find meaning and purpose in their lives were

Reproduced with permission of the W. B. Saunders Company from the *Journal of Professional Nursing*, (1992), 8 (4), 209-220.

also hardier. This finding has significance for the care that is provided to persons who are HIV+ or who have diagnoses of ARC or AIDS.

T he purpose of this study was to examine the relationship of spiritual well-being and selected demographic variables to hardiness in persons who tested positive for the human immunodeficiency virus (HIV+) or who had diagnoses of acquired immunodeficiency syndrome (AIDS)-related complex (ARC) or AIDS. The Spiritual Well-being (SWB) Scale was used to measure spiritual well-being and its components, religious (RWB) and existential well-being (EWB). Hardiness and its components, challenge, control, and commitment, were measured using the Personal Views Survey (PVS). Demographic variables were measured using the Demographic Data Survey.

Although there has been a great deal of research directed to discovery of the cure for AIDS, there has been much less emphasis on an examination of the relationship of spiritual and psychological factors to the well-being of persons who are either HIV+ or who have a diagnosis of ARC or AIDS (in the remainder of the article, this group will be referred to as PWA or person with AIDS). In this same population there is limited research on the relationship of selected demographic variables to indicators of spiritual and psychological health. This type of information is needed if more than physical concerns are addressed in the care of these individuals.

THE PROBLEM

In 1981, the American public became aware of a new and terrible disease. During that year the pattern of unexpected illness and deaths in the homosexual population was attributed to AIDS. However, before that, in the late 1970s, there had been hints that in relationship to health something was amiss in the homosexual community. There had been extraordinarily high numbers of sexually transmitted diseases, strange "fatigues," and general enteric, wasting disorders in previously healthy homosexual men. There were reports of lymphomas and other opportunistic infections that were not recognized as part of an emerging pattern. In 1981, the projected rate of increase for AIDS was a doubling of cases every six months (Kayal, 1985). Although this dire prediction has not held true, the numbers are still large. The Center for Disease Control reported that as of June 30, 1990, there had been 139,765 new cases of AIDS and 85,430 deaths. These figures do not include the estimated 1.5 to two million Americans who are asymptomatic and HIV+ (Maryland AIDS Update, 1990).

The survival rate for AIDS from time of diagnosis ranges from three to 18 months, although there is indication that the survival rate is extending due to the azidothymidine, an antiviral preparation, and pentamidine, a particularly effective antibiotic for treating AIDS-related pneumonia. In addition, there are many more drug treatments on the horizon that hold promise for extending the quantity and quality of life in the AIDS patient (Chaisson, 1990; Zurlo & Lane, 1990). In 1987, AIDS moved from the eighth to the seventh leading cause of years of potential life lost, meaning quite simply that AIDS is a major cause of death of young Americans (Maryland AIDS Update, 1990).

Despite intensive research since 1981, there has been no cure discovered for AIDS. The threat and severity of the disease has not lessened in the intervening years between 1981 and the present. It is still a terrible disease. The suffering it exacts on PWAs, on their families and support systems, and on the health workers who care for them is immeasurable (Abrams, Parker-Martin, & Unger, 1989; Bellemare, 1988; Bohne, 1986; Graydon, 1988; Schofferman, 1987; Tiblier, Walker, & Rolland, 1989; Wallack, 1989; Wendler, 1987). One demonstrable change that has occurred is in the demographics of the disease. Through the 1980s homosexual men were the primary risk group. Although they still comprise the bulk of AIDS cases, the present trend is toward increasing numbers of intravenous drug users, black and Hispanic heterosexual women who have been sexually involved with a bisexual and/or intravenous drug-abusing male, and the infants born to these women (Maryland AIDS Update, 1990).

The care of the PWA is difficult, personally demanding, and humbling. The dying process is not a gentle one but is characterized by repeated infections, debilitating diarrhea, wasting of once robust bodies, intermittent but soaring fevers, unrelenting fatigue, disfiguring lesions, and sometimes dementia. In a health care system focused on cure, the ultimate death of the PWA is a constant reminder that "we don't have all the answers" (Carson, 1990).

When curing is not possible and physical ministrations prove inadequate, care providers must shift their priority to caring. Such a shift requires a transformation of thinking for many, because the tools are no longer pharmacological preparations and miracles of medical technology but rather the use of self to communicate acceptance of the sufferer, provision of emotional support through the dying process, education about the disease and its course, exploration of ways to improve quality if not duration of life, and existential support as the sufferer struggles to find meaning and purpose in his or her life (Belcher, Dettmore, & Holzemer, 1989; Carson, 1989; Carson, in press; Carson, Soeken, Shanty, & Terry, 1990; Saynor, 1988). Caring, as described, contains both psychological and spiritual elements.

In an article written by Bernard Davzer (1988) exploring the long-term survival of some PWAs, he suggests that some PWAs have been able to change their attitudes towards the disease. Instead of viewing themselves as victims, they see themselves as survivors. The PWAs attributed this transformation to participation in spiritual activities. Behaviors such as engaging in prayer, imagery and visualization, and meditation were all identified as ways of fighting back and recommitting to a life that seemed threatened and vulnerable. These strategies have been identified as possible enhancements to the immune system (Solomon & Temoshok, 1987). Gavzer (1988) quotes one PWA as saying, "I stopped hating myself for being gay. I started deep meditation for two to three hours. I started praying to God. I began body building" (p.13). This person has survived since 1983 and attributes his survival to a spiritual reawakening. The qualities described by these survivors are also characteristic of hardiness, which includes viewing stress as a challenge, taking control, and making a commitment to fight back (Kobasa, 1979).

Additional anecdotal evidence points to the importance of spirituality to the PWA. The case of William Calderon is a perfect example. In December 1982, Calderon received a diagnosis of AIDS. He developed Kaposi's sarcoma lesions all over his body. He was told that at most he had six months to live. With this news, Calderon accepted the prognosis and began preparing for his own death. In his words, "It was as if I was programmed to die, I had no hope" (p.10).

Shortly after receiving the diagnosis, Calderon encountered a friend who told him that death was not inevitable, and that Calderon could take steps to change the prognosis. This friend introduced Calderon to a variety of techniques including imagery, eradicating negative emotions, improving nutrition, engaging in exercise, using humor, nurturing faith, and most important of all, developing an attitude of love in place of hostility. Calderon practiced these techniques. He also took the experimental drug interferon, which Calderon claimed almost killed him. Two years after his diagnosis (at the time the article was written), Calderon was living a full, happy, and apparently healthy life. His physician, Dr. Richard Shames, wrote in a report to Dr. Jean Shinoda Bolen (1985, p. 15),

> I have been following William Calderson's recent progress in dealing with his AIDS situation. As you know, he is pursuing a vigorous treatment program combining optimal nutrition, physical fitness, psychotherapy, and creative visualization. It is my medical opinion that he has by these means achieved a complete remission (the lesions of Kaposi's sarcoma that were extensive on various parts of his body and orifices are now completely gone). Also, he seems to be sustaining this progress with enjoyable career work and upbeat, positive thinking. I hope his example can help other AIDS victims.

The importance of spiritual issues to the PWA also is apparent in the wide variety of publications written by and for PWAs, including the Persons with AIDS Coalition newsletters that are published across the nation and Louise Hay's (1988) *The AIDS Book*. In each of these there are listing of spiritual healing groups and activities, personal testimonials about spiritual issues, and related articles. Readers are encouraged to become involved in AIDS education, research, and support of others. These publications extol the health-promoting benefits of spiritual activities such as prayer, meditation, visualization, imagery, participation in church activities and retreats, and reading religious and other uplifting literature.

As far as empirical evidence linking SWB and AIDS, there are only two published studies. The first, reported by Belcher, Dettmore, and Holzmer (1989), examined spiritual perspective and well-being. The researchers reported that PWAs experienced tremendous changes in their spiritual perspectives since the onset of AIDS. Many of the respondents viewed spirituality as a source of comfort and a way of understanding and ordering the AIDS experience. The second study examined the relationship between SWB and hope in a group of 66 subjects who were either HIV+ or who had diagnoses of ARC or AIDS (Carson, Soeken, Shanty, & Terry, 1990). The findings indicated that the subjects scored relatively high on both SWB and hope, and that hope was related more to the existential component of SWB than to the religious component.

What is really behind long-term survival? Is there something physically, emotionally, or spiritually different in the thousands of PWAs who are numbered in this surviving group? The answer to these questions could offer hope to thousands who feel they are losing the battle with AIDS.

There are probably many interactional factors that affect whether one PWA is more hardy or resilient than another. In fact, Solomon, Temoshok, and Zich (1987) strongly suggest that a complete understanding of AIDS must proceed from a biological, psychological, and social perspective. Consequently, they are including hardiness as the personality variable in a longitudinal study of long-term survival with AIDS. Lovejoy and Sisson (1989) go as far as to suggest that even if psychogenic factors do not cause AIDS, under certain circumstances psychogenic and physiological factors of the host interact to alter the progression of the disease from HIV+ to ARC and to full-blown AIDS. Cecchi (1981) asserts that certain aspects of a homosexual life-style, such as negative self-image, inability to express negative feelings, and a lack of community support, may produce immune deficiency. Vastyn (1986) suggests that the diagnosis of AIDS can precipitate a challenge that may lead some individuals to actively resist, while other passively give in to the disease.

The presence or absence of hardiness may be a critical factor in the long-term survival of PWAs. Hardiness is a personality characteristic touted by Kobasa (1979) as a resource in resisting the negative effects of stress, thus decreasing the incidence of severity of stress-related illnesses. Hardiness is a composite measure composed of the three subdimensions of commitment, challenge, and control. These dimensions moderate the effects of stress by altering the perception of the situation and by launching activities designed to eliminate or transform the stressor.

Although most of the research on hardiness has been done by Kobasa and here colleagues (Kobasa, 1979; Kobasa, Maddi, & Purcetti, 1982) using male executive samples, an intensive longitudinal, psychoimmunological study of PWAs surviving three, four, or five years after diagnosis with AIDS is also using Kobasa's Hardiness Scale (Solomon & Temoshok, 1987). The preliminary data, based on a very small sample size, seem to be partially consistent with Kobasa's predictions that a high level of hardiness correlates with better coping and longer survival. The researchers compared the self-report measures obtained two to eight weeks after the diagnosis of pneumocystis carinii pneumonia of men who had died (n=10) by follow-up with those who were still alive (n=11). The men in the favorable outcome group had scored significantly higher (P<.05) than did those in the unfavorable outcome group on Kobasa's control measure. The researchers urge caution in interpreting these results because of the small sample size and the number of univariate tests conducted. In addition, the groups were significantly different in terms of time from initial interview to follow-up. The favorable outcome group had only been in the study for 378.3 days compared with 481.5 days for the unfavorable outcome group. Therefore, causation cannot be assumed from the correlation. In addition, Kobasa's control measure is positively correlated (r= 0.56; p=.01) with the time of the initial interview, which means that subjects with a longer time in the study score lower on the control measure. No information was given related to the commitment and challenge subdimensions of the hardiness measure.

There is no published research examining the correlation between SWB and hardiness. However, in addition to the anecdotal and qualitative data that support a relationship, there are the results of an unpublished study conducted by Carson, Soeken, and Belcher (1991) that examined the relationships of SWB, ego strength, and hardiness among PWAs. This study demonstrated a significant relationship between hardiness and ego strength (r=. 645, P<.05). There was a significant correlation between the EWB subscale of the SWB scale and the commitment subscale of the hardiness instrument (r=.6029; P<.05). These findings support the hypothesis that PWAs who have stronger egos are hardier, and also that PWAs who are spiritually well are able to make commitments. The correlations between SWB, control, challenge, and the overall hardiness scores approached significance.

This present study was unique in its examination of the relationship of SWB and selected demographic variables in persons who were either HIV+ or who had a diagnosis of ARC or AIDS.

THEORETICAL BASIS AND BACKGROUND

This study was based theoretically on Viktor Frankl's understanding of the relationship between the spiritual concern of finding meaning in life and psychological health.

Viktor Frankl's (1955, 1963, 1967) theory and therapeutic interventions, which he referred to as logotherapy, grew out of his experiences as a prisoner in a Jewish concentration camp during World War II. Frankl's father, mother, brother, and wife died in the gas chambers. Except for his sister, his entire family perished. Stripped of all physical and emotional comforts, he lived in moment-to-moment fear of his own extermination. Yet, in the midst of such loss and suffering, he found life worth preserving. He observed that there were other prisoners who also found life meaningful even in the most bestial of conditions.

From these lived and vivid experiences, Frankl defined an existential theory that recognizes that human beings are not only physical and emotional in nature but also spiritual. He was the first psychiatrist to acknowledge, first of all, that spirituality was essential to psychological health, and second, that spirituality possesses a religious component and at the same time is a uniquely human quality. Frankl believed that the spiritual tasks of finding meaning and purpose in life comprise the core issues of existentialism. This position is elucidated in the following quote:

> ...to live is to suffer, to survive is to find meaning in the suffering. If there is a purpose in life at all, there must be a purpose in suffering and dying. But no man can tell another what this purpose is. Each must find out for himself, and must accept the responsibility that his answer prescribes. If he succeeds he will continue to grow in spite of all indignities. (1963, p.xi).

The theoretical position that individuals strive for meaning and that this meaning is linked to psychological health was the foundation for this study. Frankl (1963) believed that spiritual health led to psychological hardiness. The element of meaning is found in both SWB as well as hardiness.

The SWB Scale used in this study measures both the existential aspect of meaning in life as well as the religious aspect of meaning. Although Frankl was primarily concerned with the existential aspect of meaning, he acknowledged that both sources of meaning could lead to psychological health.

Therefore, the SWB Scale is a measure that is theoretically consistent with Frankl's writings. Furthermore, the SWB SCale has shown construct validity with the Purpose in Life (PIL) measure (Ellison & Paloutzian, 1982). The PIL, one of two measures developed by Crumbaugh and Maholick (1964), was intended to measure Frankl's construct of existential vacuum. The other measure, the Seeking of Noetic Goals Test (Crumbaugh, 1977), was developed to measure Frankl's concept of will to meaning.

Hardiness, the psychological characteristic being measured in this study, basically represents an existential striving to order and derive meaning out of the stresses of life. Hardiness, in its components of commitment, control, and challenge, also incorporates the element of responsibility so important to Frankl's theory.

It follows from Frankl's position that if an individual is spiritually well, characterized by an existential sense of a meaningful and valuable life, then hardiness, an aspect of psychological health, would also be present. The more spiritually well an individual is, then the expectation follows that the capacity to order and derive meaning out of the stresses of life would be greater.

METHODOLOGY

The design of this study was a survey to determine the extent to which variation in SWB and selected demographic variables was associated with variation in the construct of hardiness.

A nonprobabilistic sample of 100 subjects was obtained. In an attempt to obtain representative samples, three methods were employed to acquire an adequate number of individuals who were either HIV+ or who had a diagnosis of ARC or AIDS. These methods included soliciting subjects through a health care facility, through advertisements placed in *The Alternative* (a newspaper published in the Baltimore metropolitan area and designed to serve the needs of the homosexual and lesbian community), and through mailed surveys to the members of the Baltimore PWA Coalition.

Three instruments were used for data collection. These included the SWB SCale (Ellison & Paloutzian, 1982), the PVS (Hardiness Institute, Inc., 1985) and the Demographic Data Survey.

SWB Scale

This scale, developed by Ellison and Paloutzian (1982), is based on the definition of SWB developed by the National Interfaith Coalition on Aging in 1975 (p. 1): "Spiritual well-being is the affirmation of life in a relationship with God, self, community and environment that nurtures and celebrates wholeness." Ellison (1983) stated that the purpose of the tool is to provide a general measure of SWB without being limited by specific theological issues.

The scale has 20 items presented in a Likert-type format, with six response options that range from *strongly agree* to *strongly disagree*. There are 11 positively worded statements and nine negatively worded items to help control for response set difficulties. Reverse scoring is used for the negatively worded items.

Items are scored from one to six points. Total scores are obtained by summing across all items. The maximum possible score is 120; the minimum possible score is 20. Higher scores represent higher levels of SWB. No national norms have been established for the scale, although there is presently effort in this direction (Bufford, Paloutzian, & Ellison, in press).

The SWB scale has two subscales and thus yields three scores: (1) a total scale score, (2) a score for religious well-being (RWB), and (3) a score for EWB. Each of the subscales contains 10 items. Reported test-retest reliability with students was .86 and above. Coefficient alphas were also obtained with students; these were .78 and above (Ellison, 1983).

Correlations between the subscales were reported to range from .32 to .62, indicating that although the subscales are not independent, they are likely to measure the same overall concept. The correlation between the total score and RWB was .90; between the total score and EWB was .59. This indicated that most of the variance in total score is explained by the RWB subscale and the EWB subscale may contain more unexplained error (Ellison, 1983).

PVS

This questionnaire was used to measure hardiness (Hardiness Institute, Inc., 1985). This is the third generation of the hardiness scale developed by Kobasa. It is a shorter and more refined composite measure of the concept, which used 50 items. This refined measure has appeared adequate in terms of reliability and validity but has not been widely tested (Maddi, 1986). The PVS seems to be an attempt by Kobasa and her associates (Maddi, 1986) to respond to some of the measurement issues that have plagued the first two versions of the hardiness measure.

Only one published study has reported using the newest version of the hardiness measure (PVS). The researcher (Okun, Zautra, & Robinson, 1987) reported coefficient alphas for the hardiness, control, commitment, and challenge scales as 0.84, 0.70, 0.70, and .075 respectively. High scores on these measures were associated with greater hardiness.

The PVS also was used in an unpublished study conducted by Carson, Soeken, and Belcher (in press) examining SWB, hardiness, and ego strength in PWAs, the PVS was also used. Coefficient alphas were obtained for the total scale and each of the subscales. These values were: hardiness: (0.82), challenge: (0.62), commitment: (0.59), and control: (0.46).

The response options range from "0", not at all true, to "3", completely true. There are 17 challenge items, 16 commitment items, and 17 control items. To obtain individual subscale scores for challenge and control, the responses are summed over all relevant items for either challenge or control and divided by 51. To obtain a subscale score for commitment, the same procedure is followed except the number is divided by 48. To create a hardiness composite, the three ratio scores are added together, multiplied by 100, and then divided by three.

Demographic Data Survey

This survey was developed from a review of the literature that indicated that there might exist relationships between selected demographic variables and SWB and/or hardiness. The survey included questions related to age; gender; source of infection; length of time since diagnosis; perception of physical, emotional and spiritual health; participation in health-promoting, spiritual, and AIDS-related activities; religious affiliation; and whether the individual considered himself or herself to be religious.

Date Collection and Recording

The researcher distributed the Demographic Data Survey, the SWB Scale, and the PVS to subjects recruited at a large clinic that serves the homosexual population in Baltimore, MD. Surveys were also mailed to members of the Baltimore PWA Coalition. In addition, subjects were also recruited through an advertisement place in *The Alternative*.

Regardless of how the subject was recruited, certain procedures were carried out to standardize the collection of data. All subjects were given the informed consent form, which specified the purpose of the research, provided assurance of the anonymity and confidentiality of their responses, stated that participation would require approximately 30 minutes, and informed them of their right to participate or withdraw from the study at any time. Participants were not asked to sign an informed consent because the decision to participate was viewed as consent. Those who chose to participate were paid a $10 stipend for their time and effort. A stipend was offered to participants in recognition of two issues: (1) this is a very "researched" group and a small payment may act as an enticement to individuals who may be tired of participating in the research process, and (2) many PWAs suffer severe financial hardships due to the disease. They may be unable to engage in full-time employment and are faced with high medical expenses. The stipend may provide them with a small amount of discretionary money.

Data Analysis

Frequency analysis of the demographic variables was used to describe the sample. Multivariate correlational, regression techniques, bivariate correlations, and analyses of variance were used.

Results

In this study the coefficient alpha for SWB was 0.92, for RWB 0.93, and for EWB 0.85. For hardiness the coefficient alpha was 0.85, for challenge 0.72, for commitment 0.80, and for control 0.59.

Because subjects were obtained in three different ways, a one-way analysis of variance was run to determine whether the groups differed across demographic variables, SWB, and/or hardiness. There was no statistical difference among the three groups with respect to age, sex, diagnosis, source of infection, SWB, or hardiness. However, there was a significant difference in respect to time since diagnosis ($F=13.13$; $P<.05$). A Student-Newman-Keuls Test was done to determine which groups were significantly different. The group obtained from the PWA Coalition reported significantly longer times since diagnosis (mean =33 months) than either the clinic group (mean = 6.5 months) or the group obtained as a result of the advertisement (mean = 15.5 months).

Descriptive Data

The analysis of the descriptive data showed that the sample of 100 was predominately males (86 percent), with a mean age of 37.18 years. Forty-five were HIV+, 24 had a diagnosis of ARC, and 30 had a diagnosis of AIDS. The most frequent source of infection was homosexual activity (62 percent) with homosexual or bisexual activity accounting for 74 percent of the sample. Over half the subjects were within two years of diagnosis. The subjects perceived their physical and emotional health to be between fair and good. Spiritual health was perceived as good. Over half the subjects rated their participation in prayer, meditation, and the use of visualization or imagery with a mean score that indicated *somewhat* to *very much* participation, with prayer receiving the highest mean score. Attendance at spiritual retreats, reading religious literature, and attendance at church services were rated by over half the participants with a mean score that indicated *none* to *very little* participation.

Over half the participants engaged *somewhat* to *very much* in exercise and the use of vitamins and *none at all* to *very little* in the use of special diets. Over half the subjects rated their participation in AIDS-related activities with a mean score that indicated *somewhat* to *very much* participation, with offering support to other PWAs as being the most frequently cited of these behaviors.

Fifty-two subjects indicated that they belonged to an organized religion, although only 48 of these identified a specific faith. Forty-seven said they did not belong to an organized religion. Sixteen belonged to the Roman Catholic Church, 24 belonged to various Protestant denominations, three were Jewish, and five identified other faith traditions. Seventy percent perceived themselves to be *somewhat* to *very* religious.

HYPOTHESES

Two hypotheses were tested. The results for each are as follows:

Hypothesis 1: Persons who are either HIV+ or who have diagnoses of ARC or AIDS have a positive relationship between SWB and hardiness.

This hypothesis was analyzed using Pearson Product-Moment Correlation Coefficients and multiple regression. The correlations showed that SWB was significantly correlated with hardiness ($r=.417$; $P<.001$). In addition, each of the subscales of SWB, EWB ($r=.505$; $P<.001$), and RWB ($r=.247$; $P<.05$) were statistically correlated with hardiness. Differences in correlation coefficients were computed and demonstrated that the correlation of EWB and hardiness was significantly greater than that for RWB and hardiness ($t=2.458$; $P<.05$). Furthermore, SWB correlated significantly with each of the hardiness subscales. However, the correlations were not significantly different from one another (correlations with challenge and commitment were $t=1.39$; $P>.05$, and for challenge and control were $t=1.42$; $P>.05$). The means and standard deviations and the correlation matrix for these variables, as well as for the components of the SWB and hardiness scales, are shown in Tables 1 and 2.

TABLE 1
Mean and SD for SWB, EWB, RWB, Hardiness,
Challenge, Commitment, and Control

Variable	Mean	SD
SWB	88.23	19.18
EWB	43.70	9.72
RWB	44.53	12.48
Hardiness	67.52	11.70
Challenge	.57	.14
Commitment	.75	.15
Control	.72	.12

TABLE 2
Correlations between SWB, EWB, RWB, Existential Hardiness
Challenge, Commitment, and Control

	SWB	EWB	RWB	Hardiness	Challenge	Commitment	Control
SWB	1.0	.82 p=.00	.896 p=.00	.417 p=.00	.203 p=.022	.449 p=.00	.459 p=.00
EWB	.82 p=.00	1.0	.484 p=.00	.505 p=.00	.269 p=.003	.54 p=.00	.53 p=.00
RWB	.896 p=.00 p=.002	.484 p=.00	1.0	.247 p=.007	.101 p=.16	.27 p=.003	.29
Hardiness	.417 p=.00	.50 p=.00	.247 p=.007	1.0	.843 p=.00	.922 p=.00	.852 p=.00
Challenge	.203 p=.00	.269 p=.003	.101 p=.16	.843 p=.00	1.0	.64 p=.00	.54 p=.00
Commitment	.449 p=.00	.54 p=.00	.27 p=.16	.922 p=.00	.64 p=.00	1.0	.76 p=.00
Control	.459 p=.00	.53 p=.00	.29 p=.002	.852 p=.00	.54 p=.00	.76 p=.00	1.0

The variables of SWB, hardiness, and the three diagnosis groups were entered into a multiple regression equation, with hardiness as the dependent variable. The interaction of diagnosis and SWB also was entered. For this analysis, the diagnosis group was dummy-coded into two dichotomous variables, ARC and AIDS. When analyzed using hierarchical regression, SWB accounted for 17 percent (adj R = .165) of the variance in hardiness (F= 20.568; P<.0001). Diagnosis groups accounted for an additional 1.5 percent of the variance in hardiness (F=.845; P>.05). Entering the interaction of diagnosis group by SWB accounted for an additional 1.1 percent of the variance in hardiness (F=.401; P>.05). The results of this analysis showed that SWB is a predictor of hardiness (R= .4165; F=20.568; P<.0001) and that the addition of diagnosis groups and diagnosis groups by SWB did not add significantly to the prediction of hardiness. The results of the regression analysis are shown in Table 3.

TABLE 3

Multiple Regression of SWB, Diagnosis, and the Interaction of Diagnosis and SWB on Hardiness

Variable	R	R^2	F	ΔR^2	ΔF
SWB	.417	.174	20.57*	.174	20.57*
Diagnosis Groups	.434	.188	7.407**	.014	.845
Diagnosis Groups X SWB	.441	.195	4.549**	.008	.008

*Significant at p<.0001
**Significant at p<.001

Hypothesis 2: Persons who are either HIV+ or who have a diagnosis of ARC or AIDS have a positive relationship between EWB and hardiness.

This hypothesis was analyzed using Pearson Product-Moment Correlation Coefficients and multiple regression. The correlations showed that EWB is significantly correlated with hardiness (r= .505; P<.001). The correlation matrix is shown in Table 2. The variables of EWB, hardiness, and the three diagnosis groups were entered into a regression equation, with hardiness as the dependent variable. The interaction of diagnosis and EWB also was entered. For this analysis, the diagnosis group was dummy-coded into two dichotomous variables, ARC and AIDS. When analyzed using hierarchical regression, EWB accounted for 26 percent (adj R =.24709) of the variance in hardiness (F = 33.4906;

P<.0001). Diagnosis groups accounted for an additional 1.3 percent of the variance in hardiness (F=.868; P>.05). Entering the interaction of diagnosis group and EWB accounted for an additional 1.6 percent of the variance in hardiness (F= 1.038; P>.05). The results of this analysis showed that EWB is a predictor of hardiness (R= .505; F=33.4096; P<.0001), and that the addition of diagnosis groups and diagnosis groups by EWB did not add significantly to the prediction of hardiness. The results of the Regression analysis are shown in Table 4.

TABLE 4

Multiple Regression of EWB, Diagnosis, and the Interaction of Diagnosis and EWB on Hardiness

Variable	R	R^2	F	ΔR^2	ΔF
EWB	.505	.255	33.4906*	.255	33.4906*
Diagnosis Groups	.518	.268	11.7113*	.013	.868
Diagnosis Groups X EWB	.533	.284	7.447*	.016	1.038

*Significant at p<.0001

The results indicated that both hypotheses were upheld. Both SWB and EWB were positively related to hardiness.

DISCUSSION

The fact that both hypotheses were upheld is predicted from Frankl's theoretical position. Frankl recognized that spirituality holds a religious as well as an existential element. He believed that persons who defined their spirituality in a religious sense had a somewhat easier task of making meaning out of life because religions provide purpose and a sense of mission. However, the existential aspect of spirituality offers a uniquely human challenge because it focuses on an individual's concern about his or her life and the meaning and significance of that life. Frankl believed that the spiritual qualities that a person possessed determined emotional hardiness. Furthermore, these spiritual qualities allowed physically frail individuals to tolerate intolerable situation (Frankl, 1963). Spirituality, specifically the existential aspects of spirituality, holds forth the promise of giving life meaning through allowing individuals to realize experiential values "by experiencing the Good, the True, and the Beautiful, or by knowing one single human being in all his uniqueness (Frankl, 1955, p.

xii)." Frankl asserted that meaning can also be achieved through suffering. Certainly this aspect of "making meaning" pertains to the PWA just as it did to the prisoners of war held in German concentration camps. The ability to believe and act on the belief that life is meaningful is essential to hardiness and its components of challenge, control, and commitment.

Affirming the value of life allows the individual to accept the challenge inherent in his or her suffering. Making choices allows the individual to transcend the bonds of suffering rather than being mired in it. It allows the individual to take control over areas of his or her life where control is possible and to let go of control where holding on would be futile. It allows an individual to commit to something greater than herself or himself even if that something is how she or her will endure pain.

An individual with spiritual resources is able to find the unique meaning that life holds forth. As Frankl (1963) stated: ". . . each new situation in life represents a challenge to man and presents a problem for him to solve, the question of the meaning of life may actually be reversed. Ultimately, man should not ask what the meaning of his life is, but rather he must recognize that it is he who is asked. In a word, each man is questioned by life; and he can only answer to life by answering for his own life; to a life he can only respond by being responsible" (p.111).

The finding that SWB and, specifically, EWB are predictive of hardiness is also consistent with the writings of Bernard Gavzer (1988) and the experiences of William Calderon (Bolen, 1985). Gavzer interviewed long-term survivors of AIDS and discovered that these individuals attributed their hardiness to spiritual renewal. William Calderon experienced a similar renewal with a subsequent reversal of the Kaposi's sarcoma lesions that covered his body. The renewal reported by Gavzer and experienced by Calderon resulted in increased participation in prayer, imagery and visualization, meditation, AIDS research, support groups, and educational programs.

The finding of the present study in relationship to both hypotheses add significant data to the limited empirical research (Belcher, Dettmore, & Holzmer, 1989; Carson, Soeken, Shanty, & Terry, 1990; Walker-Robbins & Christiana, 1989) examining the importance of spiritual issues to the PWA as well as the importance of spirituality to hardiness.

IMPLICATIONS

The findings of this study suggest implications in the areas of health care delivery, education, theory development, and research.

Health Care Delivery

The finding that SWB, specifically the EWB component of SWB, is a predictor of hardiness suggests several clinical interventions. Ellison (1989) suggested that SWB can be fostered within the context of a therapeutic relationship. Such a relationship would include the elements of Frankl's logotherapeutic techniques. Such techniques do not in themselves make meaning for the patient who has AIDS, but these strategies assist the patient to draw his or her own conclusions regarding meaning.

The role of meaning maker has been specifically explored in relationship to the nursing role (Arnold, 1989). Arnold cites the role of the nurse as one of empathetically connecting with a patient in an effort to rekindle the spark that is needed to discover the meaning and purpose in suffering and even death.

Another clinical role includes informing patients and families about the importance of finding meaning in the illness and not assuming the victim role. Perhaps if patients were told how important activities such as prayer, meditation, use of imagery or visualization, exercise, use of vitamins, and participation in AIDS-related activities are, they would be more likely to engage in these behaviors.

An additional clinical role is identifying appropriate support groups and providing referrals for PWAs and their families. Many of these support groups incorporate spiritual-and hardiness-enhancing activities that strengthen the PWA.

Bernie Siegel (1990) claims that there is something that we can teach patients so that they can live long and well. Siegel qualifies his meaning of living long as relating to the amount of time it takes to accomplish something with one's life, and living well equates with peace of mind and loving relationships rather than to a state of the body. Long-term survivors with AIDS take charge of their lives; they ask questions; they rebel against hospital routine; they accept their mortality, but they use it as a stimulus to grow and change. Siegel (1990, p. 142) states that they are likely to say things like: "I decided to experience unconditional love before I died." "I gained new appreciation and clarity about what is really important in life." "I decided to make every day count."

Education

The findings of the present study have educational implications. Because AIDS is a major public health concern the thrust of the national effort has been threefold: treatment, cure, and education. Educational efforts have been primarily directed at informing individuals about the need to avoid risky behaviors such as unprotected sexual contact and intravenous drug use. In order to allay public fears that AIDS is an easily transmitted disease, there have also been efforts to inform the public regarding the mode of transmission of the disease. Additionally, there needs to be education regarding how to "live long and well" with AIDS (Siegel, 1990). The public needs to know that the diagnosis of AIDS does not necessarily equate with a horrible, meaningless death. It is essential to change public perceptions that encourage a "victim" rather than a "survivor" attitude.

A quote from Dr Luc Montagnier of the Pasteur Institute in Paris, codiscoverer of the AIDS virus, has bearing on this aspect of education:

> AIDS does not inevitably lead to death, especially if you suppress the co-factors that support the disease. It's very important to tell this to people who are infected. Psychological factors are critical in supporting immune function. If you suppress this psychological support by telling someone he's condemned to die, your words alone will have condemned him. It simply isn't true that the virus is 100 percent fatal (P.W.A., July 1990).

Education regarding the importance of finding meaning, getting involved in care, and taking responsibility may benefit the patient as well as others who play influential roles in the lives of PWA's. Included in this group are family members, friends, teachers, representatives of various faith traditions, politicians, and health care providers.

Theory Development

The finding that SWB and EWB are predictors of hardiness lends support for Frankl's theory. There are very little empirical data examining the relationships of spirituality and psychological constructs. These findings that support a relationship between SWB and the psychological construct of hardiness suggest that other research is warranted to examine the relationship of SWB to others aspects of psychological well-being.

Research

The findings of this study suggest a number of additional research endeavors. These include:

1.   Replicating the present study except for two changes: (1) modify the sample methodology so that more women and intravenous drug users would be represented, and (2) include a qualitative aspect to the analysis. In a study that examines the importance of meaning to the hardiness of individuals, it is

appropriate to ask subjects in what ways they are making meaning of their situation.

2.   Design an intervention study in which variables are introduced to manipulate SWB and hardiness. Possibilities for such variables include: (1) the use of a hypnosis or imagery group that focuses on cognitively reframing the image of the disease as a challenge and not a death sentence and the image of the patient from a victim to a survivor; (2) the use of Kobasa's small-group approach to teaching people cognitive strategies that increase their feelings of control and commitment and allow them to see adversity as a challenge; and (3) the use of a group therapy approach using Frankl's logotherapy techniques to assist members to find meaning in their illness. The dependent variables in this design could be hardiness as well as a parameter of immune function, such as the levels of T-4 helper cells.

REFERENCES

Abrams, D., Parker-Margin, J., & Unger, K. (1989). AIDS: Caring for the dying patient. *Patient Care*, November 30, 22-35.

Arnold, E. (1989). Burnout as a spiritual issue: Rediscovering meaning in nursing practice. In V. B. Carson (Ed.), *Spiritual dimensions of nursing practice.* Philadelphia: Saunders.

Belcher, A., Dettmore, D., & Holzmer, S. (1989). Spirituality and sense of well-being in persons with AIDS. *Holistic Nursing Practice, 3*(4), 16-25.

Bellemare, D. (1988). AIDS: The challenge to pastoral care. *Journal of Palliative Care, 4*(4), 58-60.

Bohne, J. (1986). AIDS: Ministry issues for chaplains. *Pastoral Psychology, 34*(3), 173-192.

Bolen, J. (1985). William Calderon. *New Realities*, March/April, 9-15.

Bufford, R., Paloutzian, R. & Ellison, E. (in press). Norms for the   Spiritual Well-Being Scale. *Journal of Psychology and Theology.*

Carson, V. (1989). *Spiritual dimensions of nursing practice.* Philadelphia: Saunders.

Carson, V. (1990). Spiritual direction: Important issues to the AIDS patient. *Journal of Christian Healing, 12*(3), 3-7.

Carson, V., Soeken, K., & Belcher, A. (1991). Spiritual well-being, hardiness, and ego strength in persons with AIDS. *Journal of Christian Healing, 13*(2), 21.

Carson, V., Soeken, K., Shanty, J., & Terry, L. (1990). Hope and spiritual well-being: Essentials for living with AIDS. *Perspectives in Psychiatric Care, 26*(9), 28-34.

Cecchi, R. (1981). Stress: Prodrome to immune deficiency. *Annals of the New York Academy of Sciences, 137*, 286-289.

Chaisson, R. (1990). Prevention of opportunistic infections in patients with HIV. *Maryland Medical Journal, 39*(2), 156-160.

Crumbaugh, J., & Maholick, L. (1964). An experimental study in existentialism: The psychometric approach to Frankl's concept of noogenic neurosis. *Journal of Clinical Psychology, 20*, 200-207.

Crumbaugh, J. (1977). The Seeking of Noetic Goals Test (SONG): A complementary scale to the Purpose in Life test (PIL). *Journal of Clinical Psychology, 33*, 900-907.

Ellison, C. (1983). Spiritual well-being: Conceptualization and measurement. *Journal of Psychology and Theology, 11*(4), 330-340.

Ellison, E. (1989). Spirituality: A systemic view. *Journal of Psychology and Theology, 17*(3), 158-167.

Ellison, C., & Paloutzian, R. (1982, October). *Research directions on spiritual well-being*. Paper presented at the annual meeting of the Society for the Scientific Study of Religion. Providence, Rhode Island.

Frankl, V. (1955). *The doctor and the soul*. New York: Knopf.

Frankl, V. (1963). *Man's search for meaning*. Boston: Beacon.

Frankl, V. (1967). *Psychotherapy and existentialism*. New York: Washington Square Press.

Gavzer, B. (1988, September). Why do some people survive AIDS: *Parade Magazine* in the *Baltimore Sunday*, pp.4-7.

Graydon, D. (1988). AIDS: Observations of a hospital chaplain. *Journal of Palliative Care, 8(*4), 66-69.

Hardiness Institute Inc. (1985). Chicago, Ill.

Hay, L. (1988). *The AIDS book*. Santa Monica: Hay House.

Kayal, P. (1985). "Morals," medicine, and the AIDS epidemic. *Journal of Religion and Health, 24*(3), 218-237.

Kobasa, S. (1979). Stressful life events, personality, and health: An inquiry into hardiness. *Journal of Personality and Social Psychology, 37*(1), 1-11.

Kobasa, S., Maddi, S., & Pucetti, M. (1982). Personality and exercise as buffers in the stress-illness relationship. *Journal of Behavioral Medicine, 5*(4), 391-403.

Lovejoy, N., & Sisson, R. (1989). Psychoneuroimmunology and AIDS. *Holistic Nurse Practitioner, 3*(4), 1-15.

Maddi, S. (1986, August). *The great stress-illness controversy*. Paper present at the meeting of The American Psychology Association, Washington, DC.

Maryland AIDS Update. (1990, June 30). pp.1-3.

National Interfaith Coalition on Aging. (1975). *Spiritual well-being–Definition*. Athens, GA: Author.

Okun, M., Zautra, A., & Robinson, S. (1988). Hardiness and health among women with rheumatoid arthritis. *Personality and Individual Differences, 9*(1), 101-107.

P.W.A. *News and Views*. (1990, July). p.2.

Saynor, J. (1988). Existential and spiritual concerns of people with AIDS. *Journal of Palliative Care, 1*(1), 61-65.

Schofferman, J. (1987). Hospice care of the patient with AIDS. *Hospice Journal, 3*(4), 51-74.

Siegel, B. (1990). Exceptional patients live long and live well. *Maryland Medical Journal, 39*(2), 181-182.

Solomon, G., & Temoshok, L. (1987). A psychoneuroimmunological perspective on AIDS research: Questions, preliminary findings, and suggestions. *Journal of Applied Psychology, 17*(3), 286-308.

Solomon, G., Temoshok, L, & Zich, J. (1987). An intensive psychoimmunologic study of long-surviving persons with AIDS. *Annals of the New York Academy of Sciences, 496*, 6747-655.

Tiblier, K., Walker, B., & Rolland, J. (1989). Therapeutic issues when working with families of persons with AIDS. *Marriage and Family Review, 13*(1-2), 81-128.

Vastyn, E. (1986). Spiritual aspects of the care of cancer patients. *CA: A Cancer Journal for Clinicians, 36*(2), 110-114.

Walker-Robbins, C, & Cristiana, N. (1989). The spiritual needs of persons with AIDS. *Family and Community Health, 12*(2), 43-51.

Wallack, J. (1989). AIDS anxiety among health care professionals. *Hospital and Community Psychiatry, 10*(5), 507-510.

Wendler, K. (1987). Ministry to patients with acquired immunodeficiency syndrome: A spiritual challenge. *Journal of Pastoral Care, 41*(1), 1-16.

Zurlo, J., & Lane, H. (1990). The role of antiretroviral therapy in living long and living well. *Maryland Medical Journal, 39*(2), 161-165.

EDITOR'S COMMENTS

This is an important study, but read it critically and carefully. It concerns itself with why some persons survive much longer than others. These authors hunch that psychological and spiritual factors have something to do with it.

At least two points of interest emerge after reading the article critically. First, the early part of the article gives considerable attention to Frankl's theories and how survival under extreme circumstances is possible. When the authors transition into a more direct discussion of AIDS, they write:

What is really behind long-term survival? Is there something physically, emotionally, or spiritually different in the thousands of PWAs who are numbered in this surviving group? The answer to these questions could offer hope to thousands who feel they are losing the battle with AIDS.

The hypotheses follow shortly. From these hypotheses and the rest of the study it is important to realize that this research is not about long-term survival. In fact, no data are presented at all which link the participant's survival time with the scores generated in the project. Rather, the project focuses on the relationship between scores which reportedly represent spirituality and hardiness. This is the contribution of the article and the research has nothing to do with long-term survival. Readers who realize this will not "over-interpret" the results to mean that higher spirituality and hardiness scores are linked to longer survival. Those data are apparently not available.

A second point also requires critical comment. The authors report that the hardiness instrument has a history of creating low reliability coefficients and that it has now been "refined." This is a serious matter and a brief discussion of reliability is in order.

A researcher (or anyone else) who wishes to measure specific characteristics of an individual or a group constructs a test. It can be any kind of test—written, oral, or a demonstration. A test, however, is always a sampling of the broader reality under consideration. That is, since it is impossible to ask every possible question about that which needs to be measured, sample questions must be chosen. This leads to the question as to whether the chosen questions accurately represent that broader reality. Typically, two concerns emerge. First, does the test measure what it is suppose to measure. This is the concern for test validity and can not be addressed here. The second question is whether the results generated by the test are reliable. In this instance, "reliable" mean "stable." An easy way to understand test reliability is to compare it to a reliable car. Cars which are unreliable are unstable, unpredictable. Perhaps they will not run when it rains, when its too hot, when driven into a different altitude, when using a certain brand of gasoline, or when under the control of a stranger. Concerns about test reliability are similar although they usually concern the amount of diversity among the individual items. Thus reliability, which is often reported as Chronbach's alpha, declines if the questionnaire items are non-specific, worded in a confusing manner, or interpreted by respondents in different ways. The alpha is a coefficient which represents the level of correlation between the individual items and the total score, ranging between 0 and 1.00. In many psychosocial circles, a Chronbach's alpha which is below .70 is thought to be unacceptable. Many journal reviewers will not recommend publication of results in which the alpha for a new or recently developed scale is unknown or is below this level.

All this is relevant concerning the hardiness instrument because the authors report that, in one of their unpublished studies, the alpha for the control subscale was .46. Perhaps that is why the study is unpublished. Having come to the Results section, they immediately report the coefficient alphas as is appropriate. In this version of the hardiness scale, the alphas for the control and challenge subscales were .59 and .72 respectively. It must be noted that the authors do not address the low alphas as a limitation of their results.

How should these low coefficients be interpreted? Perhaps the most general response, without seeing either the items of the scale or the results of other statistical tests which they may have performed, is to lower the level of confidence in those subscale results. Perhaps the concept of control and challenge are difficult to capture in a set of items, perhaps the items are unclear, perhaps the wording of the items are interpreted by respondents in diverse ways. All of these factors can lower the coefficient and the confidence in the score of the subscale. Having said all that, it is important to note that the alpha coefficient of the total hardiness scale for this study was .85. Therein lies confidence in the results.

17

Religious Coping and Depression Among Elderly, Hospitalized Medically Ill Men

Harold G. Koenig
Harvey J. Cohen
Dan G. Blazer
Carl Pieper
Keith G. Meador
Frank Shelp
Veeraindar Goli
Bob DiPasquale

ABSTRACT

Objective: The investigators examined the frequency of religious coping among older medical inpatients, the characteristics of those who use it, and the relation between this behavior and depression. *Method*: The subjects were 850 men aged 65 years and over, without psychiatric diagnoses, who were consecutively admitted to the medical or neurological services of a southern Veterans Administration medical center. Religious coping was assessed with a three-item index. Depressive symptoms were assessed by self-rating (the Geriatric Depression Scale) and observer rating (the Hamilton Rating Scale for Depression). *Results*: One out of every five patients reported that religious thought and/or activity was the most important strategy used to cope with illness. Variables that were associated

Reproduced with permission of the American Psychiatric Association from the *American Journal of Psychiatry*, (1992), *149*(12), 1693-1700.

with religious coping included black race, older age, being retired, religious affiliation, high level of social support, infrequent alcohol use, a prior history of psychiatric problems, and higher cognitive functioning. Depressive symptoms were inversely related to religious coping, an association which persisted after other sociodemographic and health correlates were controlled. When 202 men were reevaluated during their subsequent hospital admissions an average of 6 months later, religious coping was the only baseline variable that predicted lower depression scores at follow-up. *Conclusions*: These findings suggest that religious coping is a common behavior that is inversely related to depression in hospitalized elderly men.

Medical illness that precipitates hospitalization is a stressful experience that can interrupt social and work routines, drain finances, separate families, reverse caregiver roles, and create situations of forced dependency. Physical illness also brings with it the threat of pain and long-term disability, disfiguration, the prospect of approaching death, and feelings of existential anxiety and sometimes despair. During physical illness coping resources are seriously tested and frequently overwhelmed, as evidenced by the fact that 40% or more of older hospitalized patients experience some form of clinical depression (Kitchell, Barnes, Veith, Okimoto, & Raskind, 1982; Koenig, Meador, Cohen, & Blazer, 1988). Religious beliefs and behavior, in turn, are prevalent among older persons (Princeton Religion Research Center, 1982; Koenig, Moberg, & Kvale, 1988) and are reported to serve as a coping strategy to help manage emotional distress (Koenig, Smiley, & Gonzales, 1988; Swanson & Harter, 1971; Rosen, 1982; Conway, 1985-86). The extent to which older medical inpatients use religion for this purpose, the characteristics of those who do so, and the effectiveness of this strategy are largely unknown.

National samples of Americans of all ages indicate that persons who find personal comfort and support from religion are more likely to be older, female, black, less educated, widowed, employed in manual or unskilled occupations, more economically deprived, and affiliated with conservative Protestant religious denominations (Princeton Religion Research Center, 1982). These sociological findings suggest that persons with fewer health, social, and financial resources, when facing situations over which they have little control (such as acute hospitalization), might turn to religion for solace.

Whether religious beliefs and behavior actually help to prevent or relieve emotional distress is far from clear. Psychiatric illness may be even more common among the religious (Freud, 1927; Sanua, 1969; Ellis, 1980), perhaps predisposing them to greater problems in later life when they are faced with the stress of physical illness and/or approaching death. Thus far, systematic research on the relation between religious coping and depression among older adults in clinical settings has been limited. Previous studies have been hampered by small sample sizes, less than rigorous sampling methods, and unequal sex distribution (few males) (Swanson & Harter, 1971; Rosen, 1982; Conway, 1985-86).

This report emanates from Durham Veterans Administration (VA) Mental Health Survey (Koenig *et al*, 1991; Koenig *et al.*, 1992), a cross-sectional and longitudinal epidemiologic study of depression among hospitalized medically ill men. We examine religious coping, its sociodemographic and health correlates, and its relation to depression both cross-sectionally and over time. Four major questions guided this investigation. 1) How common is religious coping in this population? 2) Is this coping behavior more likely among those with fewer socioeconomic, physical, or mental health resources? 3) When other factors are controlled, is there an association between religious coping and depression? 4) If such a relationship exists, is it especially strong in any subgroup of the population, such as those with more severe medical illness, low social support, prior mental health problems, or other attributes?

METHOD

Between Sept. 1, 1987, and Jan. 1 1989, all men aged 65 years and over who had been admitted to medical or neurological services at the Durham VA Medical Center were screened for depression. For inclusion in the study, patients were required to score 15 or higher on the Mini-Mental State examination (Folstein, Folstein, & McHugh, 1975) and to be physically capable of undergoing a psychiatric evaluation. Psychiatric patients were excluded. Patients were evaluated within 48-72 hours of admission by a social worker and/or a Fellow in geriatric medicine (H.G.K.).

Data were collected on demographic characteristics and social and economic resources, including age, race, education, prior occupation (Myers & Bean, 1968), retirement status, current living situation, marital status, yearly income, and social support. Social support was measured with a three-item index that explored size of the support network (Blake & McKay, 1986), frequency of interaction, and perceived adequacy of support (Blazer, 1982) (values for each item ranged from 1 to 5; (Cronbach's alpha=0.57). Over 40 religious denominations were represented in the study group; these were categorized into nine general religious groups according to a schema provided by Roof and McKinney (1987).

The physical health of the participants, including medical diagnoses, functional status, and cognitive status, was assessed. Functional status was determined by measuring physical (Katz, Downs, Cash, & Grotz, 1970) and instrumental (Fillenbaum, 1985) activities of daily living. Physical activities of daily living included bathing, dressing, toileting, problems with incontinence, transfer from bed to chair or vice versa, and feeding (each rated 0-2); instrumental activities of daily living involved ability to travel, shop, prepare meals, do housework, and handle finances (rated 0 or 1). These two types of ratings together produced an 11-item scale with a possible range of scores from 0 (low functioning) to 17 (high functioning). As we have mentioned, cognitive status was measured with Mini-Mental State examination scores, which ranged from 15 to 30.

The assessment of mental health included information on alcohol use, prior psychiatric problems, and family history of psychiatric problems. Depression was assessed by self-rated and observer-rated scales. The self-rated 30-item Geriatric Depression Scale (Yesavage *et al.*, 1982-83) was administered by the social worker to all patients; this scale has been validated as a measure of depression in older medical inpatients (Koenig, Meador, Cohen, & Blazer, 1988). The men aged 70 years and older were also assessed by one of us (H.G.K.) with the Hamilton Rating Scale for Depression (Hamilton, 1967), a measure used in other studies of the elderly (Kochansky, 1979) and medical inpatients (Schwab, Bialow, Clemmons, & Holzer, 1967). Depression scales were administered early in the interview, before the assessment of religious coping.

Religious coping was assessed with a three-item index. Each item measured how much the patient relied upon religion to help manage the emotional stress associated with his illness. In item 1, the patient was asked an open-ended question about how he coped. This item was chosen in order to identify the coping behavior that the patient himself felt was most helpful, and the question was asked before questions on religion that might bias responses. If the response was religious in nature (*e.g.*, faith in God or Jesus, prayer, church), the patient received a score of 10; if the spontaneous response was not religious (*e.g.*, stay busy, family support), a score of 0 was assigned. A value of 10 for religious responses was chosen in order to give this item equal weight with the others in the index.

In item 2, patients were asked to rate on a visual analog scale the extent to which they found religious beliefs or activities helpful in coping with their situation. The scale was numbered from 0 ("not much or not at all") to 10 ("the most important thing that keeps me going"). In approaching patients with the rating scale, the investigators allowed patients to define for themselves the meaning of the term "religion" but made clear that this could involve personal belief alone or include religious activity such as prayer or church attendance.

In item 3, the interviewer rated the patient on a scale of 0-10 on the basis of an overall assessment of how much the patient used religion to cope. This judgment was based on the patient's further elaboration on religious coping themes during answers to items 1 and 2 and on a separate discussion about how religion was helpful. The scores from the three items were then summed, and an index with values ranging from 0 to 30 was obtained. Cronbach's alpha (reliability) for the index in the overall sample (N=850) was acceptable (0.82).

Test-retest/interrater reliability for the religious coping index was also determined for a subgroup of 188 consecutively admitted men. The religious coping index was administered twice to these patients, each time by a different rater; ratings were separated by 12-36 hours. The Pearson correlation between scores obtained on the religious coping index at the two administrations was 0.81. The interrater agreement for the observer-rated religious coping item (item 3) was surprisingly high (Pearson's r=0.87) given that the raters came from markedly different religious backgrounds (secular humanist versus conservative Protestant).

All participants in the baseline study who were readmitted to the medical or neurological services during the 16-month study period and 5 months thereafter (designated "time 2") were reevaluated by the social worker with the Geriatric Depression Scale and the religious coping index. Again, psychiatric admissions were excluded. If more than one readmission occurred, the results from the last interview during the 21-month observation period was used for time 2. This provided information on change in depressive symptoms and religious coping over time among patients whose medical illness prompted rehospitalization during the project.

Analyses were performed with the SAS statistical package (SAS Institute, 1988). Simple statistics were used to determine the frequency of spontaneously reported, self-rated, and observer-rated religious coping. Bivariate relations of covariates with religious coping (religious coping index score) and depression (Geriatric Depression Scale and Hamilton depression scale scores) were examined with Pearson correlations. Hierarchical regression was used to examine the strength of relationships, controlling for the effects of other covariates.

To determine whether patients who used religious coping had fewer socioeconomic or health resources than other patients, the religious coping index score was regressed on a series of 16 demographic, socioeconomic, and health variables (excluding depression). A backward stepwise regression method was used to eliminate nonsignificant variables (p>0.05); missing values were dealt with by listwise deletion. The regression was performed in five stages. In the first stage, demographic variables (age, race, and occupational and retirement status) were entered into the model. In subsequent stages, religious affiliation, socioeconomic resources, and mental and physical health variables were added. The fifth stage produced a final model that contained the significant correlates.

We examined the relation between depression and religious coping in the following manner. First, a model for depressive symptoms was constructed by regressing it on the 15 sociodemographic and health variables (excluding religious variables). Once a final model had been obtained, we added religious coping and religious affiliation variables. Interactions between religious coping and all other variables in the model were tested and included in the final model if alpha was less than or equal to 0.05. Regression models were developed for both self-rated symptoms (Geriatric Depression Scale) and observer-rated symptoms (Hamilton Rating Scale for Depression).

We analyzed the longitudinal data as follows. Pearson correlations determined bivariate relations between baseline (time 1) group characteristics and follow-up (time 2) Geriatric Depression Scale score. Hierarchical regression was then used to assess the relation between time 1 religious coping index score and time 2 Geriatric Depression Scale score, controlling for time 1 Geriatric Depression Scale score and other significant baseline correlates.

RESULTS

There were 1,110 consecutively admitted new patients during the study period. Eight hundred fifty men (77%) underwent comprehensive social, psychological, and physical health examinations; 260 did not participate because of advanced dementia or delirium (12% with Mini-Mental State scores less than 15), communication problems (2%), refusal or discharge before being seen (5%), or other reasons (4%). Nonparticipants were more likely to be older, black, and residents of nursing homes and to have diagnoses of neurological or respiratory illness.

TABLE 1
*Sociodemographic and Health Characteristics of 850
Elderly Male Medical Inpatients*

Characteristics	Mean	SD	N	%
Demographic				
Age (years)	69.8	4.9		
Black race			240	28.3
Education (years)	8.9	3.8		

(Table 1, continued)

Unskilled occupation			333	39.2
Retired more than 5 yrs.			589	69.3
Social/economic				
Married			577	67.9
Living alone			160	18.8
Income (dollars/year)	8,582	3,316		
Social support rating[a]	10.6	1.8		
Mental health				
History of psychiatric problems			216	25.7
Family history of psychiatric problems			76	9.1
Alcohol use			153	18.2
Geriatric Depression Scale score $\geq$ 11			186	22.1
Hamilton depression score $\geq$ 15			49	14.7
Physical health				
Medical diagnosis				
Cancer			188	22.1
Gastrointestinal disease		125	14.7	
Neurological disease			122	14.4
Respiratory disease			87	10.2
Renal disease			40	4.7
Cardiovascular disease		216	25.4	
Other			72	8.5
Functional status (activities of daily living)[b]	14.1	4.0		
Cognitive status (Mini-Mental State score)[c]	26.4	2.8		

[a]Range of possible scores=3-15.
[b]Range of possible scores=0-17.
[c]Range of possible scores=0-30.

The sociodemographic and health characteristics of the subjects are presented in Table 1. The distributions of race, marital status, and medical diagnoses were similar to those among elderly male patients discharged from VA hospitals in District 8, which covers most of North Carolina and parts of Virginia, Kentucky, Tennessee, and South Carolina (Koenig *et al.*, 1991). Table 2 presents the religious affiliations of the participants. The distribution was comparable to that of elderly men living in central North Carolina; compared to the population of the nation as a whole, however, a disproportionate number of men came from conservative or black Protestant denominations (63% in this study, 54% in central North Carolina, and 17% nationally).

TABLE 2

Distribution of Religious Affiliations Among 850 Elderly Male Medical Inpatients, Elderly Men in Central North Carolina, and in the United States as a Whole

Religious Group[a]	% of Elderly Male Medical Inpatients	% of Elderly Men in Central N.C.[b]	% in the U.S. Population[a]
Liberal Protestant (Episcopal, United Church of Christ, Presbyterian)	8.0	7.1	8.7
Moderate Protestant (Methodist, Lutheran, Disciples of Christ, Reformed)	12.5	17.2	19.9
Conservative Protestant White Baptist, Church of Christ, Nazarene, Seventh-Day Adventist)	40.8	54.7[c]	11.3
Black Protestant (Methodist, Baptist)	22.2		5.8
Fundamentalist/evangelical (Pentecostal, Holiness, Assemblies of God, Church of God)	5.1	5.1	4.5
Protestant (unspecified)	3.3	5.9	
Catholic	2.6	1.5	25.0
Jewish	0.00	.32	.3
Nontraditional Christian (Mormon, Jehovah's Witnesses, Christian Science, Unitarian)	3.2	3.3	8.0
No religious preference	2.4	5.1	6.9

[a]See Roof and McKinney (18).

[b]Men aged 55 years and over who participated in the Piedmont Epidemiological Catchment Area study (central North Carolina)(27).

[c]Includes conservative Protestants and black Protestants.

In response to the open-ended question directed at how they coped, 20% (N=167) of the subjects (24% of those aged 70 years and over) spontaneously replied that religion was a primary factor. Religion in this sense typically involved having trust or faith in God, praying, reading the Bible or other religious literature, listening to religious programs on the radio or watching religious programs on television, participating in church services or other related activity, and receiving emotional support from church members or a pastor. On the visual analog scale, which ranged from 0 to 10, the mean rating by patients was 6.5 (SD=3.1). More than half of the subjects (56%, N=471) rated themselves 7.5 or higher, and 21% gave themselves a rating of 10 (religion being "the most important thing that keeps me going"). Observer ratings of religious coping for the group ranged from 0 to 10, with a mean 5.7 (SD=3.2). The religious coping index scores for the group ranged from 0 to 30; the mean was 14.3 (SD=8.7).

Sociodemographic and Health Correlates of Religious Coping

The bivariate relations of covariates to religious coping are presented in Table 3 (column 1). Race, retirement status, social support, family history of psychiatric problems, and alcohol use were significant correlates. Liberal Protestants, Catholics, and patients with no affiliation were less likely to use religious coping (negative correlations), whereas black Protestants and members of fundamentalist/evangelical groups were more likely to use religious coping than were members of other religious groups.

TABLE 3

Bivariate Relation of Covariates to Religious Coping and Depression (Pearson correlations) Among 850 Elderly Male Medical Inpatients

Covariate	Religious Coping[a] (N=842)	Depression[b]	
		Geriatric Depression Scale (N=841)	Hamilton Depression Scale (N=333)
Demographic characteristics			
Age	0.05	-0.02	-0.02
Race	0.15[c]	-0.09[d]	-0.04
Education	-0.00	-0.09[d]	-0.11[e]
Occupation	0.00	0.06	0.05
Retirement status	0.08[e]	-0.11[d]	-0.02

(Table 3, Continued)

Social/edonomic resources			
Living situation	-0.01	0.03	0.03
Marital status	0.06	0.10[d]	-0.10
Income	0.05	-0.09[d]	-0.13[e]
Social support	0.12[c]	-0.24[c]	-0.21[c]
Mental health			
History of psychiatric problems	0.03	0.30[c]	0.27[c]
Family history of psychiatric problems	0.08[e]	0.13[c]	0.11[e]
Alcohol use	0.16[c]	-0.08[e]	-0.15[c]
Physical health			
Functional status (activities of daily living)	0.01	-0.26[c]	-0.17[d]
Cognitive status	0.05	-0.19[c]	-0.11[e]
Medical diagnosis			
Cancer	-0.01	-0.00	-0.01
Gastrointestinal disease	0.02	0.01	0.02
Neurological disease	-0.02	-0.03	-0.01
Respiratory disease	-0.03	0.16[c]	0.14[d]
Renal disease	0.03	0.02	-0.02
Cardiac disease	0.04	-0.08[e]	0.00
Miscellaneous	-0.02	-0.03	-0.12[e]
Religious affiliation			
Liberal Protestant	-0.07[e]	-0.00	0.07
Moderate Protestant	-0.06	-0.06	-0.12[e]
Conservative Protestant	-0.02	0.11[c]	0.02
Black Protestant	0.12[c]	0.10[d]	-0.04
Fundamentalist/evangelical	0.17[c]	0.00	0.07
Protestant (unspecified)	-0.05	0.04	-0.10
Catholic	-0.11[d]	-0.06	0.09
Nontraditional Christian	0.04	-0.01	-0.07
No religious preference	-0.15[c]	0.06	0.14[d]

[a]Measured with the religious coping index.

[b]Scores on the Hamilton depression scale were available only for men aged 70 years and over. For categorical variables, point biserial correlations are reported. The correlation between Geriatric Depression Scale and Hamilton depression scale scores was 0.66.

[c]$p \leq 0.001$.

[d]$p \leq 0.01$.

[e]$p \leq 0.05$.

Using hierarchical stepwise regression, we examined the relations between religious coping and sociodemographic and health characteristics. In stage 1, age, race, education, and occupational status were entered as independent variables into a model with religious coping index score as the dependent variable. In stages 2 through 5, religious affiliation, social/economic resources, and mental and physical health variables were added successively to the model. At each stage, nonsignificant variables were excluded by using backward stepwise elimination. Variables unrelated to religious coping and thus dropped from the model were education and occupational status (stage 1), living situation, marital status, and income (stage 3), family history of psychiatric problems (stage 4), and functional status and medical diagnosis (stage 5). The fifth and final model is presented in Table 4.

TABLE 4

Religious Coping Regressed on Sociodemographic and Health Variables for 850 Elderly Male Medical Inpatients[a]

Variable	Beta[b]
Demographic characteristics	
Age	0.12[c]
Race	0.20[c]
Retirement status	0.07[d]
Religious affiliation[e]	
Liberal Protestant	0.20[f]
Moderate Protestant	0.27[c]
Conservative Protestant	0.49[c]
Black Protestant	0.38[c]
Fundamentalist/evangelical	0.37[c]
Protestant (unspecified)	0.12[d]
Catholic	0.05
Nontraditional Christian	0.21[c]
Social support	0.12[c]
Mental Health	
History of psychiatric problems	0.07[d]
Alcohol use	-0.14[c]
Cognitive status	0.10[f]

[a]Regression analysis was performed in five stages: this table represents the fifth and final model (model F=9.5, df=15, 810, p≤0.001; total R^2=0.15).

[b]Betas are standardized; for every 1 standard deviation change in the independent variable there is a beta standard deviation change in religious coping, with all other variables in the model controlled.

(Table 4, Continued)
^{c}p≤0.001
^{d}p≤0.05.
^{e}Dummy variables were created to represent each religious group and were then compared to variables for patients with no religious affiliation (partial F=7.8, df=8, 828, p≤0.001).
^{f}p≤0.01.

Religious affiliation accounted for the largest proportion of explained variance (46%). Men from conservative, black, and fundamentalist Protestant denominations were especially likely to use religion to cope. Demographic variables (age, race, and retirement status), social support, and mental health variables (history of psychiatric problems and use of alcohol) each accounted for about 15% of the explained variance in religious coping. Patients who were older, were black, had a history of psychiatric problems, and reported greater social support were more likely to use religion as a coping behavior. Patients who used alcohol, on the other hand, were less likely to do so. The only physical health factor related to religious coping was cognitive status, which accounted for about 8% of the explained variance. Contrary to expectation, there was no significant relation between religious coping and functional status or medical diagnosis.

Religious Coping and Depression

Bivariate analyses indicated inverse correlations between religious coping index scores and both self-rated and observer-rated depression scores (Geriatric Depression Scale score, r=-0.16, p≤0.001; Hamilton depression score, r=-0.14;p≤0.01). We then used hierarchical regression to control for the confounding effects of other sociodemographic and health correlates of depression. Stepwise procedures were used to construct two models for depression (Geriatric Depression Scale scores and Hamilton depression scores as dependent variables). Fifteen sociodemographic and health variables (excluding religion) were examined as possible correlates of depression in each model.

In the development of the Geriatric Depression Scale model, variables unrelated to Geriatric Depression Scale score and thus eliminated were marital status, retirement status, occupational status, income, education, and living situation. Variables included in the final model were age, race, social support, history of psychiatric problems, family history of psychiatric problems, alcohol use, cognitive status, functional status, and six medical diagnoses (respiratory disease in particular) (Koenig *et al.*, 1992) (model F=20.7, df=14, 807, p≤0.001; R^2 =0.26). Religious affiliations were then added but did not contribute significantly (partial F=0.8, df=8, 799, p>0.50). Finally, religious coping index score was added to the model, yielding a partial F of 19.8, df=1, 799; p≤0.001 (Table 5, first column). The inverse relation between religious coping and depressive symptoms was stronger among men who had more severe disability (partial F=3.9, df=1, 798, p≤0.05). Religious coping index score did not interact significantly with any other correlates of depression, although the relation between religious coping index score and depression did tend to be stronger in men who had a prior history of psychiatric problems (partial F=3.3, df=1,797, p=0.07).

We then examined the relation between religious coping index score and observer-rated depressive symptoms (in men aged 70 years and over). A model of significant correlates of Hamilton depression scale score was created (religious factors excluded). Variables related to Hamilton depression score and controlled for in the model were social support, history of psychiatric problems, alcohol use, and functional status (model F=15.0, df=4, 318, p≤0.001; R^2=0.16). The addition of religious affiliations contributed significantly to the model—largely a result of inverse associations between Hamilton depression scale score and moderate Protestant and Catholic affiliations. Finally, religious coping index score was added; it was inversely correlated with Hamilton depression scale score (partial F=12.2, df=1, 306, p≤0.001) (Table 5, second column). There were no significant interactions between religious coping index score and other variables in the model.

TABLE 5

Self-Rated and Observer-Rated Depressive Symptoms
Regressed on Religious Coping,
With Other Correlates of Depression Controlled,
for Elderly Male Medical Inpatients

	Beta[a]	
	Self-Rated Depressive Symptoms[b]	Observer-Rated Depressive Symptoms[c]
Religious Variable		
Religious coping index score	-0.14[d]	-0.19[d]
Religious coping index score by functional status	0.25[e]	0.21
Religious affiliation[f]		
Liberal Protestant	n.s.	-0.06
Moderate Protestant	n.s.	-0.25[e]

(Table 5, Continued)

Conservative Protestant	n.s.	-0.23
Black Protestant	n.s.	-0.17
Fundamentalist/evangelical	n.s.	0.01
Protestant (unspecified)	n.s.	-0.00
Catholic	n.s.	-0.17[g]
Nontraditional Christian	n.s.	-0.12[e]

[a]Betas are standardized; for every 1 standard deviation change in the independent variables (i.e. religious coping index score) there is a beta standard deviation change in Geriatric Depression Scale score or Hamilton depression score, with all other variables in the model controlled. For religious coping index (Table 5 continued)
score, SD=8.7; for Geriatric Depression Scale score, SD=5.3; for Hamilton depression scale score, SD=6.0.
[b]Geriatric Depression Scale (model F=20.1, df=16, 798, p≤0.001; total R^2=0.29).
(Table 5, Continued)
[c]Hamilton depression scale (only for men aged 70 years and over) (model F=7.4; df=13,306, p≤0.001; total R^2=0.24).
[d]p≤0.001
[e]p≤0.05.
[f]Religious groups compared to patients with no religious affiliation (for religious affiliation in the Hamilton depression scale model, partial F=2.7, df=8, 310, p≤0.01).
[g]p≤0.01.

Follow-Up Phase

In the follow-up phase, 256 (30%) of the 850 participants were readmitted to the hospital one or more times during the 16-month study and 5 months thereafter. Of these patients, 202 (79%) received complete follow-up evaluations, including both Geriatric Depression Scale and religious coping index assessments. The time from index hospitalization to readmission evaluation ranged from 0 to 20 months (mean= 6 months). Compared with the 850 participants in the baseline study, readmitted patients were more likely to have a diagnosis of cancer (33% versus 22%) and less likely to have neurological disease (7% versus 14%); otherwise, they were similar in all other sociodemographic and health characteristics. The overall mean changes in both religious coping index score and Geriatric Depression Scale score (time 1 to time 2) were small (1 point or less). There was no relation between change in religious coping index score and change in depressive symptoms (Pearson's r=0.06, p=0.45).

TABLE 6

*Follow-Up (Time 2) Geriatric Depression Scale Score
Regressed on Baseline (Time 1) Religious Coping Index Score,
With Other Baseline Predictors Controlled,
for 202 Elderly Male Medical Inpatients*

Variables[a]	Beta[b]
Time 1 Geriatric Depression Scale score	0.62[c]
Medical diagnosis	
Cancer	-0.06
Gastrointestinal disease	-0.06
Neurological disease	-0.04
Respiratory disease	-0.08
Renal disease	0.15[d]
Cardiovascular disease	-0.11
Time 1 religious coping index score	-0.18[e]

[a]Fourteen baseline variables were not significantly related to time 2 Geriatric Depression Scale score and were dropped from the model. Dummy variables were created for each medical diagnosis; the missing category was other medical diagnoses. For medical diagnoses in the model, partial $F=2.1$, $df=6, 196, p \leq 0.05$ (model $F=20.0$, $df=8, 193, p \leq 0.001$; total $R^2=0.45$).

[b]Betas are standardized; for every 1 standard deviation change in the independent variable (e.g., time 1 religious coping index score), there is a beta standard deviation change in time 2 Geriatric Depression Scale score, with all other variables in the model controlled. For time 1 religious coping index score, SD=8.7; for time 2 Geriatric Depression Scale score, SD=5.8.

[c]$p \leq 0.001$.

[d]$p \leq 0.05$.

[e]$p \leq 0.01$.

Baseline predictors of time 2 Geriatric Depression Scale score were then examined. Bivariate analyses demonstrated significant correlations between time 2 Geriatric Depression Scale score and time 1 Geriatric Depression Scale score (r=0.64), social support (r=-0.16), functional status (r=-0.20), diagnosis of renal disease (r=0.15), and time 1 religious coping index score (r=-0.24). To control for confounding, hierarchical stepwise regression was again used (Table 6). Time 1 Geriatric Depression Scale score was entered first into the model, followed by 15 other predictors, with time 1 religious coping index score entered last. The final model contained three variables that predicted 45% of the variance in time 2 Geriatric Depression Scale score: time 1 Geriatric Depression Scale score, six medical diagnoses (renal disease in particular), and time 1 religious coping index score. No interactions between variables in the final model were significant. Thus, religious coping was the only baseline variable that predicted lower depression scores on follow-up (partial $F=10.4$, df$=1$, 193, $p=0.002$).

DISCUSSION

We found that religious beliefs and behavior were commonly used to manage stress in this medically ill group of older adults. When asked how they coped with their situations, 20% of the men spontaneously gave a response involving religion. Patients reported that trust or faith in God, prayer, Bible reading, and strong church relationships gave them comfort and a feeling of peace. We recognize that this finding may be in part due to the nature and location of our sample (southern VA hospital). A relatively high proportion of these patients were affiliated with conservative or black Protestant groups, whose traditions place strong emphasis on religion as a source of comfort in times of stress. The high rate documented among this all-male study group, however, is notable because religious coping is generally more common among women than men (Princeton Religion Research Center, 1982; Koenig, George, & Siegler, 1988), suggesting that this behavior might be even more prevalent in hospital samples that include women.

What are the characteristics of men who use religion to cope? Do they experience greater stress than other patients? Do they possess fewer socioeconomic or physical or mental health resources? In general, this was a group of older patients who had relatively severe medical illnesses, often advanced functional disabilities, low educational levels (the majority with less than a high school education), and yearly incomes averaging less than $10,000. The high rate of religious coping in this population, as we have discussed, suggests that it may indeed be characteristic of those with fewer coping resources. *Within* this group, however, there was no association between religious coping and level of functional disability, income, education, or previous occupation. On the other hand, religious coping was more common among those who were older, were black, or reported prior psychiatric problems— patients who may be more vulnerable to psychosocial or health stressors.

Furthermore, the strongest correlate of religious coping was religious affiliation (conservative, black, and fundamentalist/evangelical Protestant groups). This association by itself may have socioeconomic and health implications. The Piedmont Epidemiologic Catchment Area study showed that older members with these affiliations were more likely to come from lower socioeconomic classes, have lower educational levels, and have more chronic health problems and physical disabilities (Koenig, George, Blazer, Meador, & Pritchett, in press). Because these affiliations encourage affective release and emphasize religion as a source of comfort to those who are suffering, they may draw socioeconomically deprived or physically impaired elders into their congregations.

Some correlates of religious coping suggest mechanisms by which this behavior may help reduce stress and facilitate adaptation. Religious coping was positively related to both high level of social support and avoidance of alcohol, factors which in a VA hospital population could help to protect against emotional illness. Social support was one of the strongest inverse correlates of depression in these subjects (Koenig *et al.*, 1991). Religion may enhance social support by providing contacts with age-matched peers and/or by encouraging the development of supportive relationships within the religious community. In a study of older medical outpatients in Springfield, Ill., more than one-half of the subjects indicated that nearly all of their five closest friends came from their church congregations (Koenig, Moberg, & Kvale, 1988). For older black persons in particular, the church is reported to be a major source of informal social support (Taylor & Chatters, 1988).

Although many older men claimed that religion was helpful in coping with their illness, is there any evidence to substantiate these reports? We found religious coping to be inversely related to depression, whether assessed by self-report (Geriatric Depression Scale) or by clinician rating (Hamilton Rating Scale for Depression). This relationship was stronger among men who were more functionally disabled, and tended to be so among patients who reported histories of psychiatric problems. Note that these were also the groups who were the most depressed. Other investigators have similarly found an inverse correlation between religious cognition/behavior and depression in physically ill elders (Pressman, Lyons, Larson, & Strain, 1990; Idler, 1987) and those with psychiatric illness (Wolff, 1959; Kroll & Sheehan, 1989). Thus, these findings provide further evidence that religious coping behavior is especially helpful to older patients with few other physical or emotional resources. Studies have shown that when older persons are in situations over which they have little control, religious beliefs and behavior may counteract feelings of helplessness, provide meaning and order to experiences, and give back a sense of control (Kivett, 1979; Nelson, 1977).

As alternative explanation for the inverse relation between depression and religious coping is that as depression worsens, religious faith weakens. Depressed, physically ill persons may lose interest in religion (just as they do in other aspects of life) or may become angry at God for their poor health and dismal situation. Our data, however, provide little support for this explanation. In the follow-up portion of the study, religious coping did not decrease as depressive symptoms increased. If anything, increasing depression tended to be associated with increases in religious coping (r=0.06). Thus, our data and those of others (Crogg & Levine, 1972; O'Brien, 1982) indicate that when changes in religious coping occur during a period of increasing emotional stress in the context of physical illness, there is no decline in religious coping behavior.

Furthermore, in the longitudinal phase of our study, the baseline religious coping index score was the only sociodemographic or health variable that predicted lower depression scores on follow-up. Although the strength of the relationship was only modest, this finding provides additional evidence that the inverse relation between religious coping and depression in our cross-sectional study might have been due to a buffering effect of religious coping on depression, rather than to an inimical effect of depression on religious coping.

In this study, religious coping was measured with an index made up of both self-rated and observer-rated items. Religion was not defined, other than to say that it might include either belief or activity. However, religion was interpreted as Judeo-Christian by virtually all participants in the study. While this made assessment easier and allowed for high interrater reliability (Pearson's r=0.81) on the religious coping measure, it limits the generalizability of these results to religious cognition and behavior in the Judeo-Christian tradition.

Our finding of a high frequency of religious coping among older medical inpatients should alert consultation-liaison psychiatrists and nonpsychiatric health care providers to such behavior and to the possibly useful function it may serve. For elderly persons with health problems and stressful life situations, the immediate aim of psychotherapy is often to support healthy coping behavior (Dewald, 1971). Thus, knowledge of strategies that older persons use and find effective in facilitating adjustment is essential. Furthermore, because clinicians may play a role in controlling access to chaplains, religious reading materials, and religious services, identification of patients who rely heavily on religion as a coping behavior is necessary in order to direct resources appropriately.

The inverse relation between religious coping and depression documented here, while only moderate in strength, nevertheless has clinical importance because coping behavior is changeable and, unlike other health variables, can be affected by psychotherapeutic strategies. Religious cognition and behavior may be especially helpful to older patients with severe functional disability and in other situations where a sense of control is lost and other resources are limited. We recognize, however, that while the results of the present study are suggestive, only an intervention trial can definitively establish that religious behavior either prevents or relieves depression in this setting.

REFERENCES

Blake, R., & McKay, D. (1986). A single-item measure of social supports as a predictor of morbidity. *Journal of Family Practice, 22,* 82-84.

Blazer, D. (1982). Social support and mortality in an elderly community population. *American Journal of Epidemiology, 115,* 684-694.

Conway, K. (1985-86). Coping with the stress of medical problems a m o n g black and white elderly. *International Journal of Aging and Human Development, 21,* 39-48.

Crogg, S., & Levine, L. (1972). Religious identity and response to serious illness: a report on heart patients. *Social Science and Medicine, 6,* 17-32.

Dewald, R. (1971). *Psychotherapy: a dynamic approach.* New York: Basic Books, pp. 127-128.

Ellis, A. (1980). Psychotherapy and atheistic values: a response to A.E. Bergin's "Psychotherapy and religious values." *Journal of Consulting and Clinical Psychology, 48,* 642-645.

Fillenbaum, G. (1985). Screening the elderly: a brief instrumental activities of daily living measure. *Journal of the American Geriatrics Society, 33,* 698-705.

Folstein, M., Folstein, S., & McHugh, P. (1975). Mini-Mental State:A practical method for grading the cognitive state of patients for the clinician. *Journal of Psychiatric Research, 12,* 189-198.

Freud, S. (1927). *The future of an illusion. In Complete Psychological Works* (1961). vol 21. London, Hogarth Press.

Hamilton, M. (1967). Development of a rating scale for primary depressive illness. *British Journal of Social and Clinical Psychiatry, 6,* 278-296.

Idler, E. (1987). Religious involvement and the health of the elderly: some hypotheses and an initial test. *Social Forces, 66,* 226-238.

Katz, S., Downs, T., Cash, H., & Grotz, R. (1970). Progress in development of the index of ADL. *Gerontologist, 10,* 20-30.

Kitchell, M., Barnes, R., Veith, R., Okimoto J., & Raskind, M. (1982). Screening for depression in hospitalized geriatric medical patients. *Journal of the American Geriatrics Society, 30,* 174-177.

Kivett, V. (1979). Religious motivation in middle age: correlates and implications. *Journal of Gerontology, 34,* 106-115.

Kochansky, G. (1979). Psychiatric rating scales for assessing psychopathology in the elderly: a critical review. In A. Raskin & L. Jarvik (Eds.). *Psychiatric symptoms and cognitive loss in the elderly.* New York: John Wiley & Sons.

Koenig, H., Meador, K., Cohen, H., & Blazer, D. (1988). Depression in elderly hospitalized patients with medical illness. *Archives of Internal Medicine, 148,* 1929-1936.

Koenig, H., Moberg, D., & Kvale, J. (1988). Religious and health characteristics of patients attending a geriatric assessment clinic. *Journal of the American Geriatrics Society, 36,* 362-374.

Koenig, H., Meador, K., Cohen, H., & Blazer, D. (1988). Self-rated depression scales and screening for major depression in the older hospitalized patient with medical illness. *Journal of the American Geriatrics Society, 36,* 699-706.

Koenig, H., Smiley, M., & Gonzales, J. (1988). *Religion, health, and aging: A review and theoretical integration.* Westport, Conn: Greenwood Press, pp. 13-21.

Koenig, H., George, L., Blazer, D., Meador, K., & Pritchett, J. (in press). The relationship between religion and anxiety in a sample of community-dwelling older adults. *Journal of Geriatric Psychiatry.*

Koenig, H., George, L., & Siegler, I. (1988). The use of religion and other emotion-regulating coping strategies among older adults. *Gerontologist, 28,* 303-310.

Koenig, H., Meador, K., Shelp, F., Goli, V., Cohen, H., & Blazer, D. (1991). Major depressive disorder in hospitalized medically ill patients: an examination of young and elderly male veterans. *Journal of the American Geriatrics Society, 39,* 881-890.

Koenig, H., Meador, K., Goli, V., Shelp, F., Cohen, H., & Blazer, D. (1992). Self-rated depressive symptoms in medical inpatients: age and racial differences. *International Journal of Psychiatry in Medicine, 22,* 11-31.

Kroll, J., & Sheehan, W. (1989). Religious beliefs and practices among 52 psychiatric inpatients in Minnesota. *American Journal of Psychiatry, 146,* 67-72.

Myers, J., & Bean, L. (1968). Two-factor index of social position (Hollingshead). In J. Myers & L. Bean (Eds). *A decade later: A follow-up of social class and mental illness.* New York: John Wiley & Sons.

Nelson, F. (1977). Religiosity and self-destructive crises in the institutionalized elderly. *Suicide and Life Threatening Behavior, 7,* 67-73.

O'Brien, M. (1982). Religious faith and adjustment to long-term hemodialysis. *Journal of Religion and Health, 21,* 68-80.

Pressman, R., Lyons, J., Larson, D., & Strain, J. (1990). Religious belief, depression, and ambulation status in elderly women with broken hips. *American Journal of Psychiatry, 147,* 758-760.

Princeton Religion Research Center. (1982). *Religion in American.* Princeton, N.J.: Gallup Poll.

Roof, W., & McKinney, W. (1987). *American mainline religion.* New Brunswick, NJ: Rutgers University Press, 253-265.

Rosen, C. (1982). Ethnic differences among impoverished rural elderly in use of religion as a coping mechanism. *Journal of Rural Community Psychology, 3,* 27-34.

Sanua, V. (1969). Religion, mental health, and personality: a review of empirical studies. *American Journal of Psychiatry, 125,* 1203-1213.

SAS Institute. (1988). SAS Introductory Guide, release 6.03. Cary, N.C.

Schwab, J., Bialow, M., Clemmons, R., & Holzer, C. (1967). Hamilton rating scale for depression with medical inpatients. *British Journal of Psychiatry, 113,* 83-88.

Swanson, W., & Harter, C. (1971). How do elderly blacks cope in New Orleans? *International Journal of Aging and Human Development, 2,* 210-216.

Taylor, R., & Chatters, L. (1988). Church members as a source of informal social support. *Review of Religious Research, 30,* 193-203.

Wolff, K. (1959). Group psychotherapy with geriatric patients in a state hospital setting: results of a three year study. *Group Psychotherapy, 12,* 218-222.

Yesavage, J., Brink, T., Rose, T., Lum, O., Huang, V., Adey, M., & Leirer, V. (1982-83). Development and validation of a geriatric depression screening scale: a preliminary report. *Journal of Psychiatric Research, 17,* 37-49.

EDITOR'S COMMENTS

This study along with others in this volume demonstrates that the patient's religious/spiritual resources are valuable during illness and hospitalization because they "were commonly used to manage stress ...." The unique contribution of this study is its population, one which is widely regarded by the medical and nursing establishments as being difficult to manage in our high-tech hospitals. When ill, this population does not draw on its extensive education and scientific understanding of health and illness. Instead, as this study demonstrates, these persons rely on their religious/spiritual resources. This suggests that chaplains and pastors need to be especially tuned to these patients to provide them the support they need.

18

Assessment of Pastoral Needs Among Medical Outpatients

Larry VandeCreek
Susan Benes
Christina Nye

ABSTRACT

Reports research findings on samples of hospital outpatients, hospital inpatients, and well persons from the community in an attempt to explore the content and extent of pastoral needs among medical/surgical outpatients. Analyzes and presents statistical data which lead to the conclusion that the spiritual needs of outpatients manifest greater similarity to healthy persons in the community than to hospital inpatients. Notes limitations of the study and discusses praxis implications for chaplains.

The chaplain's ministry to medical/surgical outpatients is commanding increased attention. Holst (1987), near the end of his book, *Hospital Ministry: The Role of the Chaplain Today*, describes changes which hospitals are facing and notes that more services will be delivered on an outpatient basis. He adds, "Yet these patients and their families will face the same anxieties and have the same needs that in-patients have today who go through the same procedure...The patient needs will not

Reproduced with the permission of the Journal of Pastoral Care Publishers, Inc. from *The Journal of Pastoral Care*, (1993), 47(1), 44-53.

change, only the context" (p. 236). We believe that this opinion is widely held within the pastoral care field. We can find no empirical study in the published literature, however, which explores this claim or similar assumptions. Stelling (1988) describes a number of approaches to an outpatient ministry at a large tertiary cancer center, but his report contains no explicit evaluation of patient needs. An empirical study is needed which describes the needs of these patients, comparing them to inpatients and to healthy persons in the community.

This project was undertaken to explore the content and extent of pastoral needs among medical/surgical outpatients. It was one project within a broad strategic plan which sought to assess empirically the spiritual well-being among various populations of interest to hospital chaplains. Results of four studies from this effort have been published previously (VandeCreek, 1991; VandeCreek, 1992; VandeCreek & Smith, 1992a; VandeCreek & Smith, 1992b). These evaluation efforts identified and used established multi-dimensional questionnaires which generated baseline data to which outpatient results could be compared. Based on the outcome from these studies, we made directional (one-tailed) hypotheses concerning the results of this current study. Thus, rather than simply proposing that scores of healthy community persons, outpatients, and hospital inpatients would differ, we hypothesized the direction of the differences–that the scores of outpatients would demonstrate more similarity to healthy community persons than to hospital patients. This hypothesis contradicts Holst's statement quoted above and is based on our belief that the pastoral needs of outpatients remain lower because they continue to live with their families as well as in the community and because their disease process is often less severe. We believe that in this era of cost containment, persons are increasingly more ill when admitted to the hospital and that this is reflected in increased spiritual need, a level of need not experienced by those who remain outpatients.

We also generated directional hypotheses concerning differences within the outpatient subsample. We hypothesized that those patients whom the physician described as possessing chronic, organic disease with a more serious involvement of the "whole person" would reflect more spiritual needs on the assessment instruments. We believed that these patients would also require more time from the physician.

One difficulty with a study of outpatients lies with the diversity within this group. Outpatients include at least expectant mothers who visit their obstetrician, patients receiving routine care from their family physician, persons who come to their physician with serious symptoms expecting a new diagnosis, those under continuing specialist care for chronic disease, and cancer patients receiving chemotherapy or radiation. How can a single study group represent this diversity? In this project we respond to this problem simply by gathering data from persons who are outpatients of one specific medical/surgical specialist. These patients possess serious symptoms which often relate to a variety of diseases or traumas. We believe that this sample represents at least those outpatients with serious medical problems who are cared for by specialists.

METHODS

Subjects

We constructed a project with three convenient, unselected subsamples: outpatients, hospital patients, and well persons from the community. The first subsample consisted of 70 ophthalmology outpatients who sought medical attention from a surgeon at a large tertiary care medical center who specialized in eye problems secondary to traumas or chronic diseases such as diabetes, AIDS, or cancer. Thus, most of these patients possessed far more serious problems than the typical ophthalmology patient with cataracts or detached retinas. We believed they represented outpatients with a broad range of serious medical concerns although all had the ophthalmology problems in common. Many required long term care with monthly to biannual appointments, approximately 22% of whom eventually required eye surgery.

The second subsample consisted of 70 hospitalized patients in a large tertiary care hospital. These patients were from medical (n=18; 26%), surgical (n=33; 47%), and obstetrical (n=19; 27%) services. Most of these patients lived within 100 miles of the hospital (n=48; 68%), regarded themselves as not seriously ill(n=40; 57%), and had known their diagnosis for 6 months or less (n=43; 61%).

The third subsample contained 70 healthy volunteers from the community. These persons were members of a hospital volunteer corps or a Kiwanis Club. The demographic characteristics of the three subsamples are reported in Table 1.

TABLE 1
Demographics Of Patient And Community Subsamples

	Community Subsample*	Outpatient Subsample*	Hospital Patients*
Gender (male/female)	22/48	27/43	27/40
Age (mean years)	54.4	50.0	43.0
Race (Black/White)	3/66	6/64	8/62
Marital Status			
Never Married	13	11	15
Married	37	40	46
Divorced/Widowed	18	17	9
Educational Level			
High School	12	29	34
Some College	30	18	21
College Graduate	28	23	15
Religious Background			
Protestant	41	50	32
Catholic	8	12	14
Other	20	6	16
None	0	1	7
Pattern of Worship Attendance			
Not A Member	1	11	9
Once/Twice per Week	46	29	32
Once/month to once/year	14	16	22
Never/almost never	7	7	11

* N of all subsamples=70. Totals within the columns may not add to the sample size because of missing data.

Materials: Life Attitude Profile-Revised (LAP-R):

Reker has reported his development of the multidimensional Life Attitude Profile and his revision which refined and improved its psychometric properties (LAP-R) (Reker & Peacock, 1981; Reker, 1992). We believed this instrument assessed pastoral care needs and provided results relevant to the chaplain's work. The instrument, composed of 36-items in 6 dimensions, measured selected attitudes toward life and death on a 7-point Likert scale, responses ranging from strongly disagree (1) to strongly agree (7). We have described elsewhere the validity, reliability, and mean scores of this instrument when used with hospital patients, family members and community persons (VandeCreek, 1992).

Each dimension is now described. The *Purpose* dimension tests for the presence of life goals, a mission in life, a sense of direction and personal worthwhileness. A sample items reads, "I have discovered a satisfying life purpose." The *Coherence* dimension refers to a sense of order in one's life and a reason for existence. One of its items reads, "I have a framework that allows me to understand or make sense of my life." The *Existential Vacuum* dimension is a negative one which describes the lack of meaning in life, a lack of goals or direction and a free-floating anxiety. A sample item is, "I feel that some element which I can't quite define is missing from my life." The *Life Control* dimension reflects the freedom to make life choices and to exercise personal responsibility. It includes a sense of the internal control of life events, as for example, in the item, "I determine what happens in my life." The *Death Acceptance* dimension describes the absence of anxiety about death and the acceptance of it as "a natural, unavoidable aspect of life." The *Goal Seeking* dimension is also negative and refers to the need to reach out beyond the routine of life, to search for new experiences and challenges as exemplified in the item, "A new challenge in my life would appeal to me now." The *Personal Meaning Index* (PMI) is the sum of the purpose and coherence dimension scores. The *Life Attitude Balance Index* (LABI) is a total score obtained by summing the results of all the dimensions except for Existential Vacuum and Goal Seeking which are subtracted from the total. The range of possible scores is -60 to 156.

Reker has produced alpha coefficients for the 6 dimensions of this revised scale which range from 0.84 (Death Acceptance) to 0.71 (Goal Seeking). He has reported its validity in relation to many personal and psychological characteristics (1992).

Beck Depression Inventory (BDI):

The BDI was included because we believed depressive symptoms were associated with variations in the attitudes measured by the LAP-R. Beck introduced the BDI in 1961 and published a 25-year evaluation of it in 1988. It has become one of the most widely used instruments in assessing depressive symptoms in normal and psychiatric populations. Consisting of 21 items, each contains 4 statements which describe with increasing severity a particular depressive feature. Respondents circle the statement which "best describes the way you have been feeling the past week." The number of points assigned to each statement (0 to 3) increases with the severity of symptomatology described by the statement and their sum forms the total score of the instrument (range =

0 to 63). Typically, scores between 0 and 9 are regarded as normal, 10 through 18 as mild/moderate depression, 19 through 29 as moderate to severe, and 30 through 63 as severe depression.

A third evaluation component consisted of the ophthalmologist's judgements concerning the functional/organic and chronic/acute aspects of the patient's illness, registering these on two Likert scales, (0=functional/chronic; 10=organic/ acute). Additionally, she scored the seriousness of the patients' condition as regards eye disease and its impact on the "whole person" (Likert scale: 0=less serious;10=more serious). A record of the amount of time spent with each patient was also recorded.

Procedures

The two questionnaires were combined into a packet in counterbalanced order with a face sheet which explained the project, invited participation and promised confidentiality.   The outpatients were invited to participate by a research assistant as they waited for their appointment. The ophthalmologist author, blind to the questionnaire responses, made her patient evaluation at the end of the appointment on a separate sheet. Hospital patients were invited to participate by the research associate after she determined that they possessed the mental clarity and necessary stamina to complete the questionnaires. Data from the community subsample were gathered at their group meetings except for the hospital volunteer corps. Their responses were solicited by placing the packets and return envelopes in a lounge which they used when they arrived at the hospital.   The data were entered into a personal computer and analyzed with SPSSPC with statistical significance set at one-tailed p=0.05.

RESULTS

The first question of concern was whether the LAP-R and BDI scores would demonstrate that the outpatients in this study were similar to healthy community persons or to hospital patients. We hypothesized the former.

Past research suggested that demographic data such as that listed in Table 1 and depression results influenced some of the LAP-R scores. The ANOVA statistical procedure takes account of such influences and provides a clear picture concerning the real differences attributable to the three-subsample structure. We used the one-way analysis of variance to determine the level of demographic and depression influence on the LAP-R total and dimension scores and when these were less than p=0.05 we included that variable in the ANOVA analysis model. The ANOVA results of LAP-R total score are now described, followed by an analysis of each dimension score. Lastly, the depression scores are presented.

Life Attitude Balance Index (LABI):

The one-way analysis of variance demonstrated that the total score of the LAP-R was associated with the respondent's age and the depression data. These were included in the ANOVA model and both the age data (F=3.82; one-tailed p=0.001) and the depression scores (F=2.77; one-tailed p=0.05) were significant. When these influences were taken into account, the LAP-R total scores still distinguished between the three subsamples at a significant level (F=3.54; one-tailed p=0.02) as reported in Table 2 because inpatients generated significantly lower scores (M=73.30) than outpatients (M=75.87) and healthy persons in the community (M=74.98). The analysis of the dimension scores will provide more details concerning these differences.

TABLE 2
ANOVA Results of LAP-R Dimensions and BDI Scores For Three Populations

	Community Persons	Outpatients	Hospital Inpatients	ANOVA F Scores
LAP-R Dimensions				
Purpose	31.74	31.80	31.40	1.33
Coherence	31.90	31.93	32.07	0.73
Existential Vacuum	22.00	20.52	21.29	2.58*
Life Control	33.03	32.51	30.87	1.08
Death Acceptance	28.93	28.63	25.69	2.14
Goal Seeking	28.62	28.48	26.11	8.49**
PMI	63.60	63.42	64.18	2.50
LABI***	74.98	75.87	73.30	3.54**
BDI	5.91	7.22	9.71	6.45**

N of all subsamples = 70.
* indicates one-tailed p<0.05
** indicates one-tailed p<0.01
*** LABI scores are the sum of the four positive dimension scores minus the existential vacuum and goal seeking scores.

Purpose-in-Life Dimension:

The one-way analysis of variance demonstrated that the data concerning marital status, the pattern of attendance at worship and depression significantly interacted with the scores of this dimension. These were included in the ANOVA model and the results demonstrated that depression was a major influence on the scores of this dimension ($F=53.45$; one-tailed $p=0.000$) because inpatients created higher depression scores. When this influence of depression was taken into account, the data concerning marital status ($F=2.73$; one-tailed $p=0.03$) and the pattern of attendance at worship ($F=2.90$; one-tailed $p=0.03$) were still associated with the purpose-in-life scores at a significant level. As reported in Table 2, purpose-in-life scores were not significantly different between the three groups although those produced by the hospital patients were somewhat lower. Scores produced by outpatients and community persons were similar.

Coherence-in-life Dimension:

Data concerning patterns of attendance at worship and depression scores were associated with this dimension in the univariant test. When these were entered into the ANOVA model, the data concerning attendance at worship was significant ($F=5.09$; one-tailed $p=0.003$) along with depression scores ($F=3.61$; one-tailed $p=0.03$). The coherence-in-life dimension scores as reported in Table 2 were not significantly different between the three subsamples.

Existential Vacuum Dimension:

The respondent's age, marital status, and depression scores were associated with these dimension results in univariant tests. When they were entered into the model, both the depression scores ($F=47.77$; one-tailed $p=0.000$) and marital status data ($F=3.73$; one-tailed $p=0.01$) were significantly influential. The age data did not possessed a significant influence on the scores. The ANOVA also found a significant difference between the three subsamples ($F=2.58$; one-tailed $p=0.04$) after accounting for the influence of depression and marital status. The community persons displayed the most existential vacuum ($M=22.00$); outpatients generated a mean score of 20.52 and inpatients a score of 21.29. These scores described the outpatients as more like the inpatients.

Life Control Dimension:

The scores which described this dimension were associated only with the depression scores. The ANOVA results indicated that depression scores were highly influential (F=16.34; one-tailed p=0.000). The mean scores of this dimension in Table 2 were not significantly different although outpatients were more closely related to community persons than to inpatients.

Death Acceptance Dimension:

These data were associated with the respondent's age and depression scores in the univariant testing. The ANOVA results demonstrated that both were significantly influential in the model (age F=4.83; one-tailed p=0.000 and depression F=8.28; one-tailed p=0.002). When these influences were accounted for, the mean scores of this dimension between the three populations were not significantly different although a trend was evident (F=2.14; one-tailed p=0.06). Once again the scores of outpatients and community persons were very similar.

Goal Seeking Dimension:

Data concerning age, marital status, religious background and depression were significantly associated with the means of the three subsamples. In the ANOVA model only age (F=3.04; one-tailed p=0.006) and depression (F=7.25; one-tailed p=0.004) were significantly influential. Additionally, the mean scores of the three subsamples were significantly different (F=8.49; one-tailed p=0.000) because inpatients created lower goal seeking scores (M=26.11). Community persons (M=28.62) and outpatients scores (M=28.48) were similar.

Personal Meaning Index (PMI):

The PMI scores are created by adding the purpose and coherence dimension totals. Religious background, patterns of attendance at worship, and depression scores were significantly related to them. In the ANOVA, depression scores continued to be significant (F=24.59; one-tailed p=0.000) as well as the relationship to religious background (F=3.68; one-tailed p=0.01). Data concerning patterns of attendance at worship were also significantly related (F=2.71; one-tailed p=0.03). The three subsamples were distinguished on the basis of their mean scores as reported in Table 2 (F=2.50; one-tailed p=0.04). Outpatient scores were more similar to community persons than to hospital outpatients.

The depression mean scores are also reported in Table 2. While all of these means are nearly within the normal range as described by Beck, a gradual rise in the scores is noted. As indicated in the Table, these differences are statistically significant.

We also hypothesized that differences would exist within the outpatient subsample based on the physician's evaluation. We believed that patients whom the physician described as possessing chronic, organic disease with a more serious involvement of the "whole person" would generate scores on the assessment instrument which reflected more spiritual need and require more time from the physician. We proceeded to investigate this hypothesis by reducing the Likert scale data to a dichotomous variable, splitting the patient sample at the median score of each Likert scale. The organic/functional physician evaluation split the subsample into two groups (functional patients=20; organic=50) and these groups produced a statistically significant difference in the scores of two dimensions: death acceptance (t-test: t=1.74; one-tailed p=0.04) and goal seeking (t=1.64; one-tailed p=0.05) dimensions. In the death acceptance dimension, those patients whom the ophthalmologist judged to possess more organic disease produced lower mean scores (M=27.70) indicating less death acceptance than those assessed as presenting more functional involvement (M=30.85). As regards the goal seeking dimension, patients judged to be struggling with organic disease were less involved in goal seeking (M=27.70) when compared to the patients with more functional illness (M=30.20). It is important to remember that LAP-R goal seeking dimension is a negative category, reflecting the assumption that an increase in this activity reflects a lack of existing goals. None of the other LAP-R dimensions or the BDI scores produced statistically significant associations to the organic/functional evaluation.

The chronic/acute evaluation data were reduced in the same manner, in this instance splitting the 70 patients into two groups of 35 each. No statistically significant differences were found in LAP-R scores between these two groups although a trend existed in the purpose dimension (t=1.56; one-tailed p=.06) because chronically ill patients tended to produce lower mean scores (30.71) than those who were acutely ill (32.94). A significant difference in BDI scores did exist between the groups (t=1.66;one-tailed p=.05) because chronically ill patients created higher scores (M=8.54) than those acutely ill (5.85).

The ophthalmologist also evaluated each patient concerning the seriousness of eye and whole person involvement and these data were also split at the median. When the ophthalmologist's evaluation described more serious eye problems (n=31 vs 39 with less serious problems), the total LAP-R scores (LABI) reported a statistically significant poorer adjustment (t=2.78; one-tailed p=0.003). The difference in the scores on two dimensions of the scale greatly influenced this total score: death acceptance (t=2.25; one-tailed p=0.01) and goal seeking (t=1.72; one-tailed p=0.04). The death acceptance score was significant because the less seriously ill patients were more accepting of death (M=30.31) than those whose illness was more serious (M=26.45). The goal seeking scores were significant because the less seriously ill patients were involved in seeking for more goals (M=29.61) than those who were seriously ill (M=26.90).

The same trend was evident in the evaluation of the "whole person." A significant difference existed between those whose disease had less impact on the function of the "whole person" (n=33), and those who were more compromised (n=37). Death acceptance scores differed (t=2.06; one-tailed p=0.02) because the less seriously ill were more accepting (M=30.45) than those who were seriously ill (M=26.95). The association between the "whole person" evaluation and goal seeking scores was also significant (t=1.68; one-tailed p=0.05) because the less serious were more involved in seeking goals for their lives (M=29.79) than those who were seriously ill (M=27.19).

We also hypothesized differences in the length of appointment time. The median length of time spent with each patient was 45 minutes for the nurse/technician and one hour for the physician. No significant association was found between the scores and the amount of time spent with the patient.

Discussion

We believe that the pastoral care community is increasingly interested in the ministry to medical/surgical outpatients. No empirical study has examined the pastoral needs of this population and at least some in this community assume that the needs are similar to those persons in the hospital. We demonstrate that, at least in this population, the assumption needs to be challenged. Using a valid and reliable instrument, the LABI mean score of hospital patients is significantly lower than the other two subsamples, demonstrating more spiritual need. The LABI score of outpatients is, in fact, slightly higher than those of persons in the community. These differences are present even though the more seriously ill inpatients could not participate in the study. Presumable their participation would lower the scores of the inpatient subsample even further. We have also removed the influence of depression and demographic characteristics from the scores.

These findings do not suggest that outpatient ministry is meaningless or a low priority. Rather, we believe the results indicate that outpatient ministry, at least to a population such as we studied here, must focus on specific needs of specific persons. The results from this project suggest that attention to existential vacuum, goal seeking, and depressive symptoms are particularly relevant. Further, results suggest that chronicity of organic disease with increased involvement of the "whole person" leads to increased spiritual need. Thus, the LAP-R scores differ when the patient subsample is divided at the median and comparison made according to functional/organic, the seriousness of the eye problems and their impact on the "whole person". Those patients whose visit to the ophthalmologist roots in organic problems seem to sense the seriousness of their illness and to reflect this by lower death acceptance scores. The mean score of those with functional involvement are actually slightly higher (M=30.85) than those generated by the community subsample (M=28.93), but not at a level so as to be statistically significant. The goal seeking dimension is a negative one and those patients judged to be suffering with more organic disease reflect less seeking of additional goals than those with functional involvement. Those with more function involvement generate slightly higher means (30.20) than the community subsample (M=28.60). If we accept Crumbaugh's assertion that the seeking behavior takes place when life goals are diminished, these findings hint that those patients with functional involvement lack goals in their lives. The data from this research design can not determine whether these more functionally ill patients lack these goals because of the illness or whether the illness takes on increased functional proportion because the patient lacks goals. These results suggest the type of outpatient who may especially benefit from pastoral care and the themes which may be important to them.

The relationship between the LAP-R and BDI scores merit careful discussion. In the analysis presented above, we screen out the influence of the depression scores by entering them as a variable in the ANOVA model, thereby attempting to create a clearer picture of the LAP-R dimensions. We believe that this is legitimate and it demonstrates that the depression scores are very influential, more often influential than whether a respondent was a healthy person in the community, an outpatient, or an inpatient. The separation between the LAP-R dimensions and BDI scores, however, can also be artificial if carried too far. From a clinical point of view, the scores of the LAP-R and the BDI may reflect the same phenomenon. Certainly, depressive symptoms include a diminished sense of purpose in life and sense of control over it, two of the LAP-R dimensions. Indeed, a number of items on the BDI would be appropriate to include in the LAP-R. Thus it becomes clear that aspects of spiritual need overlap with depressive symptoms and that the latter as well as the former is at least to some extent an appropriate concern of chaplains. If the depression variable is not included in the ANOVA model to account for its influence, then the differences between the three subsamples are even greater.

These results must be evaluated in the context of the project's limitations. The outpatient subsample is a homogeneous one from the patient panel of one physician in one specialty at one hospital. This design made data gathering easier but it also limits the populations to which the results can be applied. We believe, for example, that spiritual need is very high when an outpatient receives a new diagnosis for a potentially life threaten disease. These patients also merit empirical study and we believe that our results are not generalizable to them. Other special populations also deserve study. Another limitation of the study is the small subsample sizes although we believe the results are reliable and valid. Generally, they are compatible with results from our previous studies. An additional limitation is the use of specific self-administered questionnaires. Such instruments, while providing empirical data, also strictly limit what respondents can report about themselves. It is likely that other pastoral care needs exist which are not addressed by these questionnaires.

We conclude that the spiritual needs of outpatients as represented by these scores demonstrate greater similarity to healthy persons in the community than to hospital inpatients. Ministry to them can helpfully focus on the specific pastoral needs of those with chronic, organic disease which is affecting their "whole persons."

REFERENCES

Holst, L. (1987). The chaplain in the future: threats and opportunity. In Lawrence Holst (Ed.), *Hospital ministry: the role of the chaplain today* (p 236). New York: Crossroads Publishing Co.

Reker, G., & Peacock, E. (1981). The life attitude profile (LAP): a multidimensional instrument for assessing attitudes toward life. *Canadian Journal of Behavioral Science, 13*, 264-273.

Reker, G. (1992).*Manual of the life attitude profile and the life attitude profile-revised.* Peterborough, Ontario: Gary Reker, Department of Psychology, Trent University, Peterborough, Ontario K9J 7B8.

Stelling, J. (1988). Outpatient ministry: University of Texas System Cancer Center. *Caregiver Journal, 5*, 109-114.

VandeCreek, L. (1991). Identifying the spiritually needy patient: the role of demographics." *Caregiver Journal, 8*(3), 38-47.

VandeCreek, L. (1992). Pastoral assessment of selected attitudes among hospital patients and family members," *Pastoral Sciences 11*, 67-80.

VandeCreek, L., & Smith, D. (1992a). Measuring the spiritual needs of hospital patients and their families. *The Journal of Pastoral Care 46*(1), 46-52.
VandeCreek, L., & Smith, D. (1992b). The spiritual well-being and needs of parishioners. *Journal of Religion and Health, 30* (4), 299-309.

19

Factors Associated with Meaning in Life Among People with Recurrent Cancer

Elizabeth Johnston Taylor

ABSTRACT

Attribution theory proposes that negative or unexpected events challenge one's sense of meaning. The purpose of this correlational, cross-sectional study was to determine what factors were associated with the sense of meaning in life among people with recurrent cancer. A convenience sample of 74 subjects completed 6 survey instruments, including the Purpose in Life (PIL) Test, Symptom Distress Scale, Enforced Social Dependency Scale, and Psychosocial Adjustment to Illness Scale, as well as two surveys developed by the author to assess aspects of the search for meaning, and demographic and illness variables. Significant negative Pearson correlations were found between sense of meaning and the following variables: symptom distress, social dependency, and length of time since diagnosis of recurrence. Adjustment to illness was associated with a clear sense of meaning. Analysis of variance indicated that married subjects had significantly higher PIL Test scores than single subjects. In concert, these factors accounted for 38% of the variance in sense of meaning. These findings empirically demonstrate that the sense of meaning

---

Reproduced with permission of the Oncology Nursing Society from *Oncology Nursing Forum*, (1993), 20(9), 1399-1405.

is integrally associated with the physical and psychosocial effects of illness and suggest that oncology nurses must understand how to care for those who search for meaning.

Healthcare and social psychology literature strongly suggest that people experiencing loss, change, victimization, or a traumatic life event search for meaning (Silver & Wortman, 1980; Janoff-Bulman & Frieze, 1983; Taylor, 1983; Marris, 1986; Thompson & Janigian, 1988). The experience of having cancer is one such traumatic life event, and there is substantial evidence that people living with cancer search for meaning (Bard & Dyk, 1956; Taylor, 1983; Haberman, 1987; O'Conner, Wicker, & Germino, 1990; Steeves, 1992). Indeed, there is evidence that the search for meaning may be particularly prevalent, or intensified, among people with recurrent cancer (Scott, Goode, & Arlin, 1983; Chekryn, 1984; Weisman & Worden, 1986; Mahon, Cella, & Donovan, 1990).

The experience of living with a recurrent cancer has largely been neglected by researchers (Cella, Mahon, & Donovan, 1990). This is particularly disappointing, considering the prevalence of recurrent cancer as well as the significant degree of distress that appears to be associated with it. Indeed, 52% of the more than 1 million people diagnosed with cancer today will be alive five years from now, suggesting that many of them will experience at least one recurrence of cancer (American Cancer Society, 1993).

LITERATURE REVIEW

Conceptual Framework

Frankl (1984) proposed that the "will to meaning" is a primary concern and motivating force in human life. Thus, Frankl infers that the need for meaning in life is innate and universal. Some have theorized that the search for meaning progresses through developmental phases (Fowler, 1981; Kegan, 1982). Others propose that one's sense of meaning is challenged by various life events (e.g., Janoff-Bulman & Frieze, 1983; Thompson & Janigian, 1988; Wong & Weiner, 1981). Indeed, the search for meaning has been variously defined as "making sense" of circumstances by finding reasons (Marris, 1986; Silver, Boon, & Stones, 1983), "construing good" (Taylor, Wood, & Lichtman, 1983), and understanding how an event "fits into a larger context" (Thompson & Janigian). Purpose also has often been equated with, or subsumed by, the concept of meaning (Crumbaugh & Maholick, 1981; Highfield & Cason, 1983; Thompson & Janigian; Yalom, 1980).

The sense of meaning among medically ill populations often has been studied using an approach based upon attribution theory. Although this attributional research typically investigates patients' explanations of causality (e.g. Bulman & Wortman, 1977; Gotay, 1985; Lowery, Jacobsen, & McCauley, 1987; Taylor, Lichtman, & Wood, 1983), the theory also addresses the wider phenomenon of meaning (Heider, 1958; Weiner, 1986). Attribution theory posits that negative or unexpected events precipitate the quest for causal understanding, including answers to "Why?" questions (Wong & Weiner, 1981). Attributions provide the attributor with explanations, predictions, self-protection, and social identity (Forsyth, 1980). This form of cognitive control assists people in perceiving control in the face of seemingly uncontrollable events (Lewis, 1987; Rothbaum, Weisz, & Snyder, 1982).

Previous Research

Prior studies of people with cancer have measured relationships between the sense of meaning and other factors. Acklin, Brown, and Mauger (1983) observed negative correlations between sense of meaning and despair, anger/ hostility, and isolation. Similarly, Lewis (1982; 1989) found a clear sense of meaning was positively correlated with a sense of personal (versus external) control and was predictive of low anxiety and healthy self-concept. Taylor, Lichtman, and Wood's (1984) and Gotay's (1985) research found no significant relationship between specific attributions and adjustment to cancer. These two studies demonstrate the complex relationship between attributions and adjustment, which is mediated by multiple factors and in need of further study (Michela & Wood, 1986; Turnquist, Harvey, & Andersen, 1988).

Living with Recurrent Cancer

A search of psychosocial oncology literature revealed only five reports of research and two clinical articles addressing the experience of recurrent cancer (i.e. Cella, Mahon, & Donovan, 1990; Chekryn, 1984; Mahon, 1991; Mahon, Cella, & Donovan, 1990; Schmale, 1976; Scott, Goode, & Arlin, 1983; Weisman & Worden, 1986). A salient theme to emerge from this literature was the occurrence of distress related to the patient's realization that death might be more imminent than he or she previously had thought. Existential concerns and the search for meaning were observed by several researchers (Chekryn; Weisman & Worden; Mahon, Cella, & Donovan; Scott, Goode, & Arlin). This literature also describes how physical health and disability are significant concerns for people diagnosed with recurrent cancer.

PURPOSE

A dearth of empirical knowledge regarding both the experience of recurrent cancer and the sense of meaning among physically ill populations exists. Because recurrent cancer is a life event that challenges the sense of meaning, this study explored the sense of meaning and factors associated with meaning among adults living with recurrent cancer. Thus, the purposes of this investigation were to measure the sense of meaning among people with recurrent cancer and to identify factors associated with the sense of meaning among these people.

Whereas previous studies have measured the relationship between sense of meaning and psychological factors, this study explored the associations between sense of meaning and selected illness-related factors. These illness-related factors included symptom distress, dependency, and illness variables such as cancer site, length of time since diagnosis, and length of disease-free interval. Likewise, because of the discrepancy between theory and empirical knowledge regarding the relationship between adjustment and sense of meaning, adjustment to illness was included as a variable for study.

METHODS

Sample

Power analysis determined that 68 subjects were necessary in order to achieve "good" statistical power (with a medium effect size of 0.40, power value of 0.96, and significance level of 0.05) for the correlational procedures this study initially employed for data analysis (Cohen, 1988). However, a convenience sample of 74 subjects participated in the investigation. These subjects were recruited from two oncology outpatient departments in a large university hospital in Philadelphia, PA.

Criteria for selecting subjects included (a) a diagnosis, within the past year, of recurrent cancer that had been preceded by one disease-free interval since the time of the first cancer diagnosis, (b) an age of at least 18 years, (c) verbal fluency in the English language, (d) absence of medically diagnosed mental illness (past or present), and (e) willingness to participate.

Instruments

Subjects completed four standardized instruments, and two survey tools designed by the investigator. The Crumbaugh and Maholick (1981) Purpose in

Life (PIL) Test, constructed to measure the sense of meaning in life, is a 20-item tool with 7-point Likert scale response options. In addition to establishing norms, the authors of this attitudinal scale established construct and concurrent validity and reliability with a variety of adult populations. While PIL Test scores may range from 20 to 140, scores above 112 indicate a clear sense of meaning, scores between 92 to 112 indicate indecisiveness, and scores below 92 indicate a clear lack of meaning. The internal consistency reliability of PIL Test with the present sample was acceptable, with a Cronbach's alpha of 0.88.

The **Psychosocial Adjustment to Illness Scale—Self Report** (PAIS-SR; Derogatis & Lopez, 1983) measures the multidimensional concept of adjustment to medical illness. This scale quantifies responses in seven domains: healthcare orientation, vocational environment, domestic environment, sexual relationships, extended family relationships, social environment, and psychological distress. For each of the 46 items, the subject selects one of four ranked responses. Reliability has been established for each of the instrument's domains, as have convergent and predictive validity. The overall reliability coefficient for the present sample was 0.92; likewise, the alphas for the subscales were similar to those obtained by the tool's authors. The scoring procedure employed for this study used the normative profile established for a mixed sample of patients with cancer. The sum of domain raw scores was the statistic used in data analysis because a global measure of adjustment was desired. A high PAIS-SR score indicates poor adjustment.

The **Symptom Distress Scale** (SDS; McCorkle, 1987; McCorkle & Young, 1978) was used to measure the severity of subjects' symptom distress. The 13-item SDS is a self-report instrument with 5-point Likert scale response options. A low score indicates little symptom distress. The items address nausea, appetite, insomnia, pain, fatigue, bowel pattern, concentration, appearance, breathing, outlook, and cough. The instrument's authors have documented acceptable reliability, and content and construct validity, among patients with cancer. The internal reliability of the tool with the present sample was 0.83 (Cronbach's alpha).

The **Enforced Social Dependency Scale** (ESDS; Benoliel, McCorkle, & Young, 1980) quantifies the amount of assistance with activities of daily living (ADL) required by people with a debilitating illness in order to perform their adult roles. The 10-item ESDS elicits information about eating, dressing, walking, traveling, bathing, toileting, household and vocational work roles, social roles, and communication. ESDS data are solicited by an interviewer asking questions designed to assess the degree of change in social dependency since the onset of illness. The tool offers suggested questions for each of the 10 items, as well as guidelines for scoring the response. The reliability and content validity have been demonstrated for patients with cancer. The internal reliability of the tool with the present sample was 0.85 (Cronbach's alpha). Because there was only one data collector, interrater reliability was not a concern. A low score indicates minimal dependence.

Two survey instruments were designed by the investigator for this study. The **Search for Meaning Survey** (SMS) gathered information about the subject's experience of searching for meaning. The two SMS items pertinent to the present discussion were: "With respect to your illness, have you found yourself searching for meaning?" (with yes/no response options); and "As a result of your search/questions, have you found any meaning/ answers?" (with four response options). A demographic tool was used to gather data about personal and illness characteristics.

Procedure and Setting

After the study was described to the patient and informed consent was obtained, the 6 instruments were given to the subject with instructions for completing them. Often, subjects elected to complete the instruments at home and return them by mail. Thus, 25 subjects completed at least half of the tools in their homes or offices. The ESDS was completed either by telephone or at the time the study was introduced. While 37 subjects completed the tools in an outpatient clinic setting, 12 participated in the study as hospitalized patients. A few subjects requested that the investigator read the items and responses to them. These "interviews" frequently required nearly one hour for completion. Whereas most subjects completed all of the instruments within an hour, some subjects required several days to complete the surveys. Because the study's design did not strictly control for time, it is assumed that this procedural complication did not significantly influence the data.

RESULTS

The 74 subjects with recurrent cancer reflected a variety of illness and demographic variables. Subjects' characteristics are provided in Table 1. The high number of male subjects (relative to the number in other studies of subjects with recurrent cancer) and the fairly high socio-economic status are noteworthy. Subjects typically were female, Caucasian, Protestant, married, and living with family.

Although all of these subjects had been diagnosed with recurrent cancer after one disease-free interval, illness circumstances varied in many ways (see Table 1). All but two of the subjects' recurrent cancers appear to have been related to their first cancer diagnosis. All of the subjects had received or currently were receiving some form of medical therapy or diagnostic surgery for cancer. All 74 subjects had been diagnosed with recurrent cancer within 21 months prior to their interview (90% within the past year). Subjects' disease-free intervals varied from two months to 32 years.

TABLE 1
Frequencies and Descriptive Statistics
on Major Demographic Variables

Variable	Frequency	Percent
Age[a]		
20-29	3	4.1
30-39	12	16.2
40-49	12	16.2
50-59	20	27.0
60-69	17	23.0
70-79	9	12.1
80-89	1	1.4
Marital Status		
Single	10	13.5
Married	54	73.0
Remarried	3	4.1
Divorced/separated	4	5.4
Widowed	3	4.1
Living Situation		
Lives alone	8	10.8
Lives with family	64	86.5
Lives with non-family	2	2.7
Occupation		
Student	1	1.4
Housewife	10	13.5
Unskilled worker	4	5.4
(Table 1 continued)		
Blue collar	12	16.2
White collar	23	31.1
Professional/manager	24	32.4
Gender		
Female	45	60.8
Male	29	39.2

(Table 1, Continued)

Ethnicity

Asian	1	1.4
Black	13	17.6
Caucasian	60	81.1

Religion

Roman Catholic	23	31.1
Jewish	10	13.5
Protestant	32	43.2
Other/unspecified	5	6.8
Atheist/none	4	5.4

Education (in years attended school)[b]

8-11	8	10.8
12	27	36.5
13-16	27	36.5
17-18	7	9.5
19-24	5	6.9

Site/type of recurrent cancer

Breast	31	41.9
Non-solid tumors	14	18.9

(Table 1 continued)

Melanoma	2	2.7
Colorectal	12	16.2
Genitourinary	6	8.1
Head/neck/gastric/esophagus/ lung/pancreas	9	12.2

Disease-free interval (in months)[c]

2-8	20	27.0
9-18	12	16.2
19-30	7	9.5
31-60	19	25.7
61-90	7	9.4
91-200	6	8.1
201-300	2	2.8
300-399	1	1.4

(Table 1, Continued)
Time since diagnosis of
    recurrent cancer (in months)[d]

<2	11	14.9
2-4	28	37.8
5-8	22	29.7
9-12	7	9.5
13-17	5	6.9
21	1	1.4

[a]M=53.7; SD=13.6 [b]M=14.07;SD=3.1 [c]M=46.4;SD=61.8
[d]M=5.4;SD=4.4

Subjects' physiologic and psychosocial responses to their recurrent cancer experience were measured using the SDS, ESDS, and the PAIS-SR (see Table 2). PIL Test results provide understanding regarding the sense of meaning among these subjects with recurrent cancer. Subjects' PIL Test scores ranged from 69 to 137. The average score was 108.7 (SD=17). The scores formed a moderately negative and slightly platykurtic curve.

TABLE 2
Results of Standardized Instruments[a]

Instrument	Mean	SD	Range	Possible Range	Alpha
Symptom Distress Scale	24.1	7.6	13-44	13-65	0.8339
Enforced Social Dependency Scale	22.0	6.9	11-38	10-51	0.8501
Psychosocial Adjustment to Illness Scale-Self-report (raw score)	29.2	18.0	3-91	0-138	0.9176
Purpose in Life Test	108.7	16.9	68-137	20-140	0.8832

[a]N=74, except for Psychosocial Adjustment to Illness Scale-Self report(N=71)

Using Pearson correlations, PIL Test scores were found to be significantly associated with PAIS-SR, SDS, and ESDS scores in a negative and low-moderate degree (see Table 3). PAIS-SR subscales that significantly correlated with the sense of meaning included those that assessed healthcare orientation (r=-0.47), domestic abilities (r=-0.32), psychological distress (r=-0.37, and social abilities (r=-0.29). A significant inverse relationship also was found between PIL Test scores and length of time since diagnosis of recurrence. However, correlations between PIL Test scores and income, education, and length of disease-free interval were not statistically significant.

TABLE 3

Correlations among
Sense of Meaning, Symptom Distress, Social Dependency, Adjustment to
Illness and Length of Time since Diagnosis of Recurrence[a]

	Meaning	Adjustment	Symptoms	Dependency	Time
Meaning (PIL Test)	1.00				
Adjustment (PAIS-SR)	-0.396**	1.00			
Symptom (SDS)	-0.3073*	0.6605**	1.00		
Dependency (ESDS)	-0.2840*	0.5041**	0.4704**	1.00	
Time	-0.3116*	0.2953*	0.1725	-0.0362	1.00

Abbreviations: PIL Test=Purpose in Life Test; PAIS-SR=Psychosocial adjustment to Illness Scale-Self report; SDS=Symptom distress Scale; ESDS=Enforced Social Dependency Scale. Time=number of months since subject was diagnosed with the recurrent cancer. [a]N=71. *Denotes 1-tailed significance at 0.01 level; ** Denotes 1-tailed significance at 0.001 level.

One-way analysis of variance (ANOVA) with least significant difference demonstrated that married (including remarried) subjects had significantly higher PIL Test scores than did nonmarried (including separated, divorced, and widowed) subjects (F=2.72; df=4.69; p=0.036). Because the subjects' ages reflected a very wide range, PIL Test scores were compared among the young (23-40 years), middle-aged (41-60 years), and elderly (61-81 years) subjects. The young adults had significantly lower PIL Test scores than the middle-aged adults, who scored slightly higher than the elderly subjects (ANOVA with Scheffe, F=3.87; df=2.71; p=0.025).

However, ANOVA demonstrated no significant differences in PIL Test scores by religion, degree of religiosity, gender, ethnicity, occupation, employment status, living situation, or site of diagnosis. Comparing group means revealed no significant difference between the PIL Test scores of those who answered that they had searched versus those who answered that they had not searched for meaning (per SMS). However, PIL Test scores were significantly greater for subjects who answered that they had found at least some meaning than for those who responded that no meaning had been found (F=12.64; df=2.47; p=0.000).

Partial correlational and multiple regression analysis were completed to examine multicollinearity among the various independent variables, as well as to examine their ability to determine sense of meaning (see Table 4). Multiple regression analysis demonstrated that when adjustment, dependency, symptom distress, time since diagnosis, and marital status were considered in concert, they accounted for 38% of the variance in sense of meaning (multiple $R=0.61$; adjusted $R^2=0.33$; $F=7.85$; $df=5$; $p=0.00001$). Using the stepwise method of entry (with a criterion of probability for an F-test to enter of 0.05), the regression equation demonstrated that adjustment and marital status were the best predictors of sense of meaning, accounting for 33.5% of its variance. That is, positive adjustment to illness (Beta=-0.47) and being married (Beta=0.43) predicted a clear sense of meaning. Symptom distress and dependency showed little effect on sense of meaning once adjustment was entered into the equation.

TABLE 4
Results of Multiple Regression Analysis

Variables	B	Standard Error B	Beta	Part Corr.	Partial
Psychosocial Adjustment to					
Illness-Self report	-0.357	0.410	-0.379	-0.249	-0.301
Marital Status	16.662	4.144	0.411	0.394	0.446
Time	-0.802	0.406	-0.208	-0.193	-0.238
Enforced Social Dependency	-0.302	0.297	-0.121	-0.099	-0.125
Symptom Distress Scale	0.111	0.299	0.050	0.036	0.046
(Constant)	115.156	8.194			

DISCUSSION

SDS and ESDS results suggested that these subjects with recurrent cancer experienced a moderate amount of symptom distress and were moderately dependent upon others or equipment. The PAIS-SR scores demonstrate that these subjects' adjustment to illness did not differ from that of the patients with cancer upon which the scale's normative profile was based. This result differs from Mahon, Cella, and Donovan's (1990) subjects with recurrent cancer who all scored one to two standard deviations above norm on the PAIS-SR, indicating poor adjustment. However, this difference may be accounted for by the fact that 70% of their subjects were hospitalized, compared to the 5.7% in the present study.

Comparing these subjects' mean PIL Test scores of 108.7 with the normative average 112.4 demonstrated that these subjects had significantly lower test scores than those of the general population (t=-1.88; df=73; p<0.05). Indeed, these subjects' scores are similar to undergraduates' (M=108.4) and the indigent hospitalized patients' (M=106.4) scores (Crumbaugh & Maholick, 1981). Based upon the PIL Test authors' suggestion for interpreting scores, the test results of 12 (16.2%) subjects indicated a lack of clear meaning, 30 (40.6%) indicated indecisiveness, and the majority (32, or 43.2%) had scores reflecting a clear sense of meaning.

The modest, inverse correlations between the sense of meaning and symptom distress, dependency, and adjustment indicate that both high symptom distress and increased dependence are associated with a low (or unclear) sense of meaning, and that an unclear sense of meaning is associated with poor adjustment to illness. Furthermore, people who perceive difficulty with the health care that they receive, with social and domestic disability, and with psychological distress tend to have an unclear sense of meaning. The negative correlation between sense of meaning and length of time since diagnosis demonstrates that the longer people live with the recurrent cancer, the more unclear their sense of meaning.

Although middle-aged and married subjects were found to have a significantly greater sense of meaning than young adults and elderly and unmarried subjects, no other demographic or illness factors were found to be associated with the sense of meaning in life among these patients with recurrent cancer, including education, income, length of disease-free interval, gender, ethnicity, education, income, religion (or degree of religiosity) type or status of work, living situation, or type of cancer. Furthermore (and more intriguing), sense of meaning was not related to whether or not a search for meaning was reported.

Nursing Practice Implications

These findings suggest implications and applications for nursing practice. First, the association between the physiologic and social results of illness (i.e., symptom distress and dependency) and the psychospiritual response to illness (i.e. sense of meaning) is explicitly illustrated by the results of this study. This illustration provides empirical evidence to support the view that nurses' caring must address the whole person—the physical, social, psychological, and spiritual dimensions of being.

Second, these findings suggest risk factors for an unclear sense of meaning among people with recurrent cancer. Nursing interventions designed to assist patients in ascribing meaning should be targeted particularly toward those who experience high symptom distress; are dependent, not adjusting to their illness, unmarried, and young; and who have lived with their recurrence for several months.

Whereas marital status and time since diagnosis are variables over which nurses have no control, adjustment to illness, symptom distress, and dependency are variables upon which nurses can have a profound influence. Thus, nursing interventions that decrease symptom distress and promote independence may indirectly assist patients in experiencing satisfactory meaning during their illness. Likewise, this study's findings suggest that helping patients to manage their domestic and social environments, as well as the healthcare system, may also contribute their sense of meaning.

Third, although 43% of these subjects demonstrated a clear sense of meaning, the other 57% indicated an indecisive or unclear sense of meaning. Because these subjects' sense of meaning before diagnosis is unknown, it is inappropriate to conclude that the experience of recurrent cancer either strains or strengthens one's sense of meaning. For patients who possess a clear sense of meaning, nurses must develop interventions that empower patients to provide this psychospiritual self-care. Because evidence exists that people who unsuccessfully attempt to find meaning in response to a negative life event experience greater psychological distress than do people who do not attempt to ascribe meaning, nurses presently should use caution when considering interventions for those who lack a clear sense of meaning (Lowery, Jacobsen, & McCauley, 1987; Silver, Boon, & Stones, 1983).

No specific nursing interventions have yet been tested for efficacy with a maladaptive sense of meaning. Frankl (1984) observed, however, that meaning is created through what one gives to the world, what one takes from the world, and in how one chooses to face suffering. Thus, strategies such as the following may prove useful for promoting a clear sense of meaning: encouraging patients to tell their life story, helping patients to create legacies, facilitating social support, and exploring cognitive strategies (such as downward social comparison and construing good).

Limitations and Implications for Future Research

A few recommendations for future research based upon the limitations of this study are in order. Because of its exploratory nature, the present study controlled very few illness variables. Future studies, however, may be enhanced by less inclusive sample selection criteria. Although the PIL Test has been widely used (in more than 50 studies) as "state of the art" measurement for the concept of life meaning, it is plagued by cultural insensitivity and poor content validity (Yalom, 1980). Future research should address measurement of the concept. Because the sense of meaning for subjects with a low sense of meaning was unknown prior to diagnosis, it was impossible to assess whether these subjects' sense of meaning changed in response to the diagnosis and recurrent cancer experience. Longitudinal studies exploring the sense of meaning across time would assist nurses in understanding if and when meaning changes.

CONCLUSION

This study employed quantitative methods to identify factors that are associated with a sense of meaning among people with recurrent cancer. Several variables were identified, many of which demonstrate that an individual's sense of meaning is integrally associated with the physical and psychosocial effects of cancer. Thus, nurses must address this phenomenon in practice and research.

REFERENCES

Acklin, M., Brown, E., & Mauger, P. (1983). The role of religious values in coping with cancer. *Journal of Religion and Health, 22*, 322-333.

American Cancer Society. (1993). *Cancer facts and figures—1993.* Atlanta: Author.

Bard, M., & Dyk, R. (1956). The psychodynamic significance of beliefs regarding the cause of serious illness. *Psychoanalytic Review, 43*, 146-162.

Benoliel, J., McCorkle, R., & Young, K. (1980). Development of social dependency scale. *Research in Nursing and Health, 3*, 3-10.

Bulman, R., & Wortman, C. (1977). Attributions of blame and coping in the "real world": Severe accident victims react to their lot. *Journal of Personality and Social Psychology. 35*, 351-363.

Cella, D., Mahon, S., & Donovan, M. (1990). Cancer recurrence as a traumatic event. *Behavioral Medicine, 16,* 15-22.

Chekryn, J. (1984). Cancer recurrence: Personal meaning, communication, and marital adjustment. *Cancer Nursing, 7*, 491-498.

Cohen, J. (1988). *Statistical power analysis for the behavioral sciences.* (2nd ed.). Hillsdale, NJ: Lawrence Eribaum & Associates.

Crumbaugh, J. & Maholick, L. (1981). *Manual of instructions for the Purpose in Life test.* Saratoga, CA: Viktor Frankl Institute of Logotherapy.

Derogatis, L., & Lopez, M. (1983). *PAIS & PAIS-SR administration, scoring, & procedures manual.* Baltimore: Johns Hopkins University School of Medicine.

Forsyth, D. (1980). The functions of attributions. *Social Psychology Quarterly, 43,* 184-189.

Fowler, J. (1981). *Stages of faith: The psychology of human development and the quest for meaning.* San Francisco: Harper & Row.

Frankl, V. (1984). *Man's search for meaning.* New York: Washington Square Press.

Gotay, C. (1985). Why me? Attributions and adjustment by cancer patients and their mates at two stages in the disease process. *Social Science Medicine, 20,* 825-831.

Haberman, M. (1987). *Living with leukemia: The personal meaning attributed to illness and treatment by adults undergoing a bone marrow transplantation.* Unpublished doctoral dissertation, University of Washington.

Heider, F. (1958). *The psychology of interpersonal relations.* New York: John Wiley & Sons.

Highfield, M., & Cason, C. (1983). Spiritual needs of patients: Are they recognized? *Cancer Nursing, 6,* 187-192.

Janoff-Bulman, R., & Frieze, I. (1983). A theoretical perspective for understanding reactions to victimization. *Journal of Social Issues, 39*(2), 1-17.

Kegan, R. (1982). *The evolving self: Problem and process in human development.* Cambridge, MA: Harvard University Press.

Lewis, F. (1982). Experienced personal control and quality of life in late-stage cancer patients. *Nursing Research, 31,* 113-119.

Lewis, F. (1987). The concept of control: A typology and health-related variables. *Advances in Health Promotion, 2,* 277-309.

Lewis, F. (1989). Attributions of control, experienced meaning, and psychosocial well-being in patients. *Journal of Psychosocial Oncology, 7*(1/2), 105-119.

Lowery, B., Jacobsen, B., & McCauley, K. (1987). On the prevalence of causal search in illness situations. *Nursing Research, 36,* 88-93.

Mahon, S., Cella, D., & Donovan, M. (1990). Psychosocial adjustment to recurrent cancer. *Oncology Nursing Forum, 17* (Suppl. 3), 47-52.

Mahon, S. (1991). Managing the psychosocial consequences of cancer recurrence: Implications for nurses. *Oncology Nursing Forum, 18,* 577-583.

Marris, P. (1986). *Loss and change.* London: Routledge & Kegan Paul.

McCorkle, R. (1987). The measurement of symptom distress. *Seminars in Oncology Nursing, 3,* 248-256.

McCorkle, R., & Young, K. (1978). Development of a symptom distress scale. *Cancer Nursing, 1,* 373-378.

Michela, J., & Wood, J. (1986). Causal attributions in health and illness. In P.C. Kendall (Ed.), *Advances in cognitive-behavioral research and therapy.* Vol. 5(pp.179-235). New York: Academic Press.

O'Conner, A., Wicker, C., & Germino, B. (1990). Understanding the cancer patient's search for meaning. *Cancer Nursing, 13,* 167-175.

Rothbaum, F., Weisz, J., & Snyder, S. (1982). Changing the world and changing the self: A two-process model of perceived control. *Journal of Personality and Social Psychology, 42,* 5-37.

Schmale, A. (1976). Psychological reactions to recurrences, metastases or disseminated cancer. *International Journal of Radiation Oncology, Biology, Physics, 1,* 515-520.

Scott, D., Goode, W., & Arlin, Z. (1983). The psychodynamics of multiple remissions in a patient with acute nonlymphoblastic leukemia. *Cancer Nursing, 6,* 201-206.

Silver, R., Boon, C. & Stones, M. (1983). Searching for meaning in misfortune: Making sense of incest. *Journal of Social Issues, 39*(2), 81-102.

Silver, R., & Wortman, C. (1980). Coping with undesirable life events (pp. 279-340). In J. Garber & M. Seligman (Eds.). *Human helplessness.* New York: Academic Press.

Steeves, R. (1992). Patients who have undergone bone marrow transplantation: Their quest for meaning. *Oncology Nursing Forum, 19,* 899-905.

Taylor, S. (1983). Adjustment to threatening events: A theory of cognitive adaptation. *American Psychologist, 38,* 1161-1173.

Taylor, S., Lichtman, R., & Wood, J. (1984). Attributions, beliefs about control, and adjustment to breast cancer. *Journal of Personality and Social Psychology, 46,* 489-502.

Taylor, S., Wood, J., & Lichtman, R. (1983). It could be worse: Selective evaluation as a response to victimization. *Journal of Social Issues, 39*(2), 19-40.

Thompson, S., & Janigian, A. (1988). Life schemes: A framework for understanding the search for meaning. *Journal of Social and Clinical Psychology, 7,* 260-280.

Turnquist, D., Harvey, J., & Andersen, B. (1988). Attributions and adjustment to life-threatening illness. *British Journal of Clinical Psychology, 27,* 55-65.

Weiner, B. (1986). *An attributional theory of motivation and emotion.* New York, N.Y: Springer-Verlag.

Weisman, A., & Worden, J. (1986). The emotional impact of recurrent cancer. *Journal of Psychosocial Oncology, 3*(4), 5-16.

Wong, P., & Weiner, B. (1981). When people ask "why" questions, and the heuristics of attributional search. *Journal of Personality and Social Psychology, 40*, 650-663.

Yalom, I. (1980). *Existential psychotherapy.* New York: Basic Books.

The DRG Era:
A Major Opportunity For
Increased Pastoral Care
Impact or a Crisis for
Survival?

Elisabeth McSherry
William A. Nelson

ABSTRACT

Notes how the Diagnostic Related Group (DRG) system, now being utilized by a growing number of hospitals, may provide chaplains with ways of demonstrating their worth as team members in total health care. Claims that pastoral care ought to be a major clinical service in a hospital and that chaplains therefore need to provide objective evidence of their contribution to the well-being of patients, as do other major clinical areas. Suggests specific ways for chaplains to establish such data, including the use of objective measures of the spiritual conditions of patients. Offers examples of accountability procedures and notes that such meticulous chaplain accountability along with follow-up work with patients could lead to expansions of services and new roles in the chaplaincy fields.

Reproduced with the permission of the Journal of Pastoral Care Publishers, Inc. from *The Journal of Pastoral Care*, (1987), 41(3), 201-211.

Now, and in the future, hospitals will be reimbursed prospectively for patient care according to a case-mix classification system—DRGs, Diagnostic Related Groups. For the hospital's predicted case-mix load, tallied by each of these diagnostic groups (and treatments), a fixed reimbursement will be made for expected costs. Under the DRG system, in order to operate in the black hospitals must increase the cost-effectiveness of their production functions; *i.e.*, they must reduce the average patient length of stay per DRG. They must also reduce the direct and indirect costs of the daily patient care. (Direct costs are those costs directly used in patient care whereas indirect are general support costs). The expense of Pastoral Care Departments traditionally has been factored in as part of the cluster of the hospital's indirect costs. This cluster of costs is then subdivided and tallied as part of the overhead expense items on each patient's hospital admission.

Pastoral Care Should be a Major Clinical Service

Conceptually, health care for the spiritual dimension is much better defined as a major clinical service, like psychiatry-psychology is for the psyche and, in the somatic medicine specialties, cardiovascular, renal or orthopedics, is for the body. Chaplaincy could perform in the hospital as a legitimate clinical service to the spiritual (motivation, values, meaning and belief) dimension of the patient and show how critical, full, healthy functioning of this dimension is to rapid and full patient recovery. If this were so, pastoral care services would administratively be considered a direct hospital cost, as currently inputs from medicine, surgery, laboratory, radiology and nursing are considered direct costs by most modern hospital management control structures.

TABLE 1

Chaplaincy And Hospital Organizational Structure

NOW (Most Hospitals)		FUTURE (Should Be)	
Indirect Costs	Direct Costs	Direct Costs	Indirect Cost
Housekeeping	Medicine	Medicine	Housekeeping
Laundry	Surgery	Surgery	Laundry
Dietetics	Psychiatry	Psychiatry	Dietetics
PASTORAL CARE		PASTORAL CARE	
Fiscal	Nursing	Nursing	Fiscal
Supply	OT/PT/RT	OT/PT/RT	Supply
Engineering	Others	Others	Engineering

This time in history is critical in hospital management control structuring (Anthony & Young, 1984). With the immediate installation of automated management control systems, most hospitals are in a state of flux regarding the final form of their internal management structures and are attempting to bring as many costs as possible under direct patient costs, even including housekeeping. Formerly housekeeping was an indirect cost, but for a surgical patient who used the operating room, this cost is much greater than for an outpatient or psychiatry patient. Administrators wish to find, as accurately as possible, the "real costs" that go into each type of DRG or case-mix encounter. Alert and wise chaplaincy directors now will do everything they can to upgrade their division's automated management reporting systems, and simultaneously, their clinical diagnostic acumen and classification systems. Thus they can translate their specialty's health professional effort into patient well-being output terms, and evidences of shortened lengths of stay for otherwise predictable problem patients (Florell, 1973; Peters & Waterman, 1982; Pruyser, 1976; Shelly & Fish, 1978; Proceeding of the Third Nursing Conference on Classification of Nursing Diagnosis, 1978; McSherry, 1983a; McSherry, 1983b; McSherry, 1983c, McSherry, 1990; McSherry, Nelson & Kratz, 1986; Wood, 1882). A short case history illustrates this:

A 62-year-old widowed male was admitted for a required hospitalized course of radiation therapy for treatment of residual disease in his abdomen following recuperation from a colon cancer resection. Mr. G. was cooperative yet quiet, and appeared discouraged. Following three treatments, he refused to go for further treatment, indicating that it was "not worth it since life seemed so meaningless." A psychiatry consult noted that the patient was not clinically depressed, but offered psychotherapy to enhance the patient's self-esteem. The psychiatrist asked the hospital chaplain to discuss this issue with the patient. After several meetings, the chaplain was able to theologically clarify the patient's concern and on a weekend pass the patient was able to attend church. The chaplain's contact re-established the patient's connection with basic religious resources. Mr. G. decided to continue the radiation therapy because of this enlightened collaboration between psychiatry and chaplaincy to focus upon the spiritual dimensions of meaning and purpose.

The advantage to chaplaincy of becoming a direct clinical department for one of the patient's three major health dimensions, the spirit, is major: (1) such a move automatically ensures the long-term survival of chaplaincies because a good administrator cannot cut off one-third of the major health care for the patient any more than he or she can cut cardiology from post-op intensive care units; (2) from a medical and health philosophy perspective, such a move brings balance back into the hospital's operative definition of health; previously psychiatric department misinterpretation(s) of Freudian *Imago Dei* theory allowed medicine (health care) to be practiced as if a person is constituted of only emotions and body (McSherry & Dagenais, 1981; Rizzuto, 1979; Finch, 1961). In this decade, revisions of this Freudian misinterpretation (Giargos, 1980), new spiritual dimension instrumentation, and dramatic new public health findings on the role of regularly practiced religion as the prime "protective" factor in extending population survival beyond expectations—particularly critical to elders' well-being—all work together to give dramatic new credibility to pastoral care departments (Levine, 1983; Westberg, 1977; Westberg, 1979; Reidel, 1981; Stanislav, 1984; Comstock & Partridge, 1972; Berkman & Syme, 1979).

From the opposite perspective, unfortunately some hospital administrators recently have questioned the value of pastoral care departments' existence in this era of markedly restricted resources. Some major hospitals have let all of their paid chaplains go. Administrators respect departments that know the historic data of their specialty, especially how it impacts hospital costs, and they respect and work with departments who are at least trying to undertake computerized measurement of where, to whom, and how long each of their staffs' efforts are applied. Some pastoral care directors may continue to think they can float along in non-accountability among the world of health professionals, because they consider their services unmeasurable. Sadly, these very chiefs or directors may be in for rude enlightening very soon.

OBJECTIVE EVIDENCE IS KEY TO SURVIVAL

Yet when good pastoral care reporting mechanisms are put in place, most show with very few changes in management guidance, that chaplains:
A. assist substantively in overall patient assessment and treatment,
B. can use objective instruments to:
   1. enable patient care, and
   2. communicate spiritual dimension findings more effectively with other health professionals, and
C. provide specialty interventions that reduce overall length of stay, use of hospital resources and/or distress of patients significantly. Thus effective modern chaplaincy has a direct effect on major hospital costs-containment.

For caliber of pastoral care, such objective instrumentation, good assessment format (see below), and conscientious clinical care management computer-reporting, actually (1) enhance the chaplain's ability to provide effective pastoral care, (2) equip chaplains with objective data for historical comparisons and also enhance acumen in spiritual dimension assessment and care, (3) substantiate the cost-effectiveness to the hospital of pastoral care service, (4) provide a tool to assist in patient follow-up, and (5) serve as a symbol of the hospital's concern for the spiritual dimension of the patient, thereby enhancing patient dignity and satisfaction. With new DRG management accounting systems, pastoral care accountability using such objective measures and excellent interdisciplinary outpatient follow-up also allows chaplains a new and expanded role and major impact in the DRG-era. But if chaplains fail to understand this or fail to begin immediately to implement these new methods, and thus fail to become an accountable clinical service department using precise reporting systems, increasingly programs may be cut from the hospital altogether, or at least reduced.

With the burgeoning in the last decade of spiritual assessment instrumentation, the modern chaplain is now equipped to make assessments that can be objectively recorded in charts and can suggest therapies that can be facilitated by other staff as well as the chaplain. This new objectivication moves modern chaplaincy and inpatient spiritual health care into the realm of a medical science, not merely an intuitive art in health care.

Patient Assessments

If pastoral care staff is sufficient, the modern chaplain can make an assessment on every hospital patient admitted. When the chaplain staff is small, documentation continues to be important and should be made at least on patients who are specifically referred or on any patient with significant spiritual problems. An example of a medical diagnostic format which could be used in chaplaincy follows:

MODERN PASTORAL CARE ASSESSMENT:
THE CASE OF AN 83 YEAR OLD WOMAN

Write-up chart: In telegraphic one-four point summary and attach copies of objective measures.
1. **Diagnosis**: Spiritual strengths/resources; how interface with problems/ weaknesses: Current whole person needs. A description of religious background and issues of the individual related to the diagnosis. Use also the Nursing Spiritual Diagnostic Classification, and others as needed.
2. **Objective Measures**: Use the Spiritual Profile Assessment (SPA): Personal Health Inventory, Ultimate Values, and Kasl's tests on all clients and attach

summary (or copy) in chart. When needed select other samples of Spiritual Profile Assessment forms as well as other measuring instruments.

3. **Prognosis**: (Make brief, well-priortized points; usually less than five). If no intervention is made, what are the deepest concerns for this patient? Sometimes when the condition is so unclear that a precise prognosis is not possible, just state "Close follow-up is needed, to determine what the prognosis in the case might include."

An example of a prognosis in the case of an 83 year old widow whose 15 year job as treasurer in the church is just finished; whose adult children are leaving for Texas; and whose elderly sister is terminal.

    1. Expect major losses
        A.)in housing, personal supports, home companionship
        B.)in self-esteem (treasurer job loss)
        C.)in family supports.
    2. Patient's resource of personal religion and church support group will continue strong.

4 **Intervention**: (Also brief and well-priortized, usually five points, or less). "Based on the above diagnosis and prognosis, the chaplain suggests the following intervention plan. The health provider team should consider the following help-strategies."

    1) Work with local pastor about new church role and honoring her past work.
    2) Work with MSW and pastor role-playing in advance, to prepare her for inevitable death of sister and new adjustments and housing.
    3) Find with her, new substitutes for anticipated losses; role as foster grandmother (in orphanage or with other children); new apartment with an older person from the church, etc.

5. **Follow-Up Record Keeping:** Doctors and nurses respect health professionals who are meticulous in objective record-keeping and very conscientiously see the client is not lost in follow-up.

    1) The facilitation of the treatment plan should be documented and the patient's response to this care coordinated by the spiritual health professional.
    2) Use encounter forms at every visit and list objectives measures used (McSherry, Nelson, & Kratz, 1986)
    3) A record should be kept of calls to patient's local provider (pastor), and all other pastoral counselors, chaplains and laypersons on the spiritual dimension of the case.
    4) Document consistent teamwork among the spiritual professionals in mutual contact and referral activity.

In many hospitals, where chaplaincy staffs are small, the admitting nurse can help to provide a spiritual diagnosis supplemental evaluation to the regular nursing evaluation. This can be done according to guidelines in Shelly and Fish's book *Spiritual Care for RNs* (1978) and according to the National Nursing Classification of Spiritual Diagnosis ratified in 1978 or patients can be asked if they would be willing to fill out a simple questionnaire which can be used by chaplains for determining which patients are most likely to need their support. After reviewing the instrument's results and talking to the patient, the chaplain should make a chart notation.

The advantages to the hospital's management as well as the chaplain's in making a spiritual assessment on each patient admitted are many: (a) A good spiritual assessment makes an excellent first impression that the patient is valued by the hospital management as more than just a broken machine; (b) it helps the patient and staff share in what is the most meaningful life values of the patient and draw upon the resource in dealing with the demanding requirements of hospitalization; (c) it opens up areas of need or deficiency in the individual patient's current personal perspective that may cause a disruptive or more costly hospitalization later.

As an example of this, a recent measurement of attending physician efforts in a prestigious west coast university hospital noted 62% of the medical ward attending's high cost resource time went into patient behavior problems, not diagnosis, care coordination or life sustenance planning. The case below was one of the four patients (of 12) with behavior problems who absorbed not only his, but large amounts of house officer, nurse and other highest-cost hospital input resources:

> The patient was a 27 year old Jewish law student with progressive loss of vision and degenerative cerebritis. Her entire sense of self-worth was based on her ability to successfully study and then verbally control those around her. She was not in touch with her sense of self-worth simply because she was the beloved creation of Divine Providence nor was her sense of the historical meaning of suffering addressed. In other words, existential/spiritual questions of purpose, value and meaning afflicted her as much as the progressive cerebral degeneration.

> Her admission care addressed only the technical interventions. The basic human value issues, fundamental to her response to the restrictions of her disease, were untouched. She was offered no company in the difficult journey of reordering priorities and accepting negative reality as constructively as possible. For days she disrupted an entire ward, threatening law suits on every nurse and demanding a single intern of her same faith to be the only one to stay near her or calm her for days. A major portion of the attending doctor's time was soothing beleaguered

staff and valiantly trying to find ways to calm her outward complaints. Yet the message behind her action, *i.e.* her basic spiritual need, was left unaddressed.

If a Rabbi or chaplain had been asked to evaluate her spiritual resources as a part of routine admission care, and then had regularly met with her as a partner in pastoral counseling, she could have worked through much of her hurt, desperation and loss of control and identity. Such care need not depend on a previously established depth of personal religion in the major life meanings and ultimate value concerns with which in her illness she wrestled almost alone unaided. Hospital days, resource utilization and staff morale all may have been much better served if good admission pastoral care for the whole person had been available and follow-through by the pastoral care staff or its rabbi consultant made accountable with follow-up notes and tallied clinical care units charged to the admission (McSherry, 1983c).

Chart Summaries of Patient Assessment: The way the pastoral assessment is written in the chart is critical. It should be short, telegraphic and well-priortized to communicate only the most profound and serious aspects of the patient's spiritual concerns (and resources) to other health professionals. Long theological treatises or self-indulgent inspirationals are an insult (and impediment to other health professionals' effectiveness); they block the rapid chart assimilation by other health professionals who are charged to maintain the patient's basic life functions. Chaplains must show intellectual self-discipline and rigor in priortizing and selection if they expect to deserve and maintain a co-equal relationship with other health care professionals. Despite the significance of the chaplain's charting, he or she must be sensitive to issues of patient/clergy confidentiality.

(1) In addition to assessment of the patient's major problems and strengths by interview, at least two objective measures can be appended to the chart.

(2) These objective measures provide immediate visual aids to help doctors and nurses share the chaplain's findings on the spiritual and human strengths (and problems) of the patient.

(3) Then a prognosis is made which includes a suggested intervention plan.

(4) A clear follow-up plan with the patient at specified intervals should be outlined.

Many chaplains fail to be as thorough as other health care professionals in their exactness in follow-up plans for patients. Chaplains need to be as conscientious as physicians and nurses in their plans, including referring discharged consenting patients for continuing care of the spiritual dimension through contacting local pastoral care providers to take on the case.

Clinical Care Units: In addition, pastoral care departments must develop some form of automated management accounting system. This could include reports of the number of units of time (Clinical Care Units—CCUs) (Wood, 1982) that each professional spends on patients by specific ward, age and assessment category. CCUs are in 5, 7.5, or 15 minute units, at the choice of the site's pastoral care director. Computer programs are available (Salisbury).

This allows the Director of Pastoral Care to see where the staff select to spend time; and from patient satisfaction scores and length of stay per DRG reports, he or she can then determine where changes should be made for the optimal placement of pastoral care staff to aid hospital management. This can then be reported to hospital administration and act as a credit for pastoral care. This addition to basic pastoral care functions (on) which management and pastoral care have agreed are fundamental to quality of care, regardless of their measurable effect on length of stay outcomes.

Modernized Pastoral Care Affects Overall Benefits for the DRG-Era Hospital

Pastoral care directors have been very slow in developing accountability systems that use the medical communication format described above. Yet, when the chaplain's role is evaluated objectively, unexpected major benefits for the hospital can be demonstrated. Pastoral care use of modern assessment instruments helps client satisfaction and marketing. It also conserves hospital resources input in the DRG-era.

Experimental studies at University of Virginia Medical Center (Florell, 1973) randomizing match orthopedic injury patients to daily chaplain visits or not, showed a 1-2 day decrease over controls in length of stay, one-third the pain medication ordered, and one-third the patient-originated calls on nursing time (McSherry, Nelson & Kratz, 1986). As a marketing strategy hospitals that provide both excellent technical care and resources which show that the patient is more than just a dysfunctional machine, attract clients who want to be treated with dignity and compassion. Many academic physicians prefer hospitalization in sectarian hospitals just because they perceive their care there is more respectful and conscientious.

The logic behind the value of staff resources that focus on the meaning, purpose and value (spiritual) side of people is significant. By definition, a person entering the hospital is broken in body, and socially and emotionally, involuntarily, has lost both control and productivity in his or her milieu. This sense of brokenness also impacts on the spiritual component of the patient.

The patient's spiritual life is the domain of care the modern chaplain professional has been trained to address. Explicit attention to the individual's dignity and to his worth that transcends bodily impairment or loss of job functionality is especially memorable and important to patients entering short-term hospitals. It can transform them from anxiously distressed and demanding into a more self-controlled and responsible person in regard to behavior and emotions. By responding to the patient's spiritual concerns such as the meaning of suffering, the value of life, and "why me?" issues, the patient is better equipped to cope with his or her illness and becomes a participant in health recovery. By affirming the focusing upon the patient's spiritual life, the knowing hospital manager has allowed the stage to be set to maximize patient strength and cooperation in the healing process. The attention to the patient's values and questions concerning meaning and purpose of illness promotes recovery and well-being. This support of patient resources in the spiritual dimension can help transform negative circumstances to a broader, positive encounter for patients.

Spiritual Diagnosis as a Key for Providing Health Promotion in the DRG-Era

Not only is accurate spiritual diagnosis and treatment important for the hospitalized patient, it is important for the overall patient health in his or her own community. Twentieth century health care has now reached the point where excellence and discreetness in spiritual dimension diagnosis is a key for all parts of the health care. This is not simply to save costs for the hospital. Modern health promotion theory has taught physicians and nurses that the spiritual dimension is a critical factor in motivating patients, long term, to work on behalf of their own health. Using the leading health promotion motivational theory, "The Health Belief Model"(Becker, 1977; Green, 1980), doctors have found patients work best for their own increased wellness if the professional appeals to the patient's top three ultimate values. Epidemiologist looking at large populations found that religion was the single most important factor in people's selections of healthy lifestyles, and was a major determinant of increased longevity and freedom from hypertension. The following vignette illustrates this point:

> A longterm chain-smoker, Mr. Smith's top three Ultimate Values do not include concern about his own health. On his Ultimate Values screen, Mr. Smith does, however, rank "family security" as number 1 and has other top ultimate values that include participating in events with his family. On Mr. Smith's hospital admission, the effective hospital chaplain assessed these top values of Mr. Smith with an objective test instrument and shared the findings with the other hospital providers, through the patient's chart (with the patient's consent). Both the doctors and nurses then appealed to Mr. Smith's desire to be alive in 20 years to provide his

daughters with a college education. The result of this pastoral care-provided personal values focussed approach was that Mr. Smith stopped smoking.

The chaplain who is a good diagnostician of the patient's major ultimate values with new objective measurements can now help the other health professionals identify and appeal to the patient's major values. Thus, the patient is motivated spiritually to enhance his or her own health's restoration process.

As indicated, modern pastoral care accountability can assure that discharged patients are referred back to community support systems that help sustain their constructive attitudes during post-hospital convalescence, thus promoting their long-term well-being. Discharge accountability tools and discharge notes can foster this contact (McSherry, 1986). The local pastor, rabbi or congregation support group, in such areas as cancer, stroke and Alzheimers, can be most useful even to a previously unchurched person as they continues to resolve life meaning and make new adaptations. This also enhances the hospital's profile in the community and its market position.

Another excellent role that pastoral care departments are assuming, using modern assessments, is in the outpatient setting where outpatient pastoral counseling or family counseling follow-up is done in conjunction with medical follow-up appointments. Such pastoral counseling is especially important when the patient lacks adequate community pastoral support. Follow-up sessions can enhance spiritual and health promotion while objective instruments document this client's progress.

The rationale for pastoral care in outpatient or community-based health promotion programs is based on the extraordinary 11-year success of the Kellogg Foundation-funded church-based Wholistic Health Clinics of Granger Westberg (University of Illinois Community Health Department)(Westberg, 1977, 1979). In these clinics, the pastoral counselor orchestrated the long-term health promotion plan for each client with the client, health educator nurse and family physician. Rates of hospitalization became one-half the local HMO average and one-fifth the National Health Statistics Average for the Chicago area.

Kasl's 1984 paper confirms this finding in the high-cost under-served sub-group, the elderly. Religiosity was the single most important non-fixed factor in predicting quality of health status and survival in this prospective Connecticut study of elderly undergoing forced new housing. The Comstock, Berkman and Symer, and the Tecumseh study—previously noted—all show the importance of the individual's applied religiosity in predicting prospectively the future well-being of the population.

SUMMARY OF THE DRG-ERA:
WHAT CHAPLAINS MUST DO TO SURVIVE

Crisis

Modern chaplains must use good objective measures and leave these records in the chart along with their own highly distilled, telegraphic action plan. With such accountability, chaplains can appropriately credit their professional effort to the patient's DRG-production. Modern chaplaincies must start to use on-line computer capacity to enter their clinical care units per client DRG in the hospital's overall merged financial and clinical database. Failure of chaplaincy directors to move rapidly to become accountable in the modern DRG-era can result in a loss or reduction of their chaplaincy program.

Or Opportunity?

On the contrary, good, meticulous chaplaincy accountability and patient follow-up has three major, previously unanticipated, rewards:

1. **Staffing:** Staffing may multiply several fold for chaplaincy programs that clearly document their input on wards that produce shortened and effective hospitalizations that fall below DRG reimbursement standards. Such documentation can attest that chaplains actually reduce hospital costs. Applying and documenting could convince hospital administrators that increased, not decreased, chaplain coverage is essential for greater cost-effectiveness.

2. **Extension of the Chaplain's Role to Outpatient Referral Base**: When chaplains maintain conscientious outpatient follow-up and/or referral to local pastors and pastoral counselors from consenting patients, and keep all providers informed of their observations and action plan, chaplains attain a professional respect not previously enjoyed from doctors, nurses and administrators in general.

3. **New Role as Liaison and Marketer**: Hospitals in the DRG-era need good referral bases from the community. With the rapid proliferation of church-based health promotion programs in regional and state-wide distributions, hospital chaplains can become the natural liaison with local church pastors to accept their hospital referrals and keep relations with the community referral center smooth. Modern chaplains must seek to undertake this new role if they wish to solidify chaplaincy's role long-term in a modern cost-efficient, DRG-reimbursement hospital.

CONCLUSION

The Chinese character for "crisis" has symbols for both danger and opportunity. Never before in recent history has hospital chaplaincy faced such a danger to its survival and yet such an opportunity for its greatly broadened impact and effectiveness. Chaplains need to objectively demonstrate their role in the entire hospital clinical care process. They must also objectively document their impact in facilitating renewed patient medical well-being. By this they show that patient well-being due to the fundamental nature of man is inextricable intertwined with the individual's sense of spiritual well-being.

REFERENCES

Anthony, R., & Young, D. (1984). *Management control systems.* Cambridge, MA: Harvard Press.

Becker, M. (1977). The Health Belief Model and prediction—a field experiment. *Journal of Health and Social Behavior, 18,* 348-366.

Berkman, L., & Syme, L. (1979). Social networks, host resistance and mortality: a nine year follow-up study in Alameda County. *American Journal of Epidemiology, 109,* 186-204.

Comstock, G., & Partridge, K. (1972). Church attendance and health. *Journal of Chronic Disease, 25,* 655-672.

Finch, J. (1961). *Criticisms of Freud's view of man as viewed by his major psychoanalytic dissenters.* Unpublished doctoral dissertation, University of Vancouver, B.C., Canada.

Florell, J. (1973). Crisis intervention in orthopedic surgery—empirical evidence of the effectiveness of a chaplain working with surgery patients. *Bulletin of the American Hospital Association,* March, 29-36.

Giargos, P. (1980). *Psychoanalytic study of basic human drive for metaphysical union with the deity.* Unpublished doctoral dissertation, Duke University.

Green, L. (1980). *Health education and planning: a diagnostic approach.* Palo Alto, CA: Mayfield.

Kasl, S. (1984). Psychosocial predictors of mortality among elderly poor: The role of religion, well-being and social contracts. *American Journal Of Epidemiology, 119,* 410-442.

Levine, S. (1983). The hidden healthcare system: Mediating structures and medicine. *Medical Care, 21,* 378.

McSherry, E. (1983a). Comprehensive health promotion for elders. *Journal of the Western Society of Gerontology Generations, 7,* 18-21.

McSherry, E. (1983b). Regional networds of Church-based wellness centers. *Public Health Reports, 96*, 159.

McSherry, E. (1983c). The scientific basis of whole person healthcare. *Journal of the American Scientific Affiliation, 18*, 217-224.

McSherry, E. (1984). Observations: physician costing. *VA Cooperative Studies*, 189-199.

McSherry, E. (1990). Maturity, immaturity: concept. *Dictionary of Pastoral Care And Counseling*. Nashville: Abingdon.

McSherry, E., & Dagenais, F. (1981). A model of human life cycle spiritual development for use in medical sciences. *Proceedings of Society Scientific Study of Religion Abstracts*.

McSherry, E., Nelson, W., Kratz, D. (1986). Pastoral care in the DRG-era: New accountability allows overall medical cost savings. *Health Care Management Review, 11*(1), 47-59.

Peters, T., & Waterman, R. (1982). *In search of excellence.*NewYork: Warners.

Proceeding of the Third Nursing Conference on Classifications of Nursing Diagnosis. (1978). Classification of nursing diagnosis. *Nurses Lamp (NCF)*.

Pruyser, P. (1976). *The minister as diagnostician*. Philadelphia, PA: Westminster Press.

Reidel, J. (1981). Second University of Illinois survey of wholistic health clinics. *Inc, 137*.

Rizzuto, A. (1979). *The birth of the living God*. Chicago: University of Chicago Press, 47.

Salisbury, S. (no date). VAMC, 1400 V. F. W. Parkway, West Roxbury, MA, 02132.

Shelly, J., & Fish, S. (1978). *Spiritual care: The nurse's role*. Downers Grove, Ill: Intervarsity Press.

Westberg, G. (1977). The wholistic health center project: An action-research model for providing preventative whole-person health care at the primary level. *Medical Care, 15*(3), 217-227.

Westberg, G. (1979). Multiplying wholistic health centers. *Increasing the Impact*. Battle Creek, Mich: Kellog Foundation, 123-141.

Wood, C. (1982). Nursing clinical care units at MEEI. *Harvard Business Review, 60*(2), 123-128.

EDITOR'S COMMENTS

This author has consistently called for chaplains and their Departments to become more proactive and responsible in making a contribution to hospital medical care. This article is an example and I place it here as the leader for the three articles which follow. These three appear to represent most of the literature in the field which evaluates hospital pastoral care. Hopefully, the future will contain more studies.

21

The Impact of Chaplaincy Services in Selected Hospitals In The Eastern United States

Kurt H. Parkum

ABSTRACT

Surveys a stratified sample of patients in six different hospitals and compares their perceptions of hospital chaplaincy and other pastoral care efforts with related hospital services. Reports the presence of a strong impact of pastoral care services and discusses these findings from the perspective of a theory of expressive and instrumental social orientations as explicated by the sociologist Talcott Parsons.

Health status and social support indicators are closely related. While the medical component may be dominant, factors relevant to patient satisfaction and morale have an influence on both the reputation of a hospital and on the medical component itself, *e.g.* patients' efforts at self-care as they recover. Cobb (1976), for example, found that social support can help protect people from a wide variety of pathological states ranging from depression to death and may also accelerate recovery. Cassel (1976) reached

Reproduced with permission of the Journal of Pastoral Care Publishers, Inc. from *The Journal Of Pastoral Care*, (1985), 39(3), 262-269.

similar conclusions in a review of studies comparing disease and mortality statistics for populations with and without supportive social environments.

This article focuses on hospital patient satisfaction and the patients' perception of the role of pastoral counselors during the patients' hospitalization. Comparisons are made with their perceptions of other related services. The hypothesis of this study is that the more expressive the hospital-based support mechanisms, the greater the positive impact on patient satisfaction (Note 1).

A previous statewide survey (Parkum, 1982-83) showed that hospital administrators have demonstrated their awareness and concern by providing not only medical services for their patients but also personnel specifically charged with the task of giving non-medical support. The latter include pastoral care givers, social workers, patient representatives, and volunteers. Although the patients' perception of the impact of the services is not the principal basis for evaluating the effectiveness of the services or assessing the importance of the professions or volunteer roles, the relative influence of pastoral care efforts as perceived by patients should be of considerable interest both to those who administer to patients and to hospital administrators. Patient-perceived benefits of expressive care are relevant to budgetary, organizational, and administrative planning (Note 2).

METHODS

Six hospitals were selected on the basis of size, organizational characteristics (Catholic/Protestant, medical school-affiliated/non-medical school-affiliated), rural/urban, population-base characteristics, and willingness to participate (Note 3). The aim was to include a cross-section of different institutions. Based on the assumption that acute and chronic patients have different non-medical problems, an equal number of surgery (acute) and diabetic (chronic) patients were interviewed.

A sample of 432 patients was taken, 36 diabetic patients and 36 surgery patients in each of the six hospitals. Because the preliminary study indicated that sex and socioeconomic status are especially important discriminating variables for patient satisfaction-related issues, the sample was then stratified by socioeconomic status and gender (Fox & Storms, 1981). People who did not respond due to inability or unwillingness to be interviewed were replaced with randomly selected subjects in the same respondent category (hospital, disease, gender, socioeconomic status) as the non-respondent.

INSTRUMENTAL AND EXPRESSIVE
SERVICES: A GROUND FOR COMPARISON

The sociologist Talcott Parsons (1951) theorized that both expressive and instrumental orientations can be found throughout society. Instrumental orientations concern conditions necessary to obtain a given goal, and expressive orientations concern the "flow" of gratifications. For example, at the institutional level, economic institutions are primarily instrumental and religious institutions are primarily expressive.

For patient support mechanisms, services will range from instrumental to expressive. Some services will be a mixture, and it will be difficult to determine whether a caregiver such as a volunteer provides expressive or instrumental services.

The complex nature of the concepts does not eliminate the potential influence of other related dimensions. An instrumental or expressive patient service may be either elementary or profound in nature. For example, a volunteer may bring a patient a glass of water (instrumental), or a hospital chaplain may offer Communion (expressive).

It is generally agreed that a hospital is established to achieve instrumental goals, although the nature of these goals is often complex. Primary goals may be patient services, research, monetary gain, or a combination of these and other instrumental goals. In any case, it is apparent that hospital-based support mechanisms will encounter the most unfilled needs at the expressive end of the instrumental-expressive dimension.

Hospital social workers serve instrumental needs especially in regard to discharge problems, although they take an interest in expressive needs as well. Patient representatives are primarily assigned to handle instrumental administrative needs, especially when patients express dissatisfaction with administrative procedures. Volunteers appear to fall somewhere between the expressive and instrumental extremes of the theoretical dimension because their services can vary depending upon the nature of their involvement and upon their special qualifications. However, it is unlikely that a volunteer responds to deeply felt expressive patient needs. Self-help volunteers have had the same problems and illnesses as the patients and assist them in adjusting to their condition. All other volunteers are classified as regular volunteers.

The service of pastoral caregivers are definitely more expressive in nature than those of other hospital-based support givers. In terms of Parsons' theory, patients have expressive needs that pastoral counselors are especially suited to meeting needs that remain unmet by any of the other hospital medical and non-medical patient support mechanisms. The data analysis focuses on how helpful the patients felt the support services were.

FINDINGS

One or more of the non-medical services are considered helpful by 80 percent of the patients, but the rating differs greatly among the services. Table 1 shows that pastoral counseling is considered helpful by an impressive 67 percent of the patients. Volunteers are divided into self-help volunteers, rated helpful by seven percent, and regular volunteers, who are considered helpful of 23 percent. Social workers are rated helpful by 16 percent of the patients and patient representatives are recognized as helpful by five percent. In comparing these figures a number of differences should be noted: (1) There are few self-help volunteers; (2) social workers are not primarily assigned to patient satisfaction issues; (3) patient representatives in some hospitals are supposed to concern themselves only with exceptional cases, and in other hospitals the position does not exist.

TABLE 1
Helpfulness of Hospital Based
Non-Medical Support Services to the Patient

	Helpful(%)	Not Helpful(%)
Social Worker	70(16%)	361(84%)
Patient Representative*	14(5%)	277(95%)
Pastoral Counselor	291(67%)	141(33%)
S-H Volunteer	29(7%)	402(93%)
Regular Volunteer	101(23%)	331(77%)
Average	(23%)	(77%)

*There are no patient representatives in two of the six hospitals.
Chi-Square=572.14, significant at .01 level.

TABLE 2
Type of Help Given by Hospital Based
Non-Medical Support Services to the Patient

	Expressive(%)	Instrumental(%)
Social Worker	22(37%)	38(63%)
Patient Representative	7(78%)	2(22%)
Pastoral Counselor	241(100%)	0(0%)
S-H Volunteer	20(74%)	7(26%)
Regular Volunteer	14(11%)	109(89%)
Average	(66%)	(34%)

Chi-Square=312.42, significant at .01 level.

The issue on which the data analysis and hypothesis testing depend, however, concerns the extent to which the support services differ in degree of instrumentality and expressiveness. The difference is substantial, as shown in Table 2. Figure 1 provides a graphic description of Tables 1 and 2.

FIGURE 1
Relationship Between Levels of Impact and Dimensions

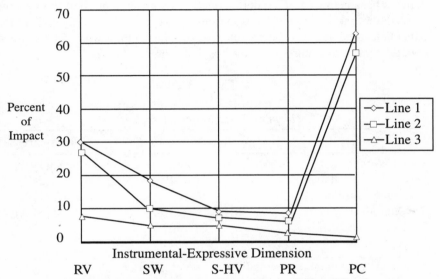

Line 1=Total Helpfulness; Line 2=Instrumental line; Line 3= Expressive line. RV=Regular Volunteer; SW=Social Worker; S-HV=Self-Help Volunteer; PR=Patient Representative; PC= Pastoral Counselor

In addition to showing the relative impact of the individual services as noted by the patients, Figure 1 also shows their location on the instrumental-expressive dimension. Pastoral counseling is located at the extreme expressive end and, as indicated vertically , is also the service that has the highest overall impact—67% of the patients note expressive assistance by a pastoral counselor. Regular volunteers fall at the other end of the dimension, providing primarily instrumental assistance. These volunteers are noted by 23% of the patients as being helpful on the vertical dimension of the graph. The graph also shows that the other services—social workers, self-help volunteers, and patient representatives—fall between the extremes of the instrumental-expressive dimension and that their impact as noted by the patients in each case is quite small in comparison with the impact of pastoral counselors and volunteers. The first step in helping patients to utilize the various support services is to make the patients aware of their existence. Table 3 shows that over 80% are aware of pastoral counselors and social workers, and that somewhat fewer patients (60%) are aware of regular volunteers. Patients' lower awareness of patient representatives and self-help volunteers (45%) may reflect the absence of these services in some hospitals. A separate count of the method by which patients became aware of support services shows that about half the patients learned about them from non-hospital-related sources. Thus only 40% of the patients learned about self-help volunteers in the hospital while 54% learned about the pastoral counselor from a hospital source.

TABLE 3
Patient Awareness of
Hospital Based Support Services

	Aware(%)	Not Aware(%)
Social Worker	348(81%)	83(19%)
Patient Representative*	128(44%)	165(56%)
Pastoral Counselor	360(83%)	72(17%)
S-H Volunteer	195(45%)	236(55%)
Regular Volunteer	259(60%)	172(40%)
Average	(64%)	(36%)

*There are no patient representatives in two of the six hospitals.
Chi-Square=243.45, significant at .01 level.

A close look at the extent to which different patient categories find the pastoral counselor helpful reveals some interesting findings. Men and women find the service helpful at about the same rate, 69% for female patients and 66% for males. Older patients aged 55 and above make use of the pastors in 70% of the cases, while the percentage is somewhat lower but still high at 63% for patients below the age of 55.

Patients were also rated according to socioeconomic status (SES), but the differences in use of chaplaincy services were small. Sixty-six percent of the low SES patients found the services helpful as compared with 69% of the high SES patients. In comparing surgery patients, who are primarily patients with an acute illness, with diabetics, whose illness is chronic, it was found that more surgery patients (72%) than diabetic patients (63%) made use of a pastoral counselor.

Finally, a comparison was made of institutional differences. While only six hospitals were compared and differences may be due to many variables unique to the individual hospital, it is notable that, as indicated in Table 4, 76% of the patients in Catholic-affiliated hospitals found the pastoral counseling service helpful, while the percentage is 72% in non-Catholic hospitals and only 55% in medical school-affiliated non-Catholic hospitals. This difference is the only one of these comparisons among patient categories that is statistically significant. It should also be noted that pastoral counseling services are, in each type of institution, considered helpful by many more patients than are the other support mechanisms.

TABLE 4
Helpfulness of Hospital Based, Non-Medical
Support Services to the Patient by Hospital Type

	Catholic		Medical School		Independent	
	Helpful	Not Helpful	Helpful	Not Helpful	Helpful	Not Helpful
SW	20(14%)	123(86%)	26(37%)	118(33%)	24(17%)	120(83%)
PR*			9(6%)	135(94%)	4(3%)	140(97%)
PC	109(76%)	35(24%)	79(55%)	65(45%)	103(72%)	41(28%)
S-H V	12(8%)	132(92%)	7(5%)	137(95%)	10(7%)	134(93%)
RV	48(33%)	96(67%)	31(22%)	113(78%)	22(15%)	122(85%)
Ave	(26%)	(74%)	(21%)	(79%)	(23%)	(77%)

There are no patient representatives in Catholic hospitals. This constitutes the major difference causing the Chi-Square to become significant. Chi-Square=22.5807, significant at .01 level.

DISCUSSION AND CONCLUSIONS

There is strong support for the expectation that pastoral counseling is not only more expressive in nature than other hospital-based support mechanisms but also that it has more impact than any other support service. Internal validity of this finding appears to be high, as the comparison among categories of patients indicates. The comparison among hospitals also suggest high validity for hospitals in general, as the relative impact of the pastoral care service is consistently higher than that of other services. The higher overall impact of the chaplaincy service in Catholic hospitals is likely to be due to their greater emphasis on this service.

An assessment of the inherent value of the patient support services is beyond the scope of this analysis, but a few comments can be made about effectiveness. Effectiveness is usually defined as degree of goal attainment. The study indicates that chaplaincy services has a high degree of effectiveness, assuming that patient satisfaction is the goal. While this may or may not be acceptable from a theological point of view, it is likely to be important to the hospital.

The hypothesis that the more expressive the hospital-based support mechanisms the greater the positive impact on patient satisfaction is supported when chaplaincy services are compared with those of regular volunteers, the only two services present in all the hospitals. Findings for the other services do not provide a clear trend. However, it can be argued that the expressive impact on patient satisfaction of social workers, self-help volunteers, and patient representatives from a patient perspective is relatively insignificant because self-help volunteers are evidently present in limited numbers in the hospitals and the roles of both patient representatives and social workers vary from hospital to hospital along with the extent to which they are expected to be instrumental or expressive.

In conclusion, the main point that can be made with empirical certainty is that in the view of the patients the effect of pastoral counselors is considerable. Hospital chaplains are filling a role much needed and recognized by the patients. Hospital administrators and medical health care providers ought to take notice, and chaplains should feel both inspired and encouraged in their much-appreciated efforts.

REFERENCES

Cassell, J. (1976). The contribution of the social environment to host resistance. *American Journal of Epidemiology, 104*, 107-123.

Cobb, S. (1976). Social support as a moderator of life stress. *Psychosomatic Medicine, 38*, 300-314.

Fox, J., & Storms, D. (1981). A different approach to sociodemographic Predictors of Satisfaction with health care. *Social Science and Medicine, 15A*, 557-564.

Parkum, K. (1982-83). Contributions to Patient Satisfaction: A new role for hospital volunteers. *The Journal of Volunteer Administration, 1*(2), 38-42.

Parsons, T. (1951). *The Social System.* New York: The Free Press.

NOTES

1. However, the opposite is not necessarily true. Instrumental services do not necessarily lead to dissatisfaction because patients do have legitimate instrumental needs.

2. Efficiency can, from the hospital's point of view, be defined as the ratio of the output, *i.e.* the hospital service, to organizational input, *i.e.* the budget for the service. Hospital chaplains can usually operate efficiently in part because they can draw upon community-based pastoral assistance. However, a service with high effectiveness and high efficiency would from an administrative point of view be a good bet for a budget elevation, and an increase in monetary support for chaplains by hospitals interested in increasing patient satisfaction would likely be a sound investment. The timeliness of this observation is highlighted by the current change to the DRG (Diagnosis Related Grouping) regulation covering reimbursement for Medicare. It is likely to make patient satisfaction an issue of prime concern for hospital administrators.

3. The anonymity of the participating hospitals has been maintained at their request.

EDITOR'S COMMENT

This remains one of the stronger studies which demonstrates the importance and benefit of pastoral services in the hospital. Its strengths include a theoretical framework (Parsons) within which the results can be understood. The stratified random sample from six hospitals is also a strength.

Its weaknesses lie in what we are not told. How were patient data gathered? If questionnaires were used, what scales were included? Did the instruments demonstrate sufficient validity and reliability so as to be trustworthy? How were instrumental and expressive scores determined? These concerns are managed by data in Table 2. But what do the numbers in Table 2 represent? Apparently they are not the numbers of respondents (they do not add up to the totals in Tables 1 or 3). We simply are not told and this makes it difficult to get behind the results to methodologies which may have influenced the data in important ways.

22

Supplier-Induced Demand For Pastoral Care Services In The General Hospital: A Natural Experiment

John Gartner
John S. Lyons
David B. Larson
John Serkland
Mark Peyrot

ABSTRACT

Assesses the effects the elimination of a pastoral care training program and a reduction in staff had on referral rates for pastoral care. Results showed a decrease in referrals initiated by pastoral care staff but an increase in pastoral care referrals initiated by medical staff and patients. Notes that when pastoral care staff were less available, the demand for their services became more apparent.

S ince ancient times the clergy has been summoned to the bed of the sick and dying. Yet as society has become more secular and medical care more scientific, the role of the chaplain in particular has shrunk to that of a supporting player in the 20th century medical center.

A growing body of literature (McSherry, Kratz, & Nelson, 1986) suggests that the chaplain's "supporting role" is not insignificant. Hospital-based pastoral

Reprinted with permission of the Journal of Pastoral Care Publishers, Inc. from *The Journal of Pastoral Care*, (1990), 44 (3), 262-270.

care intervention has been related to decreased length of stay and decreased demands on nursing time (Florell, 1973), increased consumer satisfaction with hospitalization (Parkum, 1985), increased medical knowledge and compliance by patients (Kong & Saunders,1981; 1983) and decreased rates of hospitalization (Westberg, 1977). Nonetheless, hospitals are facing an urgent need to contain costs. McSherry, *et al.*, have predicted "...in streamlining production in the Diagnosis Related Group (DRG) era, unknowing hospital managers might consider cutting pastoral care as a 'less essential' program" (1986). Thus the question of the economic value of the pastoral care program becomes relevant. More specifically, what demand exists for pastoral care services, and to what degree is that demand "supplier-induced" (Rice, 1983), *ie.*, inflated by pastoral outreach activities?

BACKGROUND

On September 1, 1985 Northwestern Memorial Hospital eliminated the pastoral training program, reducing the multi-denominational pastoral care staff from 5 1/2 full-time chaplains and 9 students to 4 1/2 full-time chaplains and no students. These positions are full-time, paid positions and do not include volunteers or community chaplains who may visit members of their congregations while hospitalized. The decision to reduce the chaplaincy staff was based on a number of factors including an estimated cost of $90 per direct patient contact hour and the observation that referrals to Social Work, Home Care Nursing, and Consultation/Liaison Psychiatry increased with the implementation of DRGs whereas chaplaincy referrals were unaffected (Lyons, Hammer, Larson, Visotsky, & Burns, 1987). Perhaps more importantly, it was observed that 80% of the pastoral care referrals were generated by chaplaincy staff.

The elimination of the chaplaincy training program serves as a "natural experiment" in which careful study of the referral rates for chaplains both before and after the elimination of the chaplaincy training program may help to answer this question. If chaplains were indeed providing outreach services that were in low demand, then the rate of chaplain referrals initiated by patients and staff (other-initiated referrals) should remain relatively constant or perhaps decline. On the other hand, if the rate of other-initiated referrals goes up after the elimination of the training program, it suggests that the outreach effort was targeting patients who would otherwise demand service.

DATA AND METHODS

Weekly statistics regarding chaplaincy referrals were collected from March 3, 1985 to March 2, 1986, six months before and after the elimination of the program using the MICRO-CARES system (Lyons, Hammer, & White, 1987). Referral rates before and after the elimination of the program were collected. Chaplain-initiated referrals and other-initiated referrals were analyzed separately. Along with a straightforward comparison of referral rates, an additional statistical analysis, interrupted time series analysis, was required to attribute these changes to the elimination of the training program. This technique allows for the statistical control of time trends that might otherwise confound simple, pre/post comparisons.

RESULTS

Before the elimination of the chaplain training program, 81% of the referrals were initiated by chaplains, 12% by nurses, 2% by patients, and 2% by patients' families. The remaining 3% were initiated by a combination of staff. After elimination of the program, only 45% of the pastoral care referrals were initiated by chaplains, 22% by nurses, 12% by patients, 9% by social workers, 6% by patients' families, and 2% by doctors. The remaining 4% were initiated by the same combination of hospital staff enumerated above.

A t-statistic was used to compare the weekly number of referrals for pastoral care initiated by chaplains before and then after the elimination of the program. Consistent with our predictions, the number of chaplain-initiated referrals decreased ($t=8.38$, df=50, p<.001) from an average of 42.85 referrals per week (sd=23.6) before the elimination of the training program to an average of 17.23 (sd=8.48) after the elimination of the program. A t-statistic was also used to compare the weekly number of other-initiated referrals for pastoral care before and after the elimination of the program. The number of other-initiated referrals increased ($t=-4.91$, df=50,p<.01) after the elimination of the program from an average of 10.12 referrals per week (sd=5.71) to an average of 20.88 (sd=9.60).

Next, the interrupted time series analysis was performed. Weekly referral rates for the 30 weeks prior to elimination of the pastoral education program were determined and an autoregressive integrated moving averages (ARIMA p,d,q) model was built for pastoral care (McCleary & Hay, 1980). In this model, p represents the order of the autoregressive function, q represents the order of the moving averages function, and d represents the differencing parameter. The steps for model building outlined by McCleary and Hay were used to determine the models in each case.

Table 1 contains the parameters for these models. The predicted weekly referral rates were then compared with the actual referrals using paired t statistics over 30 weeks post-elimination to determine whether any change in level of referral could be accounted for by other time trends.

TABLE 1

Interrupted Time Series Analysis of Pastor-Initiated
and
Other-Initiated Referral Rates
Prior to Elimination of a Pastoral Education Program

Model Characteristics	Pastor Initiated	Other Initiated
(p,d,q)	(0,0,1)	(2,1,0)
Estimate(s)	-0.871	0.651,0.210
Standard Error(s)	0.73	0.176,0.173

The time series model for chaplain-initiated referrals built using the baseline data predicted a pre-post decline to 26.45 (sd=6.4) contacts per week (Table 1). This is significantly more contacts than the observed rate of 17.23 (sd=8.48) chaplain-initiated referrals per week following the elimination of the training program (t=2.41, df=50, p<.01). This result is consistent with the above t-tests showing the significant decrease in chaplain-initiated contact consequent to the elimination of the chaplain training program.

The baseline time series model for non-chaplain initiated referrals, predicted a decline to 1.81 (sd=1.54) non-chaplain initiated referrals per week. This again is significantly less than the observed rate of 20.8 (sd=9.6) other-initiated referrals per week following the elimination of the training program (t=9.30, df=50, p<.001). Consistent with the t-tests reported above, there remained a significant increase in other-initiated referrals consequent to the elimination of the program.

DISCUSSION

The results of the present study suggest that the elimination of the chaplain training program had a strong impact on referrals for chaplaincy services. As expected, after a dramatic reduction in chaplaincy staff the number of chaplain-initiated referrals dropped dramatically, from 42 to 17 chaplain-initiated referrals per week. However, other-initiated referrals doubled, increasing from 10 to 20 referrals per week. Thus the number of other-initiated referrals before the elimination of the program was an underestimate of the perceived need for such services by patients and staff. The outreach (case-finding) nature of hospital chaplain services may have had the paradoxical effect of masking its experienced importance.

It is possible that the increase in other-initiated referrals resulted less from the reduction in outreach and more from the increased probability of getting a senior chaplain when a post training program referral was made. That is, without students, the full-time chaplains resorted to full-time patient care and thus referrals were always served by experienced chaplains rather than students.

Though the increased demand for chaplain services is greater than was previously apparent, the level of demand for chaplains following the elimination of the training program never equaled the number of referrals pastoral care staff generated previously. From one perspective then, the pastoral care training program may have resulted in the "over-servicing" of patients. That is, supply of chaplain services may have exceeded demand and resulted in some level of "make-work."

Future research should address the patient care and cost implication of both reaching patients who do not desire pastoral care services and failing to reach patients who could benefit from this service. There has been at least one attempt at such research. A study of orthopedic patients who were randomly assigned to daily chaplain visits were found to be discharged two days earlier than those who did not receive chaplain visits, required 66% less pain medication and made 66% fewer calls on nursing time than those who had no chaplain visits (McSherry, 1986). However, this study did not determine the level of need or demand for this chaplain service.

The present findings may be generalizable to other types of hospital services which involve outreach or screening or other forms of case-finding. In prospective payment environments that emphasize cost cutting, services which have an established cost but do not appear to have an economic benefit presently are at greatest risk when hospitals attempt to maximize profit (Feder, Hadley, & Zuckerman, 1987). Without consideration of more complex interactions among services and costs (*e.g.*, cost offset and cost shifting effects), elimination of these types of programs on this basis may be short-sighted. For example, short-term gains in profits might be offset by long term declines in quality of care or patient satisfaction.

In summary, the impact of the elimination of the chaplain training program and the resulting reduction of chaplaincy staff revealed two notable findings. First, the overall referral rate was significantly reduced following the elimination of the training program. Second, the demand for chaplaincy services was greater than would be suggested by the referral rates that do not include outreach or case-finding referrals.

REFERENCES

Feder, J., Hadley, J., & Zuckerman, S. (1987). How did medicare's prospective payment system affect hospitals? *New England Journal of Medicine, 317*, 867.

Florell, J. (1973). Crisis intervention in orthopedic surgery—empirical evidence of the effectiveness of a chaplain working with surgery patients. *Bulletin of the American Protestant Hospital Association, 37*, 29.

Kong, W., & Saunders, T. (1981). Churches as high blood pressure control centers. *American Journal of Public Health, 71*, 1173.

Kong, W., & Saunders, T. (1983). The role for churches in hypertension management. *Urban Health*, May, 49.

Lyons, J., Hammer, J., Larson, D., Visotsky, H., & Burns, B. (1987). The impact of a prospective payment system on psychosocial service. *Medical Care, 25*, 140.

Lyons, J., Hammer, J., & White, R. (1987). Computerization of psychosocial services in the general hospital: collaborative data management in the human services department. *Computers in Human Services, 2*, 27.

McCleary, R., & Hay, R. (1980). *Applied time series analysis in the social sciences*. Beverly Hills, California: Sage Publications.

McSherry, E., Kratz, D., & Nelson, W. (1986). Pastoral care departments: more necessary in the DRG era?. *Health Care Management Review, 11*, 47.

Parkum, K. (1985). The impact of chaplaincy services in selected hospitals in the eastern United States. *The Journal of Pastoral Care, 39,* 262.

Rice, T. (1983). The impact of medicare reimbursement on physician-induced demand. *Medical Care, 21,* 803.

Westberg, G. (1977). The holistic health center project: An action-research model for providing preventive, whole-person health care at the primary level. *Medical Care, 15,* 217.

EDITOR'S COMMENT

This is a very important study because it asks the question on the minds of at least some administrators. The question is whether providing pastoral services to general hospital patients by an internally funded pastoral care department is necessary. If these services were eliminated, who would miss them? This question can be studied in a number of ways, including the design reported here. Here the "necessity" of pastoral care is studied by asking who initiated the pastoral visit. If the visit was made because of a referral from outside the pastoral care department, then it is assumed that legitimate need existed; if it was chaplain initiated, then, ...well, maybe it was need but maybe it was "make-work." The personnel reduction within the department lends itself to a "natural experiment." The results are supportive of an internally funded pastoral care department, but this assumption behind the design is problematic.

Is it true that genuine need for pastoral care is more likely to exist if the referral is made from someone other than a chaplain? I believe the reverse is true and that an important principle is at stake. I argue that chaplains know spiritual need when they see it better than nurses or doctors or social workers. This is simply a corollary to assumptions made in every profession, namely that persons within the profession are better judges of whether they are needed and whether they can help.

This study is relevant at another point, however—and it is not discussed in the text. A large number of pastoral care visits are "screening visits." They are initial visits to perform either a formal or informal assessment of need. They are carried out because traditionally every door is open to the chaplain. When these authors report that the number of chaplain initiated referrals decreased after the staff reduction, was this largely a reduction of assessment visits? I believe that is likely true—and that leaves assessment to other professionals. But then we are back to the issue discussed above, *e.g.* who determines the patient's need?

In the end, we are further ahead because of this study. The data suggest that chaplains are valuable. But so are doctors, nurses, social workers, and the local fire department. The latter come when they are called. The design of this study hints that the chaplain's role and function could be thought of as being like the fire fighters. They are necessary, but they are to be used when others decide to call them. The problem is that detecting a fire is far easier than assessing spiritual need and its impact on illness and recovery.

But perhaps my comparison to the fire fighter is overstated. Perhaps comparison to physical or occupational therapists is more appropriate. In most hospitals, they work with the patient on referral; they come when called. But this analogy contains two problems. First, assessing spiritual need and responding to it is more subtle than the activities of these therapists. Second, all the ancillary therapies emerged from within the medical field. Pastoral care as part of religion did not; medicine emerged from religion and this is part of the reason why the involvement of pastoral care cannot be managed like allied health sciences.

23

Patient and Family Perceptions of Hospital Chaplains

Larry VandeCreek
Arne Jessen
John Thomas
James Gibbons
Stephen Strasser

ABSTRACT

While most hospitals provide chaplaincy services for patients, families, and staff, these services are seldom studied and their contribution is poorly understood. A questionnaire created by the College of Chaplains of the American Protestant Health Association was mailed by an insurance company to patients recently dismissed from the hospital, requesting evaluation of three nonmedical services (social services, chaplaincy, and patient representatives) and how well the spiritual needs for support/counseling, prayer, and sacraments were met. Responses revealed that, in comparison to the other two nonmedical services, patients receive more visits from chaplains, evaluate these visits as more important ($p<0.000$), and report that these visits meet their expectations more highly ($p<0.000$). Regression analyses demonstrate that when the chaplain meets the patient's need for support/counseling, the respondent is more likely to select the

Reproduced with permission of the Foundation of the American College of Health Care Executives and the Health Administration Press from *Hospital and Health Services Administration*, (1991), 36(3), 455-467.

hospital again (p=0.04) and recommend it to others (p=0.05). Similarly, when chaplains meet the family's need for support/counseling, the respondent is likely to chose the hospital again. Since chaplains clearly make an important contribution to patients, their families, and the hospital, administrators should review the adequacy of their chaplaincy services in the light of these data.

Financial pressures lead hospital administrators to review every aspect of their operations. Such reviews can result in questions concerning the contribution of the various nonmedical support services, including hospital-funded staff chaplaincy positions. How are chaplains viewed by patients? What purpose do they serve?

Few studies provide data that answer these questions. Carey (1972) conducted a survey within a large metropolitan hospital and concluded that "87% of nurses, 76% of doctors, and 40% of patients attached great importance to having a chaplain... available." The study was limited to one church-related hospital, and its results were circulated privately. Parkum (1985) surveyed a stratified sample of 432 patients from six hospitals and he concluded that chaplains have "more impact than any other support service" and "are filling a role much needed and recognized by the patients." At least one other study has focused on the effectiveness of staff chaplains, revealing positive results (Florell, 1973). The data remain limited, however, and no broad-based effort has attempted to document the function of the hospital chaplain or compare it to other nonmedical services. In the current study, patient evaluation data are gathered concerning social services, chaplains, and patient representatives as regards the number of patient contacts, the importance patients attribute to these professionals, and the levels at which expectations are met. Data are also gathered to determine the level of effectiveness at which chaplains meet four common spiritual needs.

METHODS

The Research Committee of the College of Chaplains of the American Protestant Health Association and an independent consultant designed a questionnaire to measure patients' perceptions of hospital chaplains. The questionnaire was mailed by a national insurance company to claimants who had recently been discharged from a hospital (N=2,480). A cover letter from the insurance company vicepresident introduced the survey as an effort of an anonymous organization to obtain feedback on its members' performance. Respondents remained anonymous but were advised to include the zip code of the hospital. The return envelope was addressed to the consultant's office, further protecting respondent blindness to sponsorship. If the patient wasincapacitated, first-order family members were encouraged to respond.

The questionnaire asked for patient demographic information, details of the hospital experience, and perceptions of three nonmedical hospital services–social service, chaplaincy, and patient representatives. Chaplains are clergy persons who work for the hospital, providing a variety of nondenominational religious services for patients and family members. This role began in the 1920s, and their services usually focus on bedside visits with the patient or family to help them use their religious resources to cope with illness, pain, death, and grief.

Social workers provide services to patients and families that include discharge planning, referral to community agencies, as well as guidance and counseling of the patient and family. They have a long history of hospital work and their presence is mandated by the Joint Commission for Accreditation of Healthcare Organizations.

Patient representatives are advocates who help with a wide range of problems that the patient or family may experience with the hospital. Such problems include helping the patient cope with the complicated structure of the hospital as well as communication issues with hospital staff persons. Such programs have proliferated in the last decade.

Respondents used a Likert scale to report the number of times they were visited by these personnel (no visit, 1-2 visits, 3-5 visits, more than 5 visits), the level of importance attributed to these services, and the extent to which their expectations were met (1=low; 10=high). No measure of patient acuity was taken.

Respondents were repeatedly encouraged to distinguish between the contribution of their parish clergy and the hospital chaplain. Each item used the phrase "hospital staff chaplain" to remind respondents of this distinction. A separate item asked whether they had received a visit by parishclergy or their representative.

An additional item asked respondents to rank the level at which four common spiritual needs were met: (1)the patient's need for support/counseling, (2)the family's need for support/ counseling, (3)the need for prayer, and (4)the need for the sacraments. Respondents were also asked if they would choose this hospital again and whether they would recommend it to a friend.

The 484 (19.5 percent) returns were analyzed by SPSSPC+ (Version 3.0) and, since this was an exploratory study, two-tailed tests were used with a significance level of 0.05. The the data were analyzed with parametric tests, and the results were supplemented with non-parametric measures when the data were believed to contain ordinal characteristics.

RESULTS

The demographic breakdown of respondents (n=484) for this survey included: *gender*--176 (36 percent) males, 308 (64 percent) females; *age*—28 (6 percent) 18-25 years, 112 (23 percent) 26-35 years, 150 (31 percent) 36-50 years, 147 (30 percent) 51-65 years, and 47 (10 percent) 66 years or older; *income*—62 (13 percent) making less than $15,000 per year, 216 (45 percent) making $15,000-$35,000, and 194 (40 percent) making more than $35,000 (12 or 2 percent did not answer this question); *religious affiliation*—274 (57 percent) Protestant, 173 (36 percent) Catholic, 11 (2 percent) Jewish, and 26 (5 percent) other.

Questionnaire respondents include patients (n=290; 60 percent) as well as spouses (n=130; 27 percent), children (n=25; 7 percent), parents (n=22; 5 percent), and others (n=7; 1 percent).

Data From Patients and Family Members

Data from family members and the category titled "other" (hereafter referred to as "family members") were combined into one group and compared to that reported by patients in order to determine any differences. The family member data tended to produce higher means than that of patients, but these means were not significantly different for patient age, gender, mean family income, religious affiliation, whether a parish clergy visited them while in the hospital, the type of illness, or whether they required surgery. Responses from each group were evenly distributed geographically as evidenced by zip codes of the hospital in which they were a patient. Their general evaluation of medical and nonmedical services were not significantly different. The family member data, however, reported a longer hospital stay (nonpatients= 50 days; patients= 17 days; t-test $t=3.36$; $p<0.001$). The family member sources also reported a larger number of patients hospitalized multiple times for the same illness ($p<0.04$). These variations seem to indicate that family members responded for patients with chronic illness who entered the hospital repeatedly and remained there longer or had died. No other statistically significant differences were found related to the independent variables.

Data from family members for the dependent variables also tended to generate higher mean scores than data from patients. At points, these differences were significant. As regards the number of visits, family members reported more visits by social services (t-test $t=3.76$; $p=0.000$) and patient representatives t-test $t=2.19$; $p=0.03$). These data suggest that the roles of these two professions are heavily involved with families.

Families gave more importance to all three professions than patients: social services, $t=4.36$; $p=0.000$; chaplaincy, $t=2.41$; $p=0.02$; patient representative, $t=3.45$; $p=0.001$). This suggests that, at least for these families, the three professions are more important to them than to the patients themselves. The data suggest that the patient's illness is an anxious time for families and that the attention of these professionals is helpful, presumably allowing them then to aid and support the patient. The family's evaluation is likely influenced by their endurance of the patient's long hospitalization.

Concerning the level at which expectations were met, family data reported a higher mean score than patients for social services. These data extend for social services the findings concerning the number of family visits and the increased level of importance described above.

The last dependent variable in which patient and family data varied significantly concerned the family's need for support/counseling. Family members reported the chaplain's work as more helpful than the data from patients ($t=2.65$; $p=0.008$). Again, this testifies to the chaplain's role with families in the hospital.

Following these analyses, the data were combined into one group for further study. In these studies, the frequently higher means of the family data for the dependent variables accentuate the results.

The geographic characteristics of the data were traced through the hospital zip code. National zip code areas 1,4,5 and 6 contained 82 percent of the 484 responses. These zip codes represent the Northern Midwest from Montana to New York, Minnesota to Missouri. No additional information was collected concerning the number of hospitals represented in the sample or their characteristics. The median length of hospital stay was 8 days (mean= 18.3 days; range = 1-300 days). Reasons for hospitalization included circulation/ cardiac traumas (14 percent), cancer (13 percent), orthopedic problems (13 percent), maternity (11 percent), and other diagnoses (29 percent). In 72 percent of the cases, this was the first hospitalization for the diagnosis. Surgery was required by 65 percent of the cases.

The Amount of Nonmedical Services

The questionnaire asked respondents to indicate the number of bedside visits they received from these professionals and the numbers varied. Chaplains visited 245 patients, social services 158 patients, and patientrepresentatives 160 patients. In addition, 60 patients received at least one visit from all three professions (see Table 1) and when the number of visits to these patients is analyzed by nonparametric measures, no significant differences exist between professions (Friedman- 4.27; $p<0.12$). The continuous nature of the Likert scale suggests interval data and the Repeated Measures MANOVA was significant- Hotellings $t=271.0$; $p<0.000$.

TABLE 1

Patient Reported Mean Number of Visits
when Contact was Made with All Three Professions

	Mean*	SD
Social Services	2.58	0.81
Chaplaincy	2.80	0.88
Patient Representatives	2.45	0.77

N=60
*Mean scores are not significant by non-parametric measures: Friedman-4.27; $p<0.12$. The means are significant by the parametric Repeated Measures Analysis of Variance: Hotellings $t=271.0$; $p<0.000$.

Some respondents indicated that they had been visited by both their parish clergy and a hospital chaplain (n= 138). This demonstrates their ability to distinguish between services rendered by these two professionals.

The Importance of Nonmedical Services

Respondents ranked the importance of the three professions. These data described chaplaincy as more important than social services and patient representatives (see Table 2) and were statistically significant (Repeated Measures analysis of variance; Hotellings $t=415.7$; $p<0.000$). A follow-up paired test between social service and chaplaincy was significant for the 453 respondents who provided data ($t=8.34$; $p<0.000$). This means that the increased importance of chaplaincy is not likely due to chance characteristics in the data. A similar test between chaplains and patient representatives (n=435) was also significant ($t=3.13$; $p<0.002$). The total responses here exceed those who had received a visit from a chaplain because respondents were encouraged to rank the importance of these professionals even if they had not experienced a visit.

TABLE 2
Levels of Importance Attributed by Patients to Visits by Social Services, Chaplaincy, and Patient Representatives

Three Group Comparison*	Mean	SD
Social Services	3.59	3.08
Chaplaincy	5.00	3.45
Patient Representatives	4.46	3.20
N=432		
Two Group Comparisons		
Social Services+	3.66	3.11
Chaplaincy	5.04	3.43
N=453		
Patient Representatives#	4.48	3.19
Chaplaincy	5.01	3.44
N=435		

Data are produced by a ten-point Likert scale in which higher scores indicate increased importance.
*Repeated Measures Analysis of Variance: Hotellings t=415.7; $p<0.000$.
+Paired t-test: 8.34; $p<0.000$.
#Paired t-test: 3.13; $p<0.002$.

The importance given to chaplaincy was not statistically linked to Protestant, Catholic, or Jewish affiliation of the respondent when analyzed by the one-way analysis of variance.

Spearman correlations revealed that the importance of these three nonmedical services was positively linked at the $p<0.001$ level to the number of visits the patient received: social service r=0.44; chaplaincy r=0.47; patient representative r=0.36. This means that patients who received more visits rated the services as more important. At least two interpretations are possible. This may mean that patients who experienced needs that were important to them received more visits from these professionals. When these needs were met, the data reflect an increased level of importance for the professional's visits. It may also mean, however, that when the professionals visited more often, the patient concluded from the initiative that these visits were important, and responses reflected this.

The Expectation of Nonmedical Services

To what extent were the patient's expectations met by these professionals? The Repeated Measures Analysis on the 91 cases that contained complete data (see Table 3) was significant because chaplains were more successful in meeting patient expectations (Hotellings t-test; $f= 134$; $p<0.000$). Follow-up paired t-tests were also significant for chaplaincy verses social services (n=125; $t= 3.79$; $p<0.000$) and for patient representatives (n=126; $t= 2.81$; $p<0.006$). These p values indicate that there was less than one in 1000 chances (social services vs chaplaincy) and approximately 6 in 1000 chances that these findings were due to chance.

TABLE 3

**Levels at which Patient Expectations Were Met
by Social Services, Chaplaincy, and Patient Representatives**

Three Group Comparison*	Mean	SD
Social Services	5.45	3.39
Chaplaincy	6.60	3.33
Patient Representatives	5.46	3.22
N=91		
Two Group Comparisons		
Social Services+	5.86	3.37
Chaplaincy	6.71	3.23
N=125		
Patient Representatives#	5.57	3.14
Chaplaincy	6.63	3.23

N=125
Data are produced by a ten-point Likert scale in which higher scores indicate an increased level at which expectations were met.
*Repeated Measures Analysis of Variance; Hotellings $t=134.0$; $p<0.000$.
+Paired t-test: 3.79; $p<0.000$.
#Paired t-test; 2.81; $p<0.006$.

Spearman correlations were generated for each professional group between the number of visits per patient and the level at which the expectations of that patient were met. Correlation coefficients were positively linked at the

$p<0.001$ level: social services $r=0.59$; patient representative $r=0.49$; chaplains $r=0.49$. This means that when respondents reported that their expectations had been met, they also tended to report multiple visits from these professionals.

Meeting Four Spiritual Needs

Responses concerning the level at which the four spiritual needs were met was undertaken by dividing the data according to religious affiliation (Protestant, Catholic, and Jewish). All "not visited" responses were deleted from the analysis, which resulted in the exclusion of the 11 Jewish respondents. In the remaining Catholic and Protestant groups (n=173 and n=272), the need for support/counseling of the patient was more effectively met for Catholic patients (one-way analysis of variance: $f=5.25$; $p< 0.02$). The need for administration of the sacraments was also more effectively met for Catholic patients (one-way analysis of variance: $f=-31.26$; $p<0.000$). The levels at which the four needs were met were not statistically linked to respondent age, gender, income, the experience of surgery, or length of time in the hospital, as shown by the one-way analysis of variance.

What is the impact of meeting these spiritual needs for the hospital? Two factors were explored: would patients select the hospital again and would they recommend it to friends (yes, maybe, no). The data were highly skewed toward a positive response, and the maybe and no categories were combined. Regression analysis was used to determine the ability of the data concerning each of the four spiritual needs to predict selection and recommendation of the hospital. Data concerning the patient's need for support/counseling from the chaplain was positively related to selecting the hospital again ($f=4.48$; $p=0.04$) and recommending it to others ($f=3.80$; $p=0.05$). This means that the chaplain's relationship to patients and families is a significant positive influence for the hospital in the health care market in terms of the patient's self-reported perception. Data concerning the family's need for counseling/support from the chaplain demonstrated a significant positive relationship to selecting the hospital again ($f=6.29$; $p=0.01$), but not for recommending it to others. The data concerning the impact of meeting needsfor prayer or the sacraments were not significant for selecting the hospital again or recommending it to others.

DISCUSSION

The 19.5 percent survey response rate constitutes a disappointing level of returns. Future research should use Dillman's (1978) methods to increase the response rate. Analysis suggests that the data represent patients who were in the hospital for a longer length of stay—mean=18.3 days versus the national mean of 7.2 days (American Hospital Association, 1989). This length of stay provided them more contact with hospital personnel, including those studied in this project. This extended contact may have been a factor that motivated their completion of the questionnaire. Social workers, chaplains, and patient representatives typically have little or no contact with patients who require routine care during a few days of hospitalization. The data, therefore, do not appear to represent a national sample of all general hospital patients, but rather the responses of those who are of special concern to hospital administrators-- that is, those who remain in the hospital longer and require more intensive services.

The respondents are drawn from a predominately middle-aged population in the Upper Midwest. They are generally free of chronic disease, 72 percent reporting hospitalization for a new diagnosis. More than 50 percent are surgical cases.

Some respondents may have been alerted to sponsorship by explicit questions about the patient's religious affiliation, the presence of spiritual needs during hospitalization or visits of the parish pastor. This may create a sample unusually sympathetic to chaplaincy, but this appears unlikely since only 245 of 484 respondents received visits from the chaplain. Nonetheless, the external validity of this study is limited because further comparison to a national sample is problematic due to the extended hospital stay of thepatients in this sample and minimal data provided by the questionnaire concerning the nature of the hospital and actual patient diagnosis.

Family members highly valued the three nonmedical services studied here, probably in part because they, with the patients, suffered with longer and repeated hospitalizations. Their appreciation of the nonmedical services is interesting because preliminary analysis of broad-based patient satisfaction data at a large university medical center shows that family members are less satisfied than patients. This patient satisfaction data, gathered without specific regard to the three professions studied here, suggest that family member needs are not as highly met as those of the patient. This is a commentary on the impact of hospitalization on family members and implies that the hospital takes care of both the patient and the family. Family members may possess more needs than hospital staffs have typically recognized.

The comparisons between chaplaincy, social services, and patient representatives must be interpreted carefully. While the Joint Commission for Accreditation of Health Care Organizations mandates a social services department, no similar standards exist for chaplaincy or patient representatives, and these services may not even have been available to some patients. Additionally, these data may reflect levels of training, competency or staffing patterns within these fields. Moreover, the perception that chaplaincy was more important does not imply that the other services were unimportant. Patients reported more visits from chaplains which is not surprising because by tradition every door in the hospital is open to them while social services typically only responds to physician referrals. Patient representatives also usually respond only to specific requests for their services. In both of these professions, however, considerable time is spent performing tasks on the patient's behalf but away from the bedside and patients have no way of knowing about or reporting that time. Hence, these data may indicate that the chaplain's work is more cognitively salient to respondents.

Patients rank chaplaincy as the most important of the three nonmedical services. This appears to represent their need for pastoral services in times of illness and hospitalization, particularly among the sample in this study, which contains many who are in the hospital repeatedly and for longer periods of time. This suggests that chaplains are more important because serious illness or approaching death raises spiritual concerns in patients and families. As hospital financing patterns increasingly dictate the admission of only those who are seriously ill, we hypothesize that spiritual needs within the hospital will increase and the importance of chaplains will rise.

The three nonmedical services each produced strong correlations between their perceived importance and the number of visits experienced by the patient. These findings indicate that the perceived importance is at least in part a function of professional visibility and the ability to help patients or families with problems experienced during illness. This is readily understood for social services and patient representatives because they usually are requested to visit the patient in response to a problem. Conversely, chaplains call on patients routinely, uninvited. The data suggest that they too must demonstrate their importance by visibility and their ability to be of aid.

The data that compare the importance of the three nonmedical services are potentially influenced, however, by a number of factors. Many patients, particularly routine surgical cases with new diagnoses, may have no need for social services and thus rank them lower. Also, patients know the role and function of chaplains at least in a general way; the role (and thus importance) of social services and patient representatives may be less clear to them.

Additionally, the fear experienced by patients and families duringillness may lead them to rank religious resources as more important even though their ability to be of aid varies.

Patients report that chaplaincy met their expectations more fully than the other two professional groups. This may occur because chaplaincy goals are clear to most patients: they support the patient and family in well-known ways, using pastoral care, counseling, prayer, and the sacraments. Most hospitals require that chaplains receive special training and certification as provided through the Association for Clinical Pastoral Education, Inc., the National Association of Catholic Chaplains, and the College of Chaplains of the American Protestant Health Association. Additionally, chaplaincy is free from direct responsibility in conflictual situations as compared, for instance, to social services personnel who, against the patient's will but on physician orders, must find a nursing home bed for the patient. All of these factors probably contribute to patients reporting that chaplains, more than the other two services, meet their expectations.

The levels at which expectations were met were highly correlated with the number of visits. Patient needs can change dramatically from day to day in the hospital. These variations range from anxiety concerning medical tests or surgery, relief or grief after diagnosis, anger concerning frustrations, and thankfulness for recovery. Multiple visits allow the chaplain to interact with all these spiritual needs and the results are likely reflected in these data.

The lack of significant difference in effectiveness of ministry by patient gender and by the need for surgery is somewhat surprising. Popular opinion believes that males generally make less use of religious resources. Surgery, as an invasive procedure with a general anesthetic, is often regarded as especially traumatic. Many chaplains regard these patients as being in special need. Perhaps the data do not accurately reflect patient needs becausethey are gathered days/ weeks after release from the hospital.

Catholic patients report that their need for support/counseling and their need for the sacraments were met more effectively than for Protestant or Jewish patients. It appears that, because the Catholic faith is heavily invested in the sacraments, a priest who uses the appropriate prayers and offers Holy Communion fulfills spiritual needs for Catholic patients. The benefits of this ministry are also reflected in the report that their needs for support/counseling were also met. The ability of the hospital through its Chaplaincy Department to help patients and families with these concerns has an effect on the patient's image of the hospital—that is, whether they would select the hospital again. The data report that chaplains have a significantly positive impact on this decision by helping families with their needs. This is not surprising because chaplains traditionally pay considerable attention to the emotional and spiritual needs of family members. Clearly an effective chaplaincy department that aids and supports the patient's family possesses more than incidental importance. Effective pastoral care affects both on the patients' present and future plans. These data support and extend the findings of Carey (1972) and Parkum (1985) who demonstrated that patients place a high value on pastoral services. The present study produces the same results in a broader sample of patients and hospitals.

Additional research should rely on improved methods which generate a large, stratified national sample. Survey data supplemented by interviews would be helpful. The questionnaire's level of sophistication should be increased so that acuity measures are gathered from all respondents. The religious affiliation category should be supplemented by a scale which describes the respondent's frequency of religious participation. Such data would allow for more substantial evaluation of the relationship between the patient's or family's religious commitments and their evaluation of chaplaincy.

Hospital administrators should review their chaplaincy services in the light of these data. Chaplains can make an important contribution because ill patients and anxious families require a skilled clergy person who can respond to their spiritual concerns. These data strongly suggest that this is an important activity that affects the patient's total image of the hospital's services.

REFERENCES

American Hospital Association. *Hospital Statistics.* Chicago: American Hospital Association, 840 North Lake Shore Drive, Chicago, Illinois 60611-2431, page 4, Table 1.

Carey, R. (1972). Hospital chaplains: who needs them? *Department of Pastoral Care,* Lutheran General Hospital, Park Ridge, Illinois.

Dillman, D. (1978). *Mail and telephone surveys: the total design methods.* New York: John Wiley and Sons.

Florell, J. (1973). Crisis intervention in orthopedic surgery—empirical evidence of the effectiveness of achaplain working with surgery patients. *Bulletin of the American Hospital Association, 37,* 29-36.

Parkum, K. (1985). The impact of chaplaincy services in selected hospitals in the Eastern United States. *The Journal Of Pastoral Care, 34,* 262-269.

Author Index

(r following page numbers indicates the reference to the work)

Abrams, D., Parker-Margin, J.,& Unger, K. (1989) 233,250r

Achenbach, T. (1978) 63,64r

Acklin, M., Brown, E.,& Mauger, P. (1983) 184,197r,293,304r

Aldwin, C.,& Revenson, T. (1987) 93,109r

Allport, G. (1950) 103,109r,225,228r

Allport, G. (1967) 217,225,228r

Allport, G.,& Ross, J.(1967) 103,109r,184,186,197r,202,210r,
    220,228r

American Cancer Society. (1993) 292,304r

American Hospital Association. 352,366r

American Psychiatric Association. (1975) 154,167r

Andrew, J. (1970) 24,31r

Anthony, R.,& Young, D. (1984) 311,321r

Arnold, E. (1989) 247,250r

Ashbrook, J.,& Hinkle, J.Jr. (1988) 32r

Augustine, M.,& Kalish, R. (1975) 53,64r

Baines, E. (1984) 140,148r

Bakan, D. (1968) 105,109r

Baldree, K., Murphy, S.,& Powers, J. (1982) 53,62,64r

Bard, M.,& Dyk, R. (1956) 292,304r

Bard, M. (1952) 184,197r

Bascom, G. (1984) 53,64r

Batson, C.,& Ventis, W. (1982) 85,93,109r

Batson, C. (1976) 93,109r

Batten, H.,& Prottas, J. (1987) 132,133,136r

Beahrs, O., Hensen, D., Hutter, R.,& Myers, H. (1988) 219,228r

Beck, A.,& Emery, G. (1985) 200,210r

Beck, A. (1961) (1988) 281

Becker, M. (1977) 318,321r

Belcher, A., Dettmore, D.,& Holzmer, S. (1989) 233,235,246,250r

Bellemare, D. (1988) 233,250r

Benoliel, J., McCorkle, R.,& Young, K. (1980) 295,304r

Benson, P.,& Williams, D.(1982) 93,109r

Benson, P.,& Spilka, B. (1973) 93,101,109r

Benson, H. (1975) 202,210r

Benson, H. (1984) 146,148r

Berger, P.,& Luckmann, T. (1966) 204,210r

Bergin, A. (1983) 119,123r

Berkman, L.,& Syme, L. (1979) 312,321r

Bernhardt, W. (1958) 42,49r

Billings, A.,& Moos, R.(1984) 84,109r

Blake, R., & McKay, D. (1986) 257,273r

Blazer, D. (1982) 257,273r

Bloom, J., Pendergrass, S.,& Burall, G. (1984) 184,197r

Bohne, J. (1986) 233,234,246,250r

Bowen, M., Justyn, J., Kass, J., Miller, M., Rogers, C., Rogers, N.,& Wood, J.(1978) 203,210r

Brandt, B. (1987) 218,219,228r

Bruder, E. (1962) 42,49r

Buber, M. (1970) 202,210r

Bufford, R., Paloutzian, R.,& Ellison, C. (1991) 217,220,228r

Bufford, R., Paloutzian, R.,& Ellison, C. (in press) 239,250r

Bulman, J.,& Wortman, C. (1977) 80,100,109r,293,304r

Burnard, P. (1987) 226,228r

Callendar, C., Bayton, J.,& Clark, J. (1982) 133,136r

Campbell, D.,& Stanley, J., (1963) 212,213r

Campbell, A., Converse, P.,& Rodgers, W. (1976) 56,64r

Caplan, G. (1981) 120,123r

Carey, R. (1972) 344,355,356r

Carson, V. (1989) 233,250r

Carson, V. (1990) 233,250r

Carson, V., Soeken, K.,& Belcher, A. (1991) 236,240,250r

Carson, V., Soeken, K., Shanty, J.,& Terry, L. (1990) 219,228r, 233,235,246,250r

Carson, V., Soeken, K. L.,& Grimm, P. M. (1988) 219,226,228r

Cassell, J. (1976) 325,332r

Cassem E. (1988) 120,123r

Cecchi, R. (1981) 235,250r

Cella, D., Mahon, S.,& Donovan, M. (1990) 292,293,304r

Chaisson, R. (1990) 233,250r

Chekryn, J. (1984) 292,293,304r

Chinen, A. (1984) 52,64r

Chrisman, M.,& Fowler, M. (1980) 139,146,148r

Clark, W. (1958) 80,109r

Clark, (no date) 1,3,12

Cleary, P.,& Houts, P. (1984) 81,109r

Cobb, S. (1976) 325,332r

Cohen, J. (1988) 294,304r

Cohen, C. (1982) 138,148r

Cohen, S.,& Willis, T. (1985) 102,109r

Collipp, P. (1969) 68,73,75r

Comstock, G.,& Partridge, K. (1972) 312,321r

Conrad, N. (1985) 52,53,64r

Conway, K. (1985-86) 256,257,273r

Conwill, W. (1986) 63,64r

Cook, J.,& Wimberly, D. (1983) 82,109r

Cooley, D. (1987) 138,148r

Cowles, K. (1988) 146,148r

Coyne, J.,& DeLongis, A.(1986) 102,109r

Crogg, S.,& Levine, L. (1972) 272,273r

Crumbaugh, J.,& Maholick, L. (1964) 238,250r

Crumbaugh, J.,& Maholick, L. (1981) 292,294,302,304r

Crumbaugh, J. (1977) 238,250r

Davidson, J. (1976) 202,210r

Davzer, B. (1988) 233

DeLong W. (1989) 126,135,136r

DeLongis, A., Coyne, J., Dakof, G., Folkman, S.,& Lazarus,
R. (1982) 81,109r

Derogatis, L.,& Lopez, M. (1983) 295,305r

Dewald, R. (1971) 272,273r

Dillman, D. (1978) 352,356r

Dittes, J. (1969) 106,110r

Dixon W. (1981) 69,75r

Donahue, M. (1985) 103,110r,184,197r,217,222,228r

Du Bois, P. (1965) 6,17r

Dubin, W., Field, H.,& Gastfriend, D. (1979) 138,148r

Dufault, K. J. (1981) 219,228r

Durkheim, E. (1915) 103,110r

Ebaugh, H., Richman, K.,& Chafetz, J. (1984) 107,110r

Echemendia, R.,& Pargament, K. (1982) 104,110r

Eckenrode, J. (1984) 81,110r

Edhert, L. (1964) 24,31r

Eimer, K. (1989) 154,162,167r

Ellis, A. (1960) 102,110r

Ellis, A. (1980) 256,273r

Ellison, C. (1983) 216,217,218,220,228r,239

Fromm, E. (1960) 102,110r

Galton, F. (1872) 68,73,74,75r

Gartner, J., Lyons. J., Larson, D., Serkland, J.,& Peyrot, M.
    (1990) 154,167r

Gatchel, R.,& Baum, A. (1983) 200,210r

Gavzer, B. (1988) 234,246,251r

Geertz, C. (1966) 103,111r

Germino, B.,& McCorkle, R. (1985) 52,64r

Giargos, P. (1980) 312,321r

Gibbs, H.,& Achterberg-Lawlis, J. (1978) 53,62,64r,83,111r

Gil, K., Abrams, M., Phillips, G.,& Keefe, F. (1989) 81,111r

Gilbert, K. (1989) 84,111r

Glock, C., Ringer, B.,& Babbie, R. (1967) 83,111r

Glueck, N. (1988) 226,228r

Goldberg, D. (1978) 93,111r

Gorsuch, R. (1984) 85,111r

Gotay, C. (1985) 293,305r

Granstrom, S. (1985) 52,64r

Graydon, D. (1988) 233,251r

Greeley, A. (1974) 202,210r

Greeley, A. (1972) 83,111r

Green, L. (1980) 318,321r

Grevengoed, N.,& Pargament, K. (1989) 84,93,111r

Griffith, E., Young, J.,& Smith, D. (1984) 83,111r

Gross, L. (1982) 183,197r

Gulko, J. (1983) 154,167r

Gutmann, D. (1987) 120,123r

Guy, (no date) 73

Haberman, M. (1987) 292,305r

Hadaway, C., Marler,P.,& Chaves,M. (1993) 151,152r

Hall, C. (1986) 63,64r

Hamilton, M. (1967) 258,273r

Johnson, P. (1967) 42,49r

Johnson, J., Christman, N.,& Stitt, C. (1985) 138,148r

Joyce, C.,& Welldon, R. (1965) 68,73,75r

Kahoe, R. (1982) 83,112r

Kardiner A. (1959) 12,13,17r

Kasl, S. (1984) 319,321r

Kass, J. (1983) 204,210r

Kass, J. (1991) 201,202,204,207,210r

Kass, J., Friedman, R., Leserman, J., Zuttermeister, P.,& Benson,
      H. (1991) 204,207,212,210r

Kass, J., Burton, L., Ferranti, L.,& Davis, F. (1991) 204,211r

Kass, J.,& Price, C. (1991) 207,211r

Katz, S., Downs, T., Cash, H.,& Grotz, R. (1970) 258,273r

Kayal, P. (1985) 232,251r

Kegan, R. (1982) 292,305r

Kemp, J. (1984) 53,65r

King, K. (1984) 140,147,148r

King, M.,& Hunt, R. (1975) 93,112r

Kirpatrick, L. (1989) 104,112r

Kitchell, M., Barnes, R., Veith, R., Okimoto J.,& Raskind, M.
(1982) 256,274r

Kivet, V. (1979) 272,274r

Klass, D.,& Gordon, A. (1978-9) 53,65r

Kobasa, S., Maddi, S.,& Pucetti, M. (1982) 236,251r

Kobasa, S. (1979) 234,235,236,251r

Kochansky, G. (1979) 258,274r

Koenig, H., Moberg, D.,& Kvale J. (1988) 119,123r,162,167r,256,
      271,274r

Koenig, H., Meador, K., Goli, V., Shelp, F., Cohen, H.,& Blazer,
      D. (1992) 257,267,274r

Koenig, H., Meador, K., Shelp, F., Goli, V., Cohen, H.,& Blazer,
      D. (1991) 257,261,271,274r

Lyons, J., Hammer, J.,& White, R. (1987) 337,340r

Lyons, J., Hammer, J., Larson, D., Visotsky, H.,& Burns, B. (1987) 336,340r

Maddi, S. (1986) 239,251r

Mahon, S. (1991) 293,305r

Mahon, S., Cella, D.,& Donovan, M. (1990) 292,293,301,305r

Malinowski, B. (1925) 103,112r

Marris, P. (1986) 292,305r

Martin, C., Burrows, C.,& Pomilio, J. (1983) 154,161,167r

Marx, J.,& Spray, S. (1969) 155,168r

Maryland AIDS Update. (1990) 232,233,251r

Maslow, A. (1970) 82,112r

Mason, R., Clark, G., Reeves, R.,& Wagner, B. (1969) 24,33,34, 38,39r

Maton, K. (1989) 84,102,107,108,112r

Maton, K.,& Rappaport, J. (1984) 84,112r

Matthews, P., Larson, D.,& Barry, C. (1993) VII, XIr

McCleary, R.,& Hay, R. (1980) 337,340r

McClintock, C., Spaulding, C.,& Turner, H. (1965) 155,168r

McCorkle, R. (1987) 295,306r

McCorkle, R.,& Young, K. (1978) 295,306r

McCrae, R. (1984) 80,81,90,100,112r

McGee, R. (1984) 219,229r

McLaughlin, S.,& Maloney, H. (1984) 63,65r

McSherry, E., VII

McSherry, E. (1983a) 311,321r

McSherry, E. (1983b) 311,321r

McSherry, E. (1983c) 311,322r

McSherry, E. (1984) 322r

McSherry, E. (1990) 311,322r

McSherry, E., Kratz, D.,& Nelson, W. (1986) 335,340r

McSherry, E., Nelson, W.,& Kratz, D. (1986) 311,314,317,319,322r

McSherry, E., & Dagenais, F. (1981) 312,322r

Michela, J.,& Wood, J. (1986) 293,306r

Miller, W. (1984) 154,168r

Miller, J. (1985) 53,62,63,65r,217,229r

Moberg, D. (1974) 216,229r

Moberg, D. (1982) 53,62,65r

Moos, R. (1986) 81,112r

Moos, R., Cronkite, R., Billings, A.,& Finney, J. (1984) 90,112r

Mudd, E. (1981) 53,65r

Murphy, M.,& Donovan, S. (1988) 202,211r

Myers, J.,& Bean, L. (1968) 257,275r

National Interfaith Coalition on Aging. (1975) 239,251r

Neighbors, H., Jackson, J., Bowman, P.,& Gurin, G. (1983) 84,112r

Nelson, F. (1977) 272,275r

Nelson, P. (1989) 217,229r

Neugarten, B. (1979) 52,62,65r

Newman, M. (1979) 52,65r

Newman, J.,& Pargament, K. (1990) 83,112r

Northouse, L. (1989) 218,226,229r

Nowotny, M. (1989) 220,222,229r

O'Brien, M. (1982) 53,62,63,65r,80,100,113r,154,168r,272,275r

O'Conner, A., Wicker, C.,& Germino, B. (1990) 292,306r

O'Hare, D. (1982) 52,65r

Okun, M., Zautra, A.,& Robinson, S. (1988) 240,251r

Owen, D. (1989) 219,229r

P.W.A. News and Views. (1990) 248,251r

Paloutzian, R.,& Ellison, C. (1982) 216,220,229r

Pargament, K., Sullivan, M., Tyler, F.,& Steele, R. (1982) 101,113r

Pargament K., Brannick, M., Adamakos, H., Ensing, D., Keleman, M.,
Warren, R.,Falgout, K., Cook, P.,& Myers, J. (1987) 87,94,113r

Pargament, K.,& Hahn, J. (1986) 83,88,113r

Pargament, K., Kennell, J., Hathaway, W., Grevengoed, N., Newman, J.,& Jones, W. (1988) 80,93,102,113r

Pargament, K. (1990) IX,76,82,83,85,104,108,113r

Park, C., Cohen, L.H.,& Herb, L. (in press) 107,113r

Parkum, K. (1982-83) 326,332r

Parkum, K. (1985) 336,341r,344,355,356r

Parse, R. (1981) 52,65r

Parsons, T. (1951) 327,332r

Perez, L., Schulman, B., Davis, F., Olson, L., Tellis, V.,& Matas A. (1989) 126,133,134,136r

Peteet, J. (1985) 184,185,197r

Peters, T.,& Waterman, R. (1982) 311,322r

Peterson, L.,& Roy, A. (1985) 120,123r

Piepgras, R. (1968) 218

Pollner, M. (1989) 102,113r

Press, J.,& Wilson, S. (1978) 69,75r

Pressman, R., Lyons, J., Larson, D.,& Strain, J. (1990) 271,275r

Princeton Religion Research Center. (1982) 256,270,275r

Princeton Religion Research Center. (1985) 153,155,160,168r

Princeton Religion Research Center. (1987) 83,113r

Proceeding of the Third Nursing Conference on Classifications of Nursing Diagnosis. (1978) 311,322r

Prottas, J.,& Batten H. (1988) 125,126,136r

Prottas, J. (1989) 126, 136r

Pruyser, P. (1968) 105,113r,193,197r

Pruyser, P. (1976) 312,322r

Putney, S.,& Middleton, R. (1961) 93,113r

Rabkin, J.,& Struening, E. (1976) 81,113r

Ragan, C., Malony,N.,& Beit-Hallahmi, B. (1980) 154,168r

Redlener, I.,& Scott, C. (1979) 162,168r

Reed, P. (1986) 52,53,55,56,61,62,65r

Reeves, R. (1960) 2,17r

Reidel, J. (1981) 312,322r

Reker, G. (1992) 280,289r

Reker, G.,& Peacock E. (1981) 173,182r,280,289r

Religious Education Association of the United States and Canada.
    (1987) 225,229r

Rice, T. (1983) 336,341r

Rizzuto, A. (1979) 312,322r

Rock, D., Myerowitz, B., Maisto, S.,& Wallston, K. (1987)
    140,141,145,149r

Rogers, C. (1961) 203,211r

Rogers, C. (1980) 203,211r

Rogers, M. (1970) 52,65r

Roland, C. (1970) 73,75r

Roof, W.,& McKinney, W. (1987) 161,168r,257,275r

Roozen, D.,& Carroll, J. (1989) 87,113r

Rosen, C. (1982) 256,257,275r

Rosner, F. (1975) 68,75r

Rothbaum, F., Weisz, J.,& Snyder, S. (1982) 293,306r

Rotter, J. (1966) 138,139,149r

Ruffing-Rahal, M. (1984) 53,65r

Salisbury, S. (no date) 317,322r

Sanua, V. (1969) 256,275r

SAS Institute. (1988) 259,275r

Saynor, J. (1988) 233,251r

Schaie, K. (1977) 52,66r

Schiller, P.,& Levin, J. (1988) 162,168r

Schmale, A. (1976) 293,306r

Schofferman, J. (1987) 233,251r

Schwab, J., Bialow, M., Clemmons, R.,& Holzer, C. (1967) 258,275r

Scott, D., Goode, W.,& Arlin, Z. (1983) 292,293,306r

Shelly, J.,& Fish, S. (1978) 311,315,322r

Sherrill, K.,& Larson, D. (1988) 120,123r

Siegel, B. (1990) 247,248,251r

Silver, R., Boon, C.,& Stones, M. (1983) 292,303,306r

Silver, R.,& Wortman, C. (1980) 292,306r

Snook, S.,& Gorsuch, R. (1989) 113,114r

Sodestrom, K.,& Martinson, I. (1987) 146,149r

Solomon, G.,& Temoshok, L. (1987) 234,236,252r

Solomon, G.,& Temoshok, L, Zich, J. (1987) 235,252r

Spielberger, C. (1969) 25,31r

Spilka, B., Shaver, P.,& Kirkpatrick, L. (1985) 83,85,101,103,114r

Spilka, B., Spangler, J.,& Rea, M. (1981) 42,49r

Spilka, B., Hood, R.,& Gorsuch, L. (1985) 81,82,85,113r

Spilka, B., Spangler, J.,& Nelson, C. (1983) 184,197r

Spilka, B., Stout, L., Minton, B.,& Sizemore, D. (1977) 42,49r

Spilka, B., Shaver, P.,& Kirkpatrick, L. (1985) 184,197r

Spilka, B., Spangler, J., Rea, M.,& Nelson, C. (1981) 41,49r

Spilka, B., Hood, R.,& Gorsuch, R. (1985) 184,198r

Spilka, B.,& Spangler, J. (1979) 186,198r

Spivak, C. (1917) 68,75r

Stark, R. (1963) 163,168r

Steeves, R. (1992) 292,306r

Stelling, J. (1988) 278,289r

Stevenson, J. (1979) 52,66r

Stoll, R. (1985) 140,146,149r

Stoll, R. I. (1989) 216.229r

Stone, A.,& Neale, J. (1984) 88,114r

Strunk, O. (1957) 42,49r

Swanson, W.,& Harter, C., (1971) 256,257,275r

Swatos, W. (1987) 193,198r

Szasz, T. (1970) 154

Tardy, C. (1985) 102,114r

Taylor, S. (1983) 81,82,114r,184,198r,292,306r

Taylor, R.,& Chatters, L., (1988) 271,275r

Westberg, G. (1977) 336,341r

Westberg, G. (1979) 312,319,322r

Westberg, G. (1977) 312,322r

Willets, F.,& Crider, D. (1988) 120,123r

Wolff, K. (1959) 271,275r

Wong, P.,& Weiner, B. (1981) 292,293,307r

Wood, C. (1982) 311,322r

Wright, B. (1960) 2,17r

Wright, S. Pratt, C.,& Schmall, V. (1985) 82,114r

Yalom, I. (1980) 292,304,307r

Yates, J., Chalmer, B., St. James, P., Follensbee, M.,& McKegney,
    F. (1981) 84,114r,184,198r

Yesavage, J., Brink, T., Rose, T., Lum, O., Huang, V., Adey, M.,&
    Leirer, V. (1982-83) 258,275r

Youngner, S., Landefeld, S., Coulton, C., Juknialis, B.,& Leary,
M. (1989) 126,136r

Youngner, S., Allen, M., Partlett et al. (1985) 133,136r

Zaichkowsky, L.,& Kanen, R. (1978) 146,149r

Ziemer, M. (1982) 147,149r

Zuckerman, D., Kasl, S.,& Ostfeld, A. (1984) 121,123r

Zurlo, J.,& Lane, H. (1990) 233,252r

Subject Index

Index of Scales